The Great British Festival Guide

SUMMERSDALE

Summersdale Publishers
46 West Street
Chichester
West Sussex
PO19 1RP
United Kingdom

A CIP catalogue record for this book is available from the British Library.

Printed and bound in Great Britain by Creative Print and Design, Ebbw Vale.

ISBN 1 84024 071 7

The information contained in this book was as full and correct as possible at the time of going to press. However, we do strongly recommend that you check individual festival details using the contact listed, as they may alter at short notice.

Contents

SCOTLAND 281

WALES 303

Introduction

Britain boasts a wealth of heritage and traditional customs, as well as a blend of popular culture, that is unique and special. Consequently, it seems a great shame that fascinating events are often overlooked entirely, or merely stumbled across by chance, simply because you happen to be in the right place at the right time. How often have you heard in retrospect about an event that you wished you had attended, meant to go the following year and missed the dates because you weren't informed?

Information regarding Britain's festivals, as we discovered at first hand, is fairly difficult to obtain and quite often unavailable via the usual avenues of enquiry, such as Tourist Information Centres. Therefore, unless you are in 'the know', you may be missing out on an abundance of entertainment and fun right under your very nose, merely because you are unaware that it is happening.

The Great British Festival Guide was compiled with precisely this in mind. It is designed to provide as much information about as many British festivals as possible. Therefore if you are planning a holiday in Britain or simply looking for a great day out in your own locality, look no further. This easily accessible guide contains everything that you need to know about over 500 of Britain's finest festivals and events. This book contains something for everyone from Youth Festivals to Over 50s Festivals from Morris Dancing to contemporary Dance Music from Traditional Seafood to Beer, in fact such an enormous range, that it would be impossible to mention everything here. The variety of captivating and novel events occurring all over Britain every year means that, young or old, whatever your interests, hobbies, sport or pastimes, you can't fail to find your ideal day out.

This guide includes everything to make your chosen excursion run as smoothly as possible. It contains full details about each festival, from how to get there by car or public transport and the availability of parking to ticket prices (including concessions) and full descriptions of what is going on, where and when. So if you're looking for something to do, go to our easy reference county guide and delve into any county that interests you. Events are also listed alphabetically by town, so that if you are visiting a particular town you can incorporate the corresponding festival as well, to make your day out complete.

This guide is as comprehensive as we have been able to make it. However, if you know of, or are involved in, the organisation of a festival, large or small, ancient or modern, that is not included in this edition, please let us know about it by completing the form at the back of this book and returning it to us for inclusion in next year's guide.

This edition has been made possible by the cooperation of all the festival contacts who have provided us with this mine of information – thank you for your help, without which this book would not exist.

BEDFORDSHIRE

Bedford Beer Festival

Type of Festival: **Beer**
Contact: **Mike Benyon**
Address:
Campaign for Real Ale Ltd
North Bedfordshire Branch
Bedford
Bedfordshire
Tel. No:
0171 438 7600 (work)
01234 364796 (home)
Date(s) of Festival:
7th-10th October 1998
Times of Festival:
7th: 5pm - 10.45pm. 8th: 11.30am - 2.30pm and 5pm -10.45pm
9th: 11.30am - 10.45pm
10th: 11.30 - 10.45pm
Cost for Adults:
£2 per head after 6pm, except Fridays £2.50 per head
Cost for Children:
Free. Not allowed in after 6pm
Special discounts:
CAMRA members
Tickets available from: **The door**
Venue:
Corn Exchange, St Pauls Square, Bedford
What's On:

Sample Real Ales from all over the UK. Also sample Belgian Beer. Saturday evening listen to live music.
Historical Background:
Standard CAMRA Beer Festival now in its 21st year

Bedford River Festival

Type of Festival:
Music, Sports, Arts, Traditional.
Contact: **Mr Andrew Jacques**
Address:
River Festival Office
Bedford Corn Exchange
St Pauls Square
Bedford
Bedfordshire
MK40 1SL
Tel. No: **01234 343992**
Fax No: **01234 343992**
Date(s) of Festival:
23rd - 24th May 1998
Times of Festival:
Saturday 23rd noon - 11pm
Sunday 24th noon - 7pm
Cost for Adults: **Free**
Cost for Children: **Free**
Tickets available from:
Not required
Routes by Car:
Major trunk roads to Bedford
Train/Other:
Bedford Railway Station
Venue:
Bedford
Facilities (Parking):
3 Festival Car parks
Facilities (Disabled):
Disabled parking available
What's On:
Main music stage, motor village, arts village, sports village, procession, river activities
Historical Background:
Held every 2 years since 1978. A major community event

Lazy Sunday

Type of Festival:
Music and Community
Contact: **Graham Bawden**
Address:
85 Bamford Road
Bedford
Bedfordshire
MK42 0NH
Tel. No: **01234 360601**
Fax No: **01234 360601**
Date(s) of Festival: **5th July 1998**
Times of Festival: **12 noon - 10pm**
Cost for Adults: **Free**
Cost for Children: **Free**
Tickets available from:
Not required
Venue:
By the River Great Ouse
Facilities (Parking):
Parking available. Toilets etc
Facilities (Disabled):
Access for disabled, and toilet facilities
What's On:
Live bands, sound systems, walkabout performers, storytellers, circus performances, puppet theatre, workshops, children's entertainment area, market, beer tent
Historical Background:
Started by local Unemployed Workers Centre in 1984. Now organised by community members. Attendance has grown from 400 in 1984 to 12,000 in 1997. Involves many diverse communities
Media/Public Comments:
"Nice to see so many people from so many different communities and backgrounds having such an enjoyable day"

Luton Festival of Transport

Type of Festival: **Transport**
Contact: **Miss J Parker**
Principal Promotions Officer
Address:
Luton Borough Council
146 Old Bedford Road
Luton
Bedfordshire
LU2 7HM
Tel. No: **01582 876083**
Fax No: **01582 876009**
Date(s) of Festival:
14th June 1998
Times of Festival: **10am - 5pm**
Cost for Adults: **£2**
Cost for Children: **£1**
Special discounts:
Family ticket £5; OAPs £1
Tickets available from: **The door**
Venue:
Stockwood Country Park, Farley Hill, Luton
Facilities (Parking):
Parking available
What's On:
400 veteran, vintage and classic cars plus motorbikes, fire engines, buses, commercial vehicles, tractors, 1950s/1960s double decker bus service to Vauxhall Motor Heritage Centre open day

BERKSHIRE

Bracknell Festival

Type of Festival: **Music**
Contact: **Simon Chatterton**
Address:
South Hill Park
Ringmead
Birchhill
Bracknell
Berkshire
Tel. No: **01344 427272**
Date(s) of Festival:
3rd - 5th July 1998
Times of Festival:
3rd: 6pm - late; 4th: 12 noon -
late; 5th: 12 noon - 10.30pm
Cost for Adults:
Whole weekend: £30. Friday (1
day) £10; Saturday/Sunday: £14
Cost for Children:
Over 13s half price. Under 13s free
Special discounts:
Concessions for parties of 6+
Tickets available from:
South Hill Gate Box Office:
01344 484123
Routes by Car:
M3 Junction 3; M4 Junction 10,
Birchhill area just off A322 near
the National Hilton
Train/Other:

South West Trains (0345 484950)
Bee Line Buses (01344 424938)
Venue:
South Hill Park, Birchhill,
Bracknell, Berkshire
Facilities (Parking):
Free parking for weekend ticket
holders. Camping facilities
Facilities (Disabled):
Disabled access
What's On:
Musicians, theatre performances,
cinema, circus acts, music and
dance workshops, comedy, special
children's area, exotic foods, late
bars. Eddie Reader vocalist (Fair-
ground Attraction), De La Soul,
Natacha Atlas, Red Snapper
Historical Background:
1998 celebrates 25 years of Festi-
vals at South Hill Park
Media/Public Comments:
Described by visitors as "a mod-
ern day party in an English country
garden"

Newbury Spring Festival

Type of Festival: **Arts**
Contact: **Phillipa Regan**
Address:
1 Bridge Street
Newbury
Berkshire
RG14 5BE
Tel. No: **01635 528766**
Fax No: **01635 528690**
Date(s) of Festival:
8th - 22nd May 1999
Times of Festival: **Various**
Cost for Adults: **Various**
Cost for Children: **Various**
Tickets available from:
The Administrator:
01635 528766

Routes by Car:
M4 (Junction 13) to Winchester
Train/Other:
Newbury Train Station
Venue:
Various venues within Newbury
Facilities (Parking): **Various**
Facilities (Disabled): **Some of the venues have limited wheelchair accommodation**
What's On:
Orchestral concerts, recitals, chamber music, jazz, film, children's events. Art exhibitions and lectures.
General Information:
Two weeks of outstanding arts events at a variety of beautiful venues in and around Newbury including parish churches, country houses and hotels. For further details contact: Bronwen Sutton: 01635 32421

Reading CAMRA Beer Festival

Type of Festival: **Beer**
Contact: **Peter Adams**
Address:
19 Belmont Road
Reading
Berkshire
RG30 2UT
Tel. No: **0118 9590407**
Date(s) of Festival:
29th April - 2nd May 1999
Times of Festival:
Thursday: 4.30 - 11pm
Friday/Saturday: 11am - 3pm and 4.30pm - 11pm
Sunday: 12noon - 4pm
Cost for Adults:
Sunday free otherwise £2 - £4
Cost for Children:
Children are not allowed into the marquee

Tickets available from:
Purchase tickets by post (see above)
Routes by Car:
From M4 out of London, exit at Junction 10, A329(M) into City Centre. Head for East Reading and drive through Cemetery Junction, take right hand fork to Town Centre. Right hand side of Pub
Train/Other:
5 mins from Reading Station
Venue:
Hobgoblin Public House (Broad Street), Hop Leaf (Southampton Street) Horse and Jockey (Castle Street), Bottoms Up
Facilities (Parking):
5 minutes from Town Centre
What's On:
Real ales to sample and enjoy. Outside Events: belly dancers, local bands, Morris men and on Friday night a R &B Band. Bouncy castles and children's areas to enjoy during the lunchtime sessions

Reading '98

Type of Festival:
Music (Pop and Rock)
Contact: **Dora Masullo**
Address:
Mean Fiddler
Information Line
Reading
Berkshire
Tel. No:
Info Line: 0181 963 0940
Dora Masullo: 0181 961 5490
Date(s) of Festival:
28th - 30th August 1998
Times of Festival: **Various**
Cost for Adults: **Various**
Tickets available from:

TicketMaster: 0541 500044:
Also available from 0171 344 0044
Routes by Car:
Junction 11 M4, A329(M) direct
from Bracknell, Junction 10 M4
Train/Other: **Reading Station**
Venue:
**Little John Farm, Richfield Avenue,
Reading**
What's On:
A feast of rock and pop. Attendance usually around 45,000

Windsor Festival

Type of Festival: **Music and Arts**
Contact: **Jane Krivine**
Address:
**Windsor Festival Society Ltd
P O Box 1214
Windsor
Berkshire
SL4 6YS**
Tel. No:
01753 623400 or 0171 286 8811
Fax No: **0171 286 8811**
Date(s) of Festival:
**19th September - 3rd October
1998**
Times of Festival: **Various**
Cost for Adults: **From £3 - £30**
Special discounts:
**Special discounts for friends of the
Windsor Festival and lunchtime
concerts are free to Advantage
Card holders**
Tickets available from:
Windsor Festival Society Ltd
Routes by Car:
From Junction 5 on M4
Train/Other:
Windsor Central (from Paddington)
Venue:
**Windsor Castle, State Apartments, St George's Chapel,
Library, Dungeon, Eton College,**

**Eton College Chapel and Election
Hall**
Facilities (Parking):
Town Parking
Facilities (Disabled):
**Access for disabled at some venues. Guide to Events published in
May from the Festival Office**
What's On:
Concerts
Historical Background:
**Began in 1969, up to 50 or 60
events each year from classical to
jazz and from opera to early music**
Media/Public Comments:
**"What a glorious Windsor Festival
it has been this year - an almost
exhaustible treasure chest" Windsor and Eton Observer 1997**

May Fayre and Country Fair

Type of Festival: **May Folk Festival**
Contact: **Gerald Aggett**
Address:
**Wokingham Lions Club
"Oaklands"
London Road
Binfield
Berkshire
RG42 4AB**
Tel. No: **01344 423147**
Fax No: **01344 423147**
Date(s) of Festival:
May 3rd 1999
Times of Festival: **10am - 5pm**
Cost for Adults: **Free**
Cost for Children: **Free**
Tickets available from:
Not required
Routes by Car:
**M4 Junction 10 Wokingham A329
to Town Centre**

Train/Other:
Wokingham Station
Venue:
Wokingham Town Centre
Facilities (Parking):
All town centre car parks will be open and free of charge
What's On:
Town Centre is closed. Town hall will be used for art exhibition/ flower display. Street market, maypole, Scottish and morris dancing, youth jazz service scene, jugglers, mime artists, funfair, country fair, farm animals, craft demo, steam train, games etc
Historical Background:
Wokingham is an historic town with Victorian Town Hall. Festival started 10 years ago and the May Fayre is an annual event
Media/Public Comments:
"One of the best family festivals in Berkshire"
General Information:
The Town Centre fills with thousands of people. Good family fun and entertainment. The shops are open and old pubs put on special food for example Pig Roast and Grills. Free programme can be obtained in "Help Shop"

Victorian Winter Carnival

Type of Festival:
Traditional Street Market and Parade
Contact: **Angie Gibson**
Town Centre Manager
Address:
The Town Hall
Market Place
Wokingham

Berkshire
RG40 1AS
Tel. No: **0118 9781985**
Fax No: **0118 9781985**
Date(s) of Festival:
29th November 1998
Times of Festival: **10am onwards**
Cost for Adults: **Free**
Cost for Children: **Free**
Tickets available from:
Not required
Routes by Car:
All major roads through the town centre
Train/Other:
Town Centre will be closed. Pedestrian routes and public transport
Venue: **Wokingham Town Centre**
Facilities (Parking):
Parking available
Facilities (Disabled):
Disabled parking available
What's On:
Street entertainers, charity stalls, pig roast, children's rides, carnival parade, local youth bands, carol singers, switching on the Christmas lights, Santa's Grotto
Historical Background:
4th year of Festival which raises over £20,000 for charity

BUCKINGHAMSHIRE

St Martin's Day

Type of Festival: **Religious**
Contact:
The Vicar, St Martins Church
Address:
2 Manor Road
Fenny Stratford
Milton Keynes
Buckinghamshire
MK2 2HW
Tel. No: **01908 372825**
Date(s) of Festival:
11th November 1998 and 1999
Times of Festival:
12 noon, 2pm, 4pm in Leon Recreation Ground, Bletchley and 7pm in the Church
Cost for Adults: **Free**
Cost for Children: **Free**
Special discounts: **Free**
Tickets available from:
Not required
Routes by Car:
A5, A4146 to Fenny Stratford
Train/Other:
Fenny Stratford and Bletchley Stations
Venue:
St Martins Church, Leon Recreation Ground, Bletchley

Facilities (Parking):
Parking in Queensway or George Street Car park
What's On:
St Martins Church, firing of Fenny Poppers in Leon recreation ground. Visit Bletchley Park (scene of WW2 code breaking activity)
Historical Background:
St Martins Church was built by the Lord of the Manor, Browne Willis in 1730 in memory of his grandfather, the famous physician who worshipped at St Martin-in-the-Fields, London, and died on St Martin's Day in St Martin's Lane in that same parish
General Information:
Fenny Poppers are mini cannons packed with gunpowder and paper resembling cast iron beer mugs. One exploded in 1859 and they were all recast. To celebrate St Martin's Day Browne Willis decreed that these cannons should be fired

Great Linford Waterside

Type of Festival: **Canal**
Contact: **Tracy Clark**
Address:
Courtyard Arts Centre
Parklands Way
Great Linford
Buckinghamshire
Tel. No: **01908 608108**
Date(s) of Festival:
19th - 21st June 1998
Cost for Adults: **Free**
Cost for Children: **Free**
Tickets available from:
Not required
Routes by Car:
M1 Junction 14 A422

Train/Other:
Wolverton Railway Station (Gt Linford 20 mins walk)
Venue:
Courtyard Arts Centre (see above)
What's On:
Community festival alongside Grand Union Canal, live music, stalls, displays, workshops, crafts, flower and beer festivals. Big band and big picnic in the evening

Haddenham Festival and Craft Fayre

Type of Festival:
Traditional Music and Ceilidh
Contact: **John Heydon**
Address:
5 Church Street
Haddenham
Aylesbury
Buckinghamshire
HP20 2QP
Tel. No: **01296 415333**
Fax No: **01296 397092**
Date(s) of Festival:
5th December 1998
Times of Festival:
12 noon - midnight (craft fayre 10.30am - 4pm)
Cost for Adults:
£14 for festival. £1 for craft fayre
Cost for Children:
7-17s half price. Under 7s free
Special discounts:
OAPs half price. Discounts for tickets purchased before 14/11: £12. Evening only: £8
Tickets available from:
Box Office, Haddenham Festival (see above)
Routes by Car:
M40 to Thame and then follow A413 to Haddenham. A41/413 to Aylesbury and then follow signs for Thame
Train/Other:
Marylebone to Haddenham and Thame Parkway and a 20 min walk. 280/282 bus from Oxford to Aylesbury stops outside the Venue
Venue:
Haddenham Village Hall, Haddenham, nr Aylesbury
Facilities (Parking):
Village Hall has a large car park
Facilities (Disabled):
Good access for disabled
What's On:
Concerts, dance displays, dancing, music and song sessions with participatory ceilidh in the evening, craft fayre during the day.
Historical Background:
The ceilidhs started 26 years ago. Approximately 15 years ago the ceilidhs were organised on the first Saturday of the month and the festival is an extension of the monthly ceilidh into a whole day event with a craft fayre on the first Saturday in December.
Media/Public Comments:
"Brilliant"
"Don't miss it, it's great"
"What a wonderful opportunity to buy Christmas presents from the Craft Fayre"
These are some of the comments from last year's visitors
General Information:
Haddenham is a village in Buckinghamshire; it has ceilidhs on the 1st Saturday of each month and the festival is a small informal event with concerts and workshops throughout the day culminating in a concert and a ceilidh in the evening

Wycombe Arts Festival

Type of Festival:
Music, Visual, Performing Arts
Contact: **John Beaumont**
Address:
Cagehill
Upper Stanley Road
Sands
High Wycombe
Buckinghamshire
HP12 4DB
Tel. No: **01494 523697**
Date(s) of Festival:
24th April - 22nd May 1999
Times of Festival: **Various**
Cost for Adults:
Many free events. Other events from £3 - £10
Tickets available from:
Festival Box Office, Swan Theatre, St Marys Street, High Wycombe: 01494 512000
Routes by Car:
M40 from London/Oxford
Train/Other:
High Wycombe Station
Venue:
Various venues in and around High Wycombe
Facilities (Parking):
Good Town Parking
Facilities (Disabled):
Disabled access to most venues
What's On:
Concerts, organ recitals, variety showtime, poetry readings, theatre, open art exhibition, festival antiques fair, photography exhibition, comedy, concerts, toy theatre (puppets) musicals (Hello Dolly), jazz café, children's choir, Mayor-making ceremony
Historical Background:
Festival is now in its 34th year
Media/Public Comments:

"Best wishes to the Wycombe Arts Festival for 1998. I feel sure it will be rewarding and enjoyable both for the visitors and those taking part"
Wendy Craig, President (stars in "Matters Matrimonial" Friday 22nd May)

Milton Keynes Brass Band Festival

Type of Festival: **Music**
Contact: **Beryl Lack**
Address:
24 Williams Close
Hanslope
Milton Keynes
Buckinghamshire
MK19 7BS
Tel. No: **01908 510809**
Date(s) of Festival:
Sunday 14th February 1999
Times of Festival:
All day events
Cost for Adults:
To be advised. 1998 price was £5
Cost for Children:
To be advised. 1998 price was £3
Special discounts:
To be advised. 1998 prices were £3 for OAPs, UB40s and students
Tickets available from:
On the door
Train/Other:
Milton Keynes and Wolverton Stations
Venue:
Stantonbury Leisure Centre, Milton Keynes
Facilities (Parking):
Parking available
Facilities (Disabled):
Disabled parking available and wheelchair access

What's On:
Approximately 50 brass bands from all parts of the country playing for up to 22 mins each. Listen to a wide variety of well performed music.
Historical Background:
The festival originated at the suggestion of local brass band musicians with the backing of Milton Keynes Development Corporation
Media/Public Comments:
The British Bandsman gives us very good reports
General Information:
The Festival is now recognised as one of the best brass band entertainment contests in the country. There are 4 different grades of bands. Each section has a short set of test pieces with varying degree of difficulty according to the grade of the band.

Festival Fortnight

Type of Festival:
Music, Drama, Dance
Contact: **Gerald Stratton**
Address:
3 Lakes Lane
Newport Pagnell
Buckinghamshire
MK16 8HS
Tel. No: **01908 610526**
Date(s) of Festival:
3rd - 19th July 1998
Cost for Adults: **Various**
Tickets available from:
40 page programme (£1) from Gerald Stratton (see above)
Routes by Car:
M1 Junction 14
Train/Other:
Milton Keynes Station

Venue:
Various venues within Newport Pagnell, eg Swan Hotel, Lovat Hall, Tickford Abbey and others
Facilities (Parking):
Town Centre parking. Admission to Riverside Meadows 50p for all.
What's On:
Concerts: classical, big band, jazz, drama "Talking Heads", dance and morris dancers, procession of floats, displays, bands, stalls, workshops, children's entertainment, funfair, exhibitions, flower festival, barbecue, history walks, evensong
Historical Background:
1998 heralds the 9th year the Festival and the carnival have joined forces to give Newport Pagnell a festive fortnight

Olney Pancake Race

Type of Festival: **Traditional**
Contact: **Janet Jones**
Address:
Olney Centre
The High Street
Olney
Buckinghamshire
Tel. No: **01234 711679**
Date(s) of Festival:
24th February 1999
Times of Festival: **11.55am**
Cost for Adults: **Free**
Cost for Children: **Free**
Tickets available from:
Not required
Routes by Car:
A509 Olney Town Centre
Train/Other:
Central Milton Keynes Railway Station then bus or Taxi
Venue: **Streets of Olney**
What's On:
Local townswomen's race with

frying pans from Market Square to the Church. Street entertainment in Town Centre from 10.30am. Warning bells are rung from the church steeple and the race is started. . .

Historical Background:

Tradition declares that the race was first run in 1445, pancakes at that time being a popular dish and receiving the royal favour. It was run on Shrove Tuesday, day before Lent and the whole day was given over to festivities, pranks and pastimes.

General Information:

Olney has been invaded every Shrove Tuesday by an increasing number of visitors from all parts of the country and the world at large. Buckinghamshire's most famous local custom. Featured in films, radio and TV and the National Press every year

National Folk Music Festival

Type of Festival:
Traditional Music and Song
Contact: **John Heydon**
Address:
4 Church Street
Aylesbury
Buckinghamshire
HP20 2QP
Tel. No: **01296 415333**
Fax No: **01296 397092**
Date(s) of Festival:
16th - 18th April 1999
Times of Festival:
Friday 8pm - Sunday 5pm
Cost for Adults: **£35 TBC**
Cost for Children: **Half price**
Special discounts: **None**

Tickets available from:
Box Office: 01296 415333
(see above)
Routes by Car:
M1 Junction 4, then A60 to Loughborough
Train/Other:
Loughborough Station then bus
Venue:
Sutton Bonington Campus, nr Loughborough
Facilities (Parking):
Good parking
Facilities (Disabled):
Good access for disabled at all venues
What's On:
Concerts, lectures, workshops, informal sessions. There are participatory informal sessions where anyone who wishes to can take part either in a song session or in a music session
Historical Background:
The Festival started 35 years ago and was organised by the English Folk Dance and Song Society but now run privately. More than a festival, it is a gathering of people with one common aim - to share that enthusiasm and to continue and nurture the traditions
Media/Public Comments:
"It's perfect"
"Best I've ever been to"
"Excellent"
These are some of the comments made by visitors last year
General Information:
"The national" is a unique experience. Not only does it attract the best traditional performers, but what is at the heart of the Festival is the warm and welcoming atmosphere that comes from the shared passion of the living traditions.

Wendover Canal Festival at Tring

Type of Festival: **Traditional**
Contact: **Richard House**
Address:
Wendover Arm Trust
8 Eythrope Road
Stone
Aylesbury
Buckinghamshire
HP17 8PG
Tel. No: **01296 748036**
Date(s) of Festival:
30th - 31st May 1999
Times of Festival: **10am - 5pm**
Cost for Adults: **£3**
Cost for Children: **£1**
Special discounts:
£2 for OAPs, UB40s, students and £7 family (in advance)
Tickets available from:
Tourist Info: 01296 330559
Box Office: 01296 748036
Routes by Car:
On B488 at Tring off the A41
Train/Other:
Euston - Birmingham/Rugby Line. Tring Station 1- 2 miles
Venue: **Canal site at Tring**
Facilities (Parking):
Large Free car park "Field Site"
Facilities (Disabled):
Limited disabled parking at Field Site, however wheelchairs welcome
What's On:
Large craft fair, arena events, novelty dog show, clowns, Punch and Judy, canal boats, live music, trade stands, classic cars, canal trips, military vehicle rides, licensed bar, children's rides, bouncy castles, inflatable games. Evening entertainment and bar
Historical Background:
9th annual event in current form.

All profits are used for restoration of Wendover arm of Grand Union Canal. Over 100 canal boats and over 60 caravans stay on site all weekend
Media/Public Comments:
"Best public event in the year"
"10,000 people kept happy and interested all day"
"Terrific value - never a dull moment"
General Information:
Varied programme of entertainments, majorettes, jugglers, children's entertainers, live music, escapologists, clowns, canal horse harness demonstrations, classic car parades, dog shows etc. Friendly, relaxed atmosphere run by volunteers

Winslow Jazz Festival

Type of Festival: **Jazz**
Contact: **Ted Griffin**
Address:
Manor Farm House
Steeple Claydon,
Winslow
Buckinghamshire
MK18 2QF
Tel. No: **01296 730575**
Date(s) of Festival:
9th - 11th April 1999
Times of Festival: **All weekend**
Cost for Adults: **Various**
Tickets available from:
Box Office (see above)
Routes by Car:
Aylesbury to Buckingham Road
Train/Other:
Milton Keynes and Aylesbury Stations
Venue:
Streets of Winslow, Winslow Parish Church and Bell Hotel

Facilities (Parking):
Free Town parking
Facilities (Disabled):
Access for disabled in all venues
What's On:
Jazz and Dine at the Bell Hotel, Jazz Parade in Winslow Streets and a Jazz service at Winslow Parish Church
Historical Background:
Third festival

CAMBRIDGESHIRE

Grass Roots Festival of the New Theatre

Type of Festival: **Theatre**
Contact:
Cambridge Drama Centre
Address:
Covent Garden
Mill Road
Cambridge
Cambridgeshire
CB1 2HR
Tel. No: **01223 322748**
Fax No: **01223 302589**
Date(s) of Festival:
22nd June - 18th July 1998
Times of Festival:
8pm each evening

Cost for Adults: **£6.50**
Cost for Children: **£4.50**
Special discounts:
UB40s, OAPs, Students: £4.50
Tickets available from:
Box Office: 01223 322748
Routes by Car:
Train/Other:
Cambridge Railway Station - 5 mins walk
Venue:
Cambridge Drama Centre
Facilities (Parking):
Queen Anne Multi Storey Car park, Gonville Place
Facilities (Disabled):
Fully accessible for disabled
What's On:
New plays by local writers, open rehearsals, informal presentations
Historical Background:
A platform for local writers to experiment with new ideas. The first festival was in 1995.
Media/Public Comments:
"A fine festival of plays and players"

Camfest

Type of Festival: **Arts Festival**
Contact: **Alexandra Wren**
Address:
ADC Theatre
Park Street
Cambridge
Cambridgeshire
CB5 8AS
Tel. No: **01223 359547**
Fax No: **01223 300085**
Date(s) of Festival:
25th June - 25th July 1998
Times of Festival:
Various daily
Cost for Adults:
Various, many events free. Others

up to £10

Special discounts:

Concessions available for students and OAPs

Tickets available from:

Box Office: 01223 359547

Routes by Car:

Access to City by all routes

Train/Other:

Cambridge Station south side of town. Regular buses to centre

Venue:

ADC Theatre, Cambridge

Facilities (Parking):

City car parks. One in Park Street 50 yds from the theatre

Facilities (Disabled):

Assistance available but please telephone 01223 359547 prior to visit

What's On:

Focus on as many different art forms as possible: Art Galleries, Musicals, Opera, Drama, Poetry Reading, Story telling, children's workshops and much much more

Historical Background:

Previously a fringe to Arts Festival but now amalgamated into one and named Camfest

Media/Public Comments:

"A good mix"

"Absolutely inclusive"

"No-one can say there's nothing for them"

Ely Folk Festival

Type of Festival: **Folk Music**

Contact: **Ely Folk Weekend**

Address:

78 West End
Haddenham
Cambridgeshire
CB6 3TE

Tel. No: **01353 741032**

Date(s) of Festival:

10th - 12th July 1998

Times of Festival:

4pm Friday -11pm Sunday

Cost for Adults:

Season Tickets: £25 (£28 from 1st June). Tickets available for day/ evenings

Cost for Children:

Under 16 half price. Under 10s free

Special discounts:

Free tickets available for Stewards.

Tickets available from:

Booking Office (see above)

Routes by Car:

20 mins from A14 and M11

Train/Other:

Main rail line to London and good rail links to the rest of the country

Venue:

Pocket Park, Ely

Facilities (Parking):

Free parking on site. Free camping for tents and caravans on the main site for season ticket holders. The river is nearby for boat moorings.

Facilities (Disabled):

Access for disabled, disabled toilet facilities

What's On:

Vin Garbutt, Cordelia's Dad, Fernhill, Cran Madigan, Calluna, Epona, Ian Bruce, Breeze Band, Sid Kiper, The Aqua Sisters, The Wide Glide Band and much more. Plus morris displays, real ale bar, concerts, sessions, workshops, children's workshops

Historical Background:

Now in its 14th year, the 1998 festival promises to be the best yet

Media/Public Comments:

"With its beautiful cathedral towering majestically above the

surrounding countryside, the city of Ely lies in the heart of Cambridgeshire Fens, famed for spectacular sunsets and the vast expanse of sky. What better location for a weekend of music and dance"

Oundle International Festival

Type of Festival: **Music**
Contact: **Trisha Ryan**
Address:
The Old Crown
Clapthorn
Peterborough
Cambridgeshire
PE8 5BJ
Tel. No: **01832 272026**
Date(s) of Festival:
10th -19th July 1998
Times of Festival:
Some lunch time recitals; mostly evening and twilight
Cost for Adults:
£4 - £14
Tickets available from:
Tourist Information Office, West Street, Oundle: 01832 274333. Credit card Hotline: 01832 275109
Routes by Car:
12 miles west of Peterborough, 7 miles north of A14 (A1-M1 link road)
Train/Other:
Peterborough Station
Venue:
Various venues in Oundle and surrounding district i.e. Peterborough Cathedral. Also concerts at Kings College, and Clare College, Cambridge University
Facilities (Parking):
Easy parking

Facilities (Disabled):
Assistance given to disabled. Prior notification required
What's On:
Lots of concerts including Evelyn Glennie, Nikolai Demidenko, Male Voice Choir from Moscow, Rimsky Korsakow Quartet, BBC Big band, Humphrey Lyttelton. Also many town and country walks, visit fine country houses like Deene Park
Historical Background:
Established in 1985 to run alongside the internationally renowned summer school for young organists. The Festival has been a magnet every July since then for organists and classical music lovers
General Information:
Oundle is a charming small Cambridgeshire market town with lovely stone houses surrounded by beautiful countryside

Peterborough Beer Festival

Type of Festival: **Real Ale, Music**
Contact: **Mike Lane**
Address:
Peterborough
Cambridgeshire
Tel. No: **0850 334203**
Date(s) of Festival:
25th - 29th August 1998
Times of Festival:
Mainly pub opening hours
Cost for Adults:
Varies from £2 - £3.50
Special discounts:
Free of charge to CAMRA members
Tickets available from: **At the event**
Routes by Car:
Peterborough Town Centre

Train/Other:
Peterborough Station
Venue:
Peterborough River Embankment
Facilities (Parking):
Town Parking
Facilities (Disabled):
Access for disabled
What's On:
Watch this space!
Historical Background:
21st year. Largest UK beer festival under canvas
Media/Public Comments:
All positive local press and radio
General Information:
Expected 32,000 visitors over the 5 days

VW Action

Type of Festival:
Music and Automobile
Contact: **Brian Burrows**
Address:
**VW Action
Enterprise House
133 Blyth Road,
Hayes
Middlesex
UB3 1DD**
Tel. No: **0181 573 8761**
Fax No: **0181 561 9114**
Date(s) of Festival:
11th - 13th September 1998
Times of Festival:
12 noon Friday - 5pm Sunday
Cost for Adults: **£20**
Cost for Children: **Half Price**
Tickets available from:
Brian Burrows (see above)
Routes by Car:
A1 sign posted from Peterborough turn off
Train/Other:
Peterborough Station

Venue:
East of England Showground, Peterborough
Facilities (Parking):
Plenty of parking. Camping available
What's On:
Live bands, top DJs, concours/show cars, trade stands, mega movie screen (all night), speedway, autojumble, club displays, stunt displays, marching bands, "Miss VW" competition, charity auction
Historical Background:
22 years old. The largest VW event in the world - fact!
Media/Public Comments:
"VW Action has finally found its feet again after a shaky hand over and now its promising to grow once more to become the grand finale of the VW show season"

Truckfest

Type of Festival:
Truck Festival
Contact: **Russell Harman**
Address:
**Live Promotions Limited
The Millstone
St Thomas Road
Spalding
Lincolnshire
PE11 2XY**
Tel. No: **01775 768661**
Fax No: **01775 768665**
Date(s) of Festival:
2nd - 3rd May 1999
Times of Festival: **9am - 6pm**
Cost for Adults: **£8**
Cost for Children: **£4**
Special discounts:
Family £20 per day. Adults £7.50 per day. Children £3.50 per day (if booked in advance)

Tickets available from:
Live Promotions Ltd/Tourist Information
Routes by Car: **A1 Peterborough**
Train/Other:
Peterborough station, then bus link
Venue:
East of England Showground, Peterborough
Facilities (Parking):
Free on site parking, camping facilities
What's On:
New trucks, stunt trucks, custom trucks, international trucks, celebrity appearances and lots of action
Historical Background:
Started in 1983 and developed into the largest event of its kind in Europe
Media/Public Comments:
"The biggest"; "The Best"; "An articulated extravaganza"
"Truckfest is a Mecca for the haulage industry" BBC's Top Gear

Stilton Cheese Rolling

Type of Festival: **Traditional**
Contact: **Mrs Main**
Address:
Stilton Community Association
8 Caldegate Road
Peterborough
Cambridgeshire
PE7 3RH
Tel. No:
01733 241206 (home)
01780 434201 (work)
Date(s) of Festival:
3rd May 1999
Times of Festival: **10am - 2.30pm**
Cost for Adults: **Free**
Cost for Children: **Free**
Tickets available from:

Not required
Routes by Car:
8 miles south of Peterborough off the A1 at Norman Cross
Train/Other:
Peterborough nearest railway station. Bus from Peterborough and Huntingdon
Venue:
Stilton Village Centre, 6 miles from Peterborough
Facilities (Parking):
Street parking
What's On:
Mayday celebrations, processions, street entertainment, stilton cheese rolling competitions, stalls, sideshows, fairground, music, fancy dress.
Historical Background:
Annual commemoration of the famous cheese
Media/Public Comments:
"Expect 3000 attendance"
"Family day out"

Wisbech Rose Fair

Type of Festival:
Flower and Craft
Contact: **Mrs Janet Stevens**
Address:
Wisbech Rose Fair Committee
Briarwood
23 Station Drive
Wisbech
Cambridgeshire
PE13 2PP
Tel. No: **01945 461393**
Date(s) of Festival:
1st - 5th July 1998
Times of Festival:
9.30am - 8.30pm daily
Cost for Adults:
Free. Can reserve for cream teas, high teas and luncheons

Cost for Children: **Free**
Tickets available from:
01945 581397/01945 582508
Routes by Car:
A47 East or West. A17, A1 from North
Venue: **Wisbech**
Facilities (Parking):
Car parking on site, coach parking next to site. Coach parties catered for.
Facilities (Disabled):
Disabled parking on site
What's On:
One of the largest flower festivals in East Anglia. See exotic blooms and traditional English blooms brought together in a themed display set against the backdrop of St Peter and St Pauls Church. Visit the gardens, browse among stalls, crafts etc
Historical Background:
The Festival was started 27 years ago for the repairs to St Peters and St Pauls Church. This is a large church with many interesting features built circa 1111AD. This year's theme is "Healing Hands" to celebrate the 50th anniversary of the NHS
General Information:
Carnival Day on Saturday 4th July 1998. Carnival processions

CHANNEL ISLANDS

Guernsey Lily International Amateur Film and Video Festival

Type of Festival: **Amateur Film**
Contact: **Joan M Ozanne**
Address:
La Geniesse
Forest
Guernsey
Channel islands
GY8 0AQ
Tel. No: **01481 38147**
Fax No: **01481 35989**
Date(s) of Festival:
25th - 27th September 1998
Times of Festival:
Morning, afternoon and evenings
Cost for Adults:
To stay in Peninsula: £28 B&B pp Double/Twin Room; Single Room supplement of £8 per night. Entry fees for competitions £5 per entry
Tickets available from:
Peninsula Hotel: 01481 48400 or fax: 01481 48706
Train/Other:
By Sea: from Poole or Dorset. A number of airports in UK and Europe
Venue:
Peninsula Hotel, Les Dicqs Vale, Guernsey.
What's On:
Screening of successful films followed by presentation of awards and dinner, films and talk by Tony Rose. The Festival is considered to be one of the most prestigious, people return year after year
Historical Background:
Now in its 7th year following a suc-

cessful inaugural festival in 1992, this Festival presents the perfect opportunity for amateur film makers to combine a holiday with a chance of winning an award.

Media/Public Comments:
The media has been very complimentary

General Information:
Only 80 miles from the South Coast of England, Guernsey is just waiting to be discovered. Its unique atmosphere inspired both Renoir and Hugo and its cobbled streets, bustling harbour and glorious coast and countryside are a pleasure to explore

Jersey Environment Week

Type of Festival:
Green Festival

Contact:
Mike Stentiford
Interpretation Officer

Address:
Jersey Tourism
Environmental Services Unit
Jersey

Tel. No:
01534 483140

Date(s) of Festival:
15th - 23rd May 1998

Times of Festival: **Various**

Routes by Car:
High speed Car Ferry from Poole

Train/Other:
Flights direct from 26 UK airports

Venue:
Various venues throughout Jersey

Facilities (Disabled):
Wheelchair wander for disabled

What's On:
Environmental lectures, wildlife lectures, Petal and Bugs walk, Puffin Paddle, cycle tours of archaeological sites, open days, presentations, walks, exhibitions, and outside activities. Top TV personalities will also be on the island for the week.

Historical Background:
The Festival is now in its 2nd year and was designed to celebrate Jersey's commitment to the environment

Media/Public Comments:
"The week aims to promote Jersey's environmental assets through the medium of discovery, enjoyment and protection." Tourist Office

The Island of Jersey Floral Festival

Type of Festival: **Floral**

Contact: **Mrs Pam Daltrey**

Address:
Jersey Tourism
Liberation Square
St Helier
Jersey

Tel. No: **01534 500700**
Fax No: **01534 500899**

Date(s) of Festival:
13th - 18th June 1998

Times of Festival: **Various**

Routes by Car:
High speed car ferry from Poole

Train/Other:
Direct air links from 26 UK airports

Venue:
Everywhere is crammed full of

blooms, with car parks, private gardens, hotels, shops, pubs putting on a magnificent floral display

What's On:

Private and commercial gardens competition, gardening demonstrations, gardening celebrities such as Fred Downham and Ashley Stephenson talking on a variety of subjects

Media/Public Comments:

Jersey's resident garden expert, Denis Shaw can be heard on BBC Radio Jersey giving the Island's gardeners regular tips and advice.

"One of the loveliest things is judging the pubs" BBC Gardeners World

General Information:

The island looks its very best during the festival as it coincides with the annual Garden Award Scheme when private gardeners and businesses have their very best floral displays on show

The Jersey Good Food Festival

Type of Festival: Cuisine
Contact: Mike Tait
Public Relations Dept
Address:
Jersey Tourism
Liberation Square
St Helier
Jersey
Tel. No: 01534 500700
Fax No: 01534 500899
Date(s) of Festival:
23rd - 31st May 1998
Times of Festival: Various
Routes by Car:

High speed car ferry from Poole
Train/Other:
Direct flights from 26 UK airports
Venue:
Various venues within St Helier and Jersey including Longueville Manor Hotel, Central and Fish Markets of St Helier etc
Facilities (Parking):
Good parking. Guest houses and hotels to suit all pockets
What's On:
A chance to taste the very best local produce, sample the cooking skills of top Jersey chefs and learn how to prepare some dishes, Jersey Chef's Circle menu competition, visiting chefs from around the world giving visitors a taste of international cuisine

Media/Public Comments:

"Encourages visitors to enjoy food in a relaxed atmosphere at different venues around Jersey"
Bournemouth Evening Echo
"Diners are spoilt for choice and quality with lots of excellent island produce and scrumptious seafood"
Herald

General Information:

There is a lot happening in Jersey in 1998 plus a brand new maritime musuem and the opening of the world's largest steam clock. There are magnificent castles and prehistoric sites, potteries, gardens and the world famous Gerald Durrell Zoo

Jersey Jazz Festival

Type of Festival: **Music**
Contact: **Alan Auld**
Address:
Jersey Jazz Promotions
8 Le Clos de la Chasse
Rue de la Guilleaumerie
St Saviour
Jersey
JE2 7H2
Tel. No: **01534 864296**
Fax No: **01534 864296**
Date(s) of Festival:
30th April - 3rd May 1999
Times of Festival:
Free afternoon sessions. Evening sessions (varying prices). 3 day pass £39. Lunch £13
Tickets available from:
Arts Centre Box Office: Philips Street, St Helier: 01534 873767
Routes by Car:
Car Ferry high speed from Poole
Train/Other:
Flights direct from UK
Venue:
Various venues within St Helier
Facilities (Parking):
Hotel and municipal car parks
What's On:
Highlights include: US Tenor Sax star Harry Allen, a tribute to Burt Bacharach starring Claire Martin - recent winner of the UK Jazz Singer Award and "Salute to Sinatra" starring Louis Hoover and Pete Cater Big Band
Historical Background:
1998 is the 13th year of the festival which features visiting US stars with the best of UK and local musicians
Media/Public Comments:
"A meaty and high powered festival, full of undiluted and uncompromising jazz" Jazz Journal
General Information:
Browse around the VAT free shops of St Helier. Explore the varied list of attractions on the beautiful island of Jersey

Jersey Festival of World Music

Type of Festival: **Music**
Contact: **Gerry Jackson**
Address:
Eskdale
5 Sunshine Avenue
St Saviour
Jersey
JE2 7TS
Tel. No: **01534 607860**
Fax No: **01534 607860**
Date(s) of Festival:
1st - 4th October 1998
Times of Festival: **Various**
Cost for Adults:
£25 (festival pass)
Cost for Children:
Under 14s free
Special discounts:
OAPs, UB40s, students: £15 (festival pass)
Tickets available from:
Jersey Arts Centre, Phillips Street, St Helier: 01534 873767
Routes by Car:
High speed car ferry from Poole
Train/Other:
Direct flights from 26 UK airports
Venue:
Various venues on the Island
What's On:
A mix of dances, concerts, informal sessions, family events
Historical Background:
1998 will be the 23rd consecutive year of the Festival. From humble begin-

nings, (it started as a folk festival) it is now an integral part of the Island's cultural calendar and is recognised in Europe and further afield as a festival of very high quality

Guernsey Eisteddfod Festival

Type of Festival:
Music, Drama, Arts
Contact: **Mrs Barbara Minta**
Guernsey Eisteddfod Society
Address:
La Chapelle
Rue des Chapelles
Vale Guernsey
GY8 5BJ
Tel. No:
01481 47606 (home)
01481 45417 (work)
Fax No: **01481 41253 (work)**
Date(s) of Festival:
9th February - 7th March 1999
Times of Festival: **TBC**
Cost for Adults: **TBC**
Venue:
Various venues on the Island
Facilities (Parking): **Ample Parking**
What's On:
Arts and crafts exhibition and competition, art, craft needlework, photography, cookery, silk painting, flower arranging (lasting 4 days). Attend competitions of French, speech and drama, roller skating etc
Historical Background:
1998 sees the festival's 69th year
Media/Public Comments:
"Acclaimed as a great success"

CHESHIRE

Chester Summer Music Festival

Type of Festival: **Music**
Contact: **Fiona England**
Address:
8 Abbey Square
Chester
Cheshire
CH1 2HU
Tel. No: **01244 320722**
Fax No: **01244 341200**
Date(s) of Festival:
10th - 25th July 1998
Cost for Adults: **From £3 to £20**
Special discounts:
Concessions available for OAPs
Tickets available from:
Box Office: 01244 320700
Routes by Car:
Chester situated near M53 and M56
Train/Other:
Main route from Euston
Venue:
Various venues within Chester
Facilities (Parking):
Good parking facilities
Facilities (Disabled):
All venues have disabled access and there are stewards to assist

What's On:
Everything from opera to pop classics
Historical Background:
Celebrating festival's 21st birthday

The Chester Literature Festival

Type of Festival: **Literature**
Contact: **Freda Headmen Administrator**
Address:
**The Chester Literature Festival Committee
8 Abbey Square
Chester
Cheshire
CH1 2HU**
Tel. No: **01244 319985**
Fax No: **01244 341200**
Date(s) of Festival:
3rd - 18th October 1998
Times of Festival:
Mostly evenings, some lunchtime, some Sunday afternoons
Cost for Adults:
Varies from £3 (individual events) - £75 (season tickets)
Cost for Children:
Individual events £2
Special discounts:
Concessions available for OAPs and "Friends of the Festival"
Venue: **Chester City Centre**
Facilities (Parking):
Parking within the City Centre
What's On:
Events within Civic Theatre eg Roger McGough and Willy Russell
Historical Background:
Founded in 1989 and organised by local bookshops, writer's groups and Chester Arts Association. The major events are sponsored by publishers. Authors who took part last year were **Michael Holroyd, Dame Cleo Laine, Sarah Harrison, Dickie Bird and many more**
Media/Public Comments:
**"Am emerging Festival"
The Times**
General Information:
Chester is a beautiful medieval walled city on the River Dee. The City contains "The Rows", these are shops built on two tiers. Birth Place of Randolph Caldecott, with Lewis Carroll's birthplace close by. Chester also has a beautiful cathedral

Easter Festival

Type of Festival:
Family Entertainment
Contact: **Christine Green**
Address:
**Tatton Park
Knutsford
Cheshire**
Tel. No: **01565 654822**
Fax No: **01565 650179**
Date(s) of Festival:
10th - 12th April 1999
Times of Festival:
10.30am - 4.30pm
Cost for Adults:
£4.50 (1998 price) 1999 TBC
Cost for Children:
£2.50 (1998 price)
Tickets available from:
01565 654822 or at the gate
Venue:
Tatton Park, Knutsford
Facilities (Parking):
Parking available
What's On:
Circus, family show, craft hall, fairground, rides, pottery fun, Victorian household recreation, hog bending contest, pancake race and lots more

Knutsford Royal May Day

Type of Festival: **Traditional**
Contact: **Mr A De Ruiter**
Address:
Roebuck Farm
Manchester Road
Knutsford
Cheshire
Tel. No: **01565 633143**
Date(s) of Festival:
1st Saturday in May 1999
Times of Festival:
2pm procession
Cost for Adults: **Free**
Cost for Children: **Free**
Tickets available from:
Not required
Routes by Car:
Knutsford sign posted from all major routes including M6
Train/Other:
To Knutsford Railway Station. Manchester/Chester Line
Venue:
Knutsford Town Centre
Facilities (Parking):
Town Centre parking facilities
What's On:
Procession including horse drawn vehicles, approximately 500 children in costume, bands, vintage bicycles including Penny Farthings, morris dancing, May Queen crowning, country dancing, maypole dancing, visit largest travelling funfair in the North West.
Historical Background:
Commenced 1864 to celebrate coming of Spring. Visited by the Prince of Wales in 1887 resulting in the granting of the prefix "Royal"
Media/Public Comments:
Has appeared on TV and Radio on several occasions and received good comments
General Information:
All vehicles are horse drawn - no mechanical vehicles. Dancers are trained by the Knutsford Royal May Day Committee. There is a free firework display on the following day at dusk

Gawsworth Hall Open Air Festival

Type of Festival:
Drama, Opera, Concerts
Contact: **Mrs E Richards**
Address:
Gawsworth Hall
Macclesfield
Cheshire
SK11 9RN
Tel. No: **01260 223456**
Fax No: **01260 223469**
Date(s) of Festival:
18th June - 15th August 1998
Times of Festival: **7.30pm**
Cost for Adults: **Various**
Cost for Children:
Under 6s free
Routes by Car:
2 miles south of Macclesfield on A536
Train/Other:
Macclesfield Main Line
Venue:
Gawsworth Hall, Macclesfield
Facilities (Parking):
Free Car/coach parking
Facilities (Disabled):
Limited disabled access to some shows
What's On:
Theatre, jazz, brass, opera, classical, folk. A Gilbert and Sullivan

production, an opera, and various one night concerts

Historical Background:
Gawsworth Hall is a 15th century house home of the Fitton Family. Mary Fitton was possibly the 'dark lady' of Shakespeare's sonnets. Open Theatre has been running since 1972 and now includes 4 plays (one amateur, three professional)

Media/Public Comments:
Articles featured in the Manchester Evening News

General Information:
Covered Grandstand to see events. Famous acts attending such as Hinge and Bracket, Rolf Harris, Peter Skellern/Richard Stilgoe

Middlewich Folk and Boat Festival

Type of Festival:
Traditional Music and Dance
Contact: **Mr Dave Thompson**
Address:
33 Manor Crescent
Middlewich
Cheshire
CW10 0EW
Tel. No: **01606 836896 after 6pm**
Date(s) of Festival:
19th - 21st June 1998
Times of Festival:
8.30pm - 11pm daily
Cost for Adults: **£20**
Cost for Children:
Under 12s free. Under 16s half price
Special discounts:
£16 before 1st June
Tickets available from:
Box Office: Southway, Middlewich, Cheshire, CW10 9BL
Routes by Car:
M6 Junction 18, Middlewich 2 miles

Train/Other:
Winsford/Sandbach Station (3 miles)
Venue:
Middlewich Town
Facilities (Parking):
On site parking, camping, toilets and showers
What's On:
Over 300 musicians, singers and dancers, mainstage marquee concerts, acoustic stage on one central site. Family and children's events, 8 canalside venues, host sessions and singarounds. Also morris dancers, traditional narrowboat rallies with special events
General Information:
A unique annual event in the centre of the canal network and salt mining industry of Cheshire. 60 page event programme available early May and features all artists appearing in the festival

Arley Garden Festival

Type of Festival:
Gardening and Plants
Contact: **Judy Popley**
Address:
Arley Hall
Northwich
Cheshire
CW9 6NA
Tel. No: **01565 777353/777284**
Fax No: **01565 777465**
Date(s) of Festival:
27th - 28th June 1998
Times of Festival: **10am - 5pm**
Cost for Adults:
£5 (£1 extra to visit Arley Hall)
Cost for Children: **£2**
Special discounts: **OAPs £4.50**
Tickets available from: **Arley Hall**
Routes by Car:

Junction 19/20 M6; Junction 9/10 M56, 5 miles from Knutsford
Train/Other:
Knutsford, Northwich, Crewe. Coaches from Altringham. Book with Altringham Tourist Information
Venue:
Arley Hall, Northwich
Facilities (Parking):
Free car park, free plant creche, refreshments
Facilities (Disabled):
Close to Festival
What's On:
Plant stalls from all over UK selling rare, unusual, popular plants, trees shrubs etc. Accessories from fountains to follies, sculpture, garden tools and furniture. Refreshments, Gardener's questionnaire, view Arley Hall and gardens
Historical Background:
4th year of high quality show situated at world famous gardens. Beautiful countryside
Media/Public Comments:
"Good value, good products, good food, great atmosphere, bring your cheque book!"

Arley Music Festival

(not confirmed at time of going to print)
Type of Festival: **Music**
Contact: **Judy Popley**
Address:
Arley Hall
Northwich
Cheshire
CW9 6NA
Tel. No: **01565 777353**
Fax No: **01565 777465**
Date(s) of Festival:
12th -13th September 1998

Times of Festival: **11am - 5pm**
Cost for Adults: **TBC**
Tickets available from:
Arley Hall
Routes by Car:
M6 Junction 19/20, M56 Junction 9/10
Train/Other:
Knutsford or Northwich. Pre-book coach transport from Altringham Tourist Information Office: 0161 912 5931
Venue:
Arley Hall, Northwich
Facilities (Parking):
Free Parking
Facilities (Disabled):
Access for disabled
What's On:
Music for everyone! From opera to steel bands, tin whistle to brass band. Also children's workshops. Make your own music!

Warrington New Summer 98 Free Streets Festival

Type of Festival:
Outdoor Street Entertainment
Contact: **Stewart Leather**
Arts Development Unit
Address:
Community Services Dept
3rd Floor
New Town House
Buttermarket Street
Warrington
Cheshire
WA1 2NH
Tel. No: **01925 442887**
Fax No: **01925 442888**
Date(s) of Festival:
24th - 25th July 1998
Times of Festival: **10am - 4pm**

Cost for Adults: **Free**
Cost for Children: **Free**
Tickets available from:
Not required
Train/Other:
Town Centre is in close proximity to central and Bank Quay stations
Venue:
Warrington Town Centre (Bridge Street and Market Gate area)
Facilities (Parking):
Town Centre parking
Facilities (Disabled):
Town Centre is pedestrianised and accessible by wheelchair
What's On:
A diverse array of internationally acclaimed street entertainers.

CORNWALL

Cornwall Theatre and Heritage

Type of Festival:
Theatre and Performing Arts
Contact: **Julie Grey**
Address:
CTF
Shire House
Mount Folly Square

Bodmin
Cornwall
PL31 2DQ
Tel. No:
01208 74159 Ext 30
Box Office: 01208 76616
Fax No:
Box Office: 0128 79268
Date(s) of Festival:
27th June - 4th July 1998
Times of Festival: **Various**
Cost for Adults: **£1 - £6**
Cost for Children: **£1 - £3**
Special discounts:
Concessions available and some free shows
Tickets available from: **Box Office**
Routes by Car:
A30 to Bodmin
Train/Other:
To Bodmin Parkway - Taxi to Town Centre
Venue: **Bodmin**
Facilities (Parking):
Parking close to all venues
Facilities (Disabled):
Full disabled access to all venues
What's On:
Wide range of professional performing arts, dance, theatre, music, and cabaret
Historical Background:
Started in 1996, funded by South West Arts and involves all of Cornwall's professional practitioners and promoters
Media/Public Comments:
"A seven day extravaganza of professional performing arts and provides a yearly focus for the arts in Cornwall"

Bude Jazz Festival

Type of Festival:
Jazz (mainly Traditional)

Contact: **Jean Manuel**
Address:
**c/o Bude Visitor Centre
The Crescent
Bude
Cornwall
EX23 8LE**
Tel. No: **01288 356360**
Fax No: **01633 220422**
Date(s) of Festival:
29th August - 5th September 1998
Times of Festival:
12 noon - 11.30pm
Cost for Adults:
£11 per day, Stroller tickets for full week £49.50
Special discounts: **None**
Tickets available from:
Jean Manuel (see above)
Routes by Car:
Bude is on the A39 Atlantic Highway between Bideford and Wadebridge (off M5, Junction 27). Also from A30 Okehampton by-pass via the A3072
Train/Other:
Rail and coach passengers should travel to Exeter and use the special connecting bus service to Bude. For details contact Western National at Bodmin: 01208 79898
Venue:
More than 20 venues within Bude
Facilities (Parking):
Parking available in various car parks. Jazz venues are mostly within walking distance of one another. Continuous "Jazzbus" services, free of charge to all ticket holders, link all stroller jazz venues. Bude has many excellent hotels, bars and restaurants
What's On:
200 jazz events in 8 days - all day every day. In addition there are 5 late evening "Festival Extra" events, separately ticketed. These include: Bob Kerr's Whoopee Band, Humphrey Lyttelton and the tribute to Billie Holiday "Lady Sings the Blues"
Historical Background:
Festival is in its 11th year.
General Information:
100 bands with leading jazz musicians from all over Britain. 20 different venues hosting jazz events. Four New Orleans style street parades, two jazz services, etc

Calstock Festival

Type of Festival:
Arts, Music
Contact: **Mex Merrick**
Address:
**Calstock Village Hall
Calstock
Cornwall**
Tel. No:
Festival Office: 01822 834480
Date(s) of Festival:
23rd - 29th May 1998
Times of Festival: **Various**
Cost for Adults:
Varies per event/workshop. All events require tickets phone 01822 834480
Cost for Children: **Concessions**
Tickets available from:
Festival Office: 01822 834480
Train/Other:
Plymouth to Calstock
Venue: **Calstock**
Facilities (Parking):
Parking available
Facilities (Disabled):
Disabled access for most events
What's On:
Festival day, Saturday 24th May.

Music, market, and street theatre. Lots of workshops for children and adults art exhibition, classical concerts, rave, gigs and much more

Historical Background:
Now in its 10th year, and events differ from year to year

Falmouth Big Green Fair

Type of Festival:
Environmental and Traditional
Contact: **Suzanne Williams**
Address:
Falmouth Green Centre
Union Road
Falmouth
Cornwall
TR11 4JW
Tel. No: **01326 375158**
Date(s) of Festival: **4th July 1998**
Times of Festival: **11am onwards**
Cost for Adults: **Free**
Cost for Children: **Free**
Tickets available from:
Not required. Programmes 50p
Train/Other:
1 mile from Penmere Station, Falmouth Buses from "The Moor" Falmouth
Venue:
1 mile from Town Centre in the grounds of Falmouth school, Trescobees Rd
Facilities (Parking):
Some parking but there will be a charge
Facilities (Disabled):
Due to some steep slopes and steps, access for disabled people is slightly curtailed. However extra help is available upon request.
What's On:
Music (drumming, hurdy gurdy, belly dancing and other exotica), green art exhibition, vegan food stalls, local cider and ale, environmental stalls. Bouncy castles, workshops, complimentary healing tasters such as reflexology, massage etc

Historical Background:
4th year of the fair. Each year expands. It was originally set up to promote green issues
Media/Public Comments:
"Enjoyed the relaxed sunny atmosphere"
"It was fun to have a go at Tai Chi and drumming"

Tall Ships Race

(also see World Watersports Festival)
Type of Festival: **Watersports**
Contact: **Tabitha Smith**
Address:
Cornwall '98
Trevint House
Strangeways Villas
Truro
Cornwall
TR1 2PA
Tel. No: **01872 223527**
Fax No: **01872 242470**
Date(s) of Festival:
16th - 19th July 1998
Times of Festival:
19th July 1998 (noon) when the race starts
Cost for Adults: **Free**
Cost for Children: **Free**
Tickets available from:
Not required
Venue: **Falmouth**
What's On:
The Tall Ships are the focal point of the Watersports Festival. Concerts, music sound stage, stalls, multi-cultural crafts, maritime art exhibitions, dragon boat racing, tug of war, funfair sea shanties, street

theatre evening entertainment and culminating in firework display

Historical Background:

Falmouth has the 3rd largest natural deep water harbour in the world. Home to the Tea Clipper Cutty Sark and the main port for the Packet Ships. The 1st race was staged in 1956 between Torbay and Lisbon. Sponsored by Cutty Sark Whiskey.

Media/Public Comments:

Largest annual sailing event in the world. It is estimated that more people visited the Tall Ships Race from the 4 ports in 1996 than attended the Olympic Games in Atlanta. Approximately 100 ships will attend from 20 countries.

General Information:

Between 80 and 100 vessels joining the fleet in 1998, comprising 2500 cadets and crews from 20 nations. Old friends such as STA Schooner, Sir Winston Churchill, Malcolm Miller, square rigged ships like STS Kruzenshtern, STS Mir. Barques, Brigs, Ketches

Annual Ceremonial Assembly

Type of Festival: **Traditional**

Contact: **Mr J C Jenkin**

Address:

Crosstrees
Water Lane
Golant
Fowey
Cornwall
PL23 1LG

Tel. No: **01726 833402**

Date(s) of Festival:

5th September 1998

Times of Festival: **2pm**

Cost for Adults: **Free**

Cost for Children: **Free**

Tickets available from:

Not required

Train/Other:

To Penzance (10 miles)

Venue: **Fowey Town Centre**

What's On:

Procession of approximately 250 robed Bards, delegates from Wales and Brittany. Dancers from local primary school. Ceremony in Cornish language, translation for visitors, presentation of awards and prizes. Initiation of new Bards. Celtic dancing, stalls, evening concerts

Historical Background:

Bards - story tellers, poets and singers were important as keepers of the heritage. In Celtic times they assembled at venerated sites in Britain, revived in 1925.

Media/Public Comments:

Well known in Cornwall and is televised by BBC and ITV. A unique ceremony commemorating the Celtic nature and heritage of Cornwall

General Information:

On Sunday 6th September 1998 at 3pm there is a Cornish language evensong in the Parish Church

Daphne Du Maurier Festival

Type of Festival:

Arts and Literature

Contact:

Paul Warbey/Jonathan Aberdeen

Address:

Restormel Borough Office
Penwinnick Road
St Austell
Fowey
Cornwall
PL25 5DR

Tel. No: **01726 74466**
Fax No: **01726 68339**
Date(s) of Festival:
7th - 16th May 1999
Times of Festival: **Various**
Cost for Adults:
Various. Some venues free. Booking fee £1
Cost for Children:
Concessions for children
Special discounts:
Discounts for students, UB40's
Tickets available from:
Box Office: 01726 77477
Routes by Car:
From the M5 at Exeter, choice of routes A38 or A30. The A30 is mostly dual carriageway and runs within 5 miles of Lostwithiel leading on to Fowey
Train/Other:
All services stop at St Austell (9 miles from Fowey). National Express. Good local Bus service runs between St Austell and Fowey most of which pass through Tywardreath, Par and St Blazey
Venue:
Fowey and surrounding areas
Facilities (Disabled):
A lot of venues are not suitable for wheelchair access. Full list available on request from Festival Information Line: 01726 74324
What's On:
Celtic and folk music, art exhibitions, guided walks, street fayres, drama, comedy, day schools, camera clubs, orchestras and more
Historical Background:
This 1999 Festival will celebrate the life and works of Daphne Du Maurier and host a range of Arts and Literary events.
General Information:
The festival programme has at- tracted many well known authors and personalities. "Festival Village" is to be set in Fowey overlooking the picturesque estuary

Fowey Royal Regatta and Carnival

Type of Festival: **Sailing/Carnival**
Contact: **Mr G Jane**
Address:
24 Windmill
Fowey
Cornwall
PL23
Tel. No: **01726 832133**
Date(s) of Festival:
16th - 22nd August 1998
Times of Festival: **Various**
Cost for Adults:
Voluntary donation
Cost for Children: **Free**
Tickets available from:
Not required
Routes by Car:
B3269 or A3082 to Fowey
Train/Other:
Par 3 miles, St Austell 9 miles. Regular bus service to Fowey, National Express St Austell. Hoppa Bus 24 from St Austell
Venue: **Fowey**
Facilities (Parking):
Additional parking made available
Facilities (Disabled):
Limited disabled parking
What's On:
Sailing races, carnival, band concerts, giant pastry ceremony, Red Arrows flying display, fireworks
Historical Background:
Started more than 150 years ago
Media/Public Comments:
"Brilliant week"
"People book from one year to next"

Helston Flora Day

Type of Festival: **Street Dancing**
Contact: **C L Oliver**
Address:
Helston Flora Day Association
51 Coinage Hall Street
Helston
Cornwall
TR13 8EU
Tel. No: **01326 572082**
Date(s) of Festival:
Saturday 8th May 1999
Times of Festival:
All day. First dance starts at 7am
Cost for Adults: **Free**
Cost for Children: **Free**
Tickets available from:
Not required
Venue: **Helston Town Centre**
Facilities (Parking):
The streets of the town are closed to all traffic from 6.30am until the early evening
What's On:
Continuous programme of dancing: children's dance featuring over 1000 children dressed in white, the Hal-An-Tow pageant about the history of health. Early dance and evening dance. Thousands sing and dance their way through the town in colourful costumes and top hats
Historical Background:
This festival has been called Flora, Furry, Faddy Day. A spring Festival when nature's barrenness gives way to fertility and life (spring) over death (winter), the passing from darkness into light. Probably the survival of a pagan ritual dance. "Chorus: Hal-an-Tow, Jolly rumble, For we are up as soon as any day, O, And for to fetch the Summer home, The Summer and the May, O, For Summer is come, O,
And Winter is agone, O.
Excerpt from "Hal-An-Tow Song"
General Information:
Flora - thought to be due to 18th century classicism when it became habit to refer so much to Greek or Roman origin.
Furry - from the Latin "Feria" - feast day. Faddy - English dance

Mevagissey Feast Week

Type of Festival: **Traditional**
Contact: **Robin Hunkin**
Address:
Dealand Cottage
57 Cliff Street
Mevagissey
Cornwall
OPL26 6QL
Tel. No: **01726 842920**
Date(s) of Festival:
28th June - 4th July 1998
Times of Festival: **Various**
Cost for Adults: **Various**
Cost for Children: **Various**
Venue: **Mevagissey Town Centre**
What's On:
Choral concerts, flower festival, traditional processions and dancing, live music events, water sports, gig racing, carnivals, village fete, firework display
Historical Background:
Ancient Festival celebrating the Feast of St Peter, the Patron Saint of Mevagissey and Fishermen
Newquay 1900 Week
Type of Festival: **Victorian**
Contact: **Mrs Mary Cook**
Address:
Chairman
3 Bayview Terrace
Newquay
Cornwall
TR7 2LR

Tel. No: **01637 878735 Box Office**
Date(s) of Festival:
5th July - 10th July 1998
Times of Festival: **Various**
Cost for Adults:
**Max £2 for marquee held concerts.
Most other events free**
Cost for Children: **Half price**
Tickets available from:
Box Office (see above)
Venue:
Various venues within Newquay
Facilities (Parking):
**No Parking on the Killacourt. Car
Parks nearby**
Facilities (Disabled):
**Cars may have access to the
Killacourt for the disabled**
What's On:
**Processions, carnival, flora dance,
torchlight procession and firework
display, concerts, choirs and bands,
markets, craft fair, baby show, chil-
dren's sports etc.**
Historical Background:
**Commenced in July 1982 as part
of maritime England. Victorian
theme to celebrate the era when
Newquay became known as a holi-
day resort.**
Media/Public Comments:
**Featured on The Clothes Show
BBC1 and The Jameson's Pro-
gramme BBC Radio 2**

West Cornwall Maritime Festival

Type of Festival: **Martime, Music**
Contact:
Penwith District Council
Address:
**Tourism Dept
Penwith Council
St Clare
Penzance**

Cornwall
Tel. No: **01736 362341**
Date(s) of Festival:
10th - 14th July 1998
Times of Festival: **Daily**
Cost for Adults:
**Festival is free. Entertainment
marquees various charges.**
Tickets available from:
**Entertainment Tickets:
Martin Val Baker: 01736 366077**
Routes by Car: **A30 to Penzance**
Train/Other:
Penzance Main Line Station
Venue:
**Penzance Harbour areas. Main en-
tertainment marquee. Penzance
main car park. Marquees also at
St Antony's Gardens**
What's On:
**Music events include: Mary Black,
Sharron Sharron Band, Australian
Pink Floyd, Osbisa, Edward II, Jools
Holland R & B Band, Eliza Carthy
Band, Balham Alligators, La Cucina
etc**
Historical Background:
**First Festival was in 1996 which
was a great success**

St Marys Arts Festival

Type of Festival:
Music, Dance, Drama, Arts
Contact: **Peter Mound**
Address:
**Festival Chairman
37 Chapel Street
Penzance
Cornwall**
Tel. No: **01736 367659**
Date(s) of Festival:
22nd August - 5th September 1998
Times of Festival: **Various**
Cost for Adults: **Various**
Special discounts:

Concessions available
Tickets available from:
Peter Mound (see above)
Routes by Car:
A30 to Penzance
Train/Other:
Penzance mainline station
Venue:
St Marys Church, Church Street, Penzance
Facilities (Parking):
Parking close by
Facilities (Disabled):
Disabled parking
What's On:
Art Exhibition, (local artists), concerts. Drama, Poetry reading, light entertainment, jazz, pavement art for children, Cornish male voice choir concert
Historical Background:
St Marys Art Festival is an event dedicated to generations of highly talented young musicians. This festival gives local musicians the opportunity to play on their home ground and for Cornwall's residents and visitors to hear their music.
Media/Public Comments:
Excellent reviews. Event covered by Classic FM Radio, Radio Cornwall and local newspapers

Lowender Peran

Type of Festival:
Traditional Music and Dance Celtic Festival
Contact: **Gerald Morris**
Address:
Worthyvale House
Penhallow
Truro
Cornwall TR4 9NA
Tel. No: **01872 553413**

Fax No: **01872 553413**
Date(s) of Festival:
14th -18th October 1998
Cost for Adults: **Season Ticket £24**
Cost for Children:
Under 13s free (accompanied by adult)
Tickets available from:
Gerald Morris (see above)
Train/Other:
Truro Station and National Buses to Perranporth
Venue:
Ponshere Hotel, Perranporth, and Perranporth Town Centre
What's On:
Ceilidhs, Celtic dance spectacular, concerts, dance displays, pipers, story telling, poetry reading, singers session, dance workshops, children's sessions. Also Celtic craft market, costumed pageant through streets, guided historical walk.
Historical Background:
Started in 1978 to celebrate the Celtic connection between Cornwall and the other Celtic nations such as Scotland, Ireland, Isle of Man, Wales, Brittany
General Information:
Celtic culture is not a spectator sport. The festival has always emphasised participation and there will be opportunities for people to join in with a whole range of activities

Polperro Festival

Type of Festival:
Arts, Music, Drama
Contact: **Mr E C Pilcher**
Address:
"Village Yokel"
Fore Street

Polperro
Cornwall
Tel. No: **01503 272129**
Fax No: **01503 272775**
Date(s) of Festival:
20th - 28th June 1998
Cost for Adults:
£1 - £4. Lots of free entertainment
Cost for Children:
Concessions available
Special discounts:
Concessions available
Tickets available from: **The door**
Routes by Car:
Dual carriageway A38 to Plymouth, A38 to Trerulefoot Roundabout, turn left to Looe, and then to Polperro
Train/Other:
Plymouth, bus or taxi
Venue: **Polperro Village**
Facilities (Parking):
Main Village car park
Facilities (Disabled):
Most venues are accessible to disabled
What's On:
Bert Jansch (folk), Brian Patton (poet), poetry evening, poetry competition, steel band, Kingsmen Barbershop group, Theatre Rotto (puppets). Also street entertainment, Morris Men/Ladies. All the local Pubs have live music to suit various taste.
Historical Background:
Festival now in its 3rd year. Small village festival set up to promote the village and its heritage and aiming to provide entertainment and enlightenment for all.
"The best comments that we have, is that visitors are booking especially for the festival"

General Information:
Polperro is a small beautiful Cornish fishing village ideal for a community based friendly festival

St Ives September Festival

Type of Festival: **Music and Arts**
Contact: **St Ives Festival Limited**
Address:
Festival Office
The Guildhall
Street an Pol
St Ives
Cornwall
Tel. No: **01736 796888**
Date(s) of Festival:
7th - 19th September 1998
Times of Festival: **Evenings**
Cost for Adults: **Varies**
Tickets available from:
Box Office: 01736 366077
Train/Other: **St Ives via St Erth**
Venue:
Various venues within St Ives
What's On:
Music, poetry exhibitions, folk, jazz, world music, June Tabor Band, Ralph McTell, Nick Lowe, Gordon Giltrap, Dick Gaughan.
Outdoor pursuits such as walking, beaches, cliffs swimming etc
Historical Background:
Festival began in 1978 and ended in 1986 then revived in 1994. Now attracts thousands to St Ives in late part of the season
Media/Public Comments:
"Consistently good Festival" Venue Magazine Festival Guide.
"Best little Festival in Europe" American Magazine

St Ives Feast

Type of Festival: **Traditional**
Contact: **Town Clerk**
Address:
The Guildhall
Street an Pol
St Ives
Cornwall
TR26 2DS
Tel. No: **01736 797840**
Date(s) of Festival:
Monday nearest 3rd of February, but never on the 3rd
Times of Festival:
9.30am - 12.30pm
Cost for Adults: **Free**
Cost for Children: **Free**
Tickets available from:
Not required
Routes by Car:
St Ives A3074/B3306
Train/Other:
St Erth - St Ives branch Line. St Ives National Express
Venue: **St Ives**
Facilities (Parking):
Town Centre Car parks
What's On:
Mayoral procession followed by hurling of silver ball. Meeting of Western Hunt. Distribution of pennies to children under the age of 7 and then the Feast Monday Rugby match
Historical Background:
The silver ball is thrown by the Major, it is caught by one of the waiting crowd and passed from one to another on the beaches or streets of the town. The person holding the ball at noon takes it to the major at the Guildhall and receives a Crown piece

Wadebridge Folk Festival

Type of Festival: **Traditional Folk**
Contact:
Clare Wilson - Publicity Officer
Address:
3 Bossiney Grange
Bossiney
Tintagel
Cornwall
PL34 0AX
Tel. No: **01840 770946**
Date(s) of Festival:
28th - 31st August 1998
Times of Festival:
Friday pm to Monday midnight
Cost for Adults: **Various**
Cost for Children: **Various**
Special discounts:
Concessions available
Tickets available from:
Sue Sedgewick, Yew Cottage, Rosehill, Lanivet, Cornwall, PL30 5ES: 01208 831123
Routes by Car: **A39 /A 30/ M5**
Train/Other:
Bodmin Parkway and connecting bus service. National cycle route all the way to Wadebridge
Venue: **Wadebridge**
Facilities (Parking):
Free parking Sunday/Monday. Camp site with showers close to venues
Facilities (Disabled):
Some disabled access
What's On:
Traditionally based folk from Europe (including Ireland) and UK. Children's events, workshops, street entertainment, high profile concerts to unscheduled sessions almost continually. Festival bar and festival kitchen

Historical Background:
Originally offshoot of Sidmouth 1969-1972 in Falmouth. Moved to Wadebridge in 1973 - now in its 26th year
Media/Public Comments:
"Friendly family festival in a small market town"

Total Eclipse of the Sun

Type of Festival: **Astronomic**
Contact: **Steve Winston**
Address:
Cornwall County Council
County Hall
Truro
Cornwall
Tel. No: **01872 322000**
Fax No: **01872 323804**
Date(s) of Festival:
11th August 1998
Times of Festival:
Partial Eclipse will begin at 9.57am, followed by Total Eclipse at 11.11am, lasting until 11.13am and again followed by a partial eclipse until 12.32 pm
Cost for Adults: **Free**
Cost for Children: **Free**
Tickets available from:
Not required
Venue:
Examples: Bodmin 1 min 46 secs. Falmouth 2mins 6 secs.
What's On:
The total eclipse will last on average a little over 2 mins. The sudden darkness and drop in temperature has a marked effect on wildlife and the man made environment such as street lighting etc
Historical Background:
The track of the eclipse will follow a broad band approximately 100km wide, beginning off Nova Scotia and continuing across SW Cornwall (its first landfall) NE France, S Belgium, Luxembourg, S Germany, Austria, Hungary, Romania and so on to India
General Information:
In Falmouth a partial eclipse will begin at 9.57am followed by a total eclipse at 11.11am lasting until 11.13am and again followed by a partial eclipse until 12.32 am

World Watersports Festival

Type of Festival:
Maritime (Cornwall '98)
Contact: **Tabitha Smith**
Address:
Cornwall '98
Trevinct House
Strangeways Villas
Truro
Cornwall
TR1 2PA
Tel. No: **01872 223527**
Fax No: **01872 242470**
Date(s) of Festival:
March - October 1998
Times of Festival:
Tel: Nivea Sunday Cornwall '98 Hotline 0891 22 1998
Tickets available from:
Tel: Nivea Sunday Cornwall '98 Hotline 0891 221998
Venue:
Various venues throughout Cornwall
What's On:
Angling, canoeing, classic boats, dinghy racing, land yachting, pilot gig racing, power boating, rowing, speed sailing, surfing, surf lifesaving, swimming, Tall Ships, water skiing, windsurfing, yacht racing.

General Information:
Spans every area of Cornwall, taking in beaches, bays, estuaries, rivers and lakes with over 100 events. Alongside the watersports there are concerts, shows, exhibitions, song, dance, parties, art and fireworks

Truro Jazz Festival

Type of Festival: **Music**
Contact: **John Simpson**
Address:
Stonecutters
Keeble Park
Perranwell Station
Truro
Cornwall
TR3 7NL
Tel.No:
01872 862058 (evening)
01872 222202 (day)
Fax No: **01872 223785**
Date(s) of Festival:
1st - 5th July 1998
Times of Festival:
1st-3rd: 8pm- 11pm 4th: all day
5th: 10.30am - 12am
Cost for Adults:
Mixture of free event in pubs and ticket only events. £6 - £10 depends on gig
Venue:
Various venues within Truro town centre
Facilities (Parking):
Many parking areas around and in Truro. City Centre closed to traffic on Saturday
What's On:
New Orleans-style marching band - Parade 11am and 3pm. Stalls Carousel etc. Listen to lots of Jazz. On Sunday at 10.30am there is a Gospel service at Truro Methodist Church with Pauline Pearce.

Historical Background:
This is the 3rd Jazz Festival
General Information:
All confirm a happy occasion, lots of fun and lots of great jazz. Not to be missed

CUMBRIA

Appleby Jazz Festival

Type of Festival:
Modern Improvised Music
Contact: **Neil Ferber**
Address:
Bongate Mill
Appleby
Cumbria
CA16 6UR
Tel. No: **017683 51052**
Fax No: **017683 51052**
Date(s) of Festival:
24th - 26th July 1998
Times of Festival:
24th: 2pm -midnight
25th: 11am - midnight
26th: 11am - 9pm
Cost for Adults: **£35 per weekend**
Special discounts:
Concessions available
Tickets available from:
Box Office, Bongate Mill, Appleby

Routes by Car:
Appleby 12 miles from Junction 38 off M6. On the A66 from Scotch Corner to the Laites
Train/Other:
Settle - Carlisle Line
Venue:
The River Field, Bongate Mill, Appleby
Facilities (Parking):
Good parking in field next to venue
What's On:
The Stan Tracey Octet, Peter King Quartet, Don Weller Quartet, Art Themen Quartet, Tim Garland, Bryan Spring Trio, Gordon Beck, Gerard Presencer/Evan Parker, Alan Barnes, Bobby Wellins, Septpiece, Stacey Kent Quartet
Historical Background:
1998 is the Festival's 8th year. Previously held in the Castle, 1998 sees a new venue. All the events take place in a large marquee
Media/Public Comments:
Well received by the media and becoming more popular as the years go by
General Information:
The best of modern jazz in an idyllic setting next to the River Eden which runs through the historical town of Appleby

Bawming of the Thorn

Type of Festival: **Traditional**
Contact: **Ron Anderson**
Address:
**Appleton Thorn Primary School
Arley Road
Appleton Thorn
Cumbria
WA4 4RW**
Tel. No: **01925 266764**
Fax No: **01925 861737**

Date(s) of Festival: **20th June 1998**
Times of Festival: **1.30pm**
Cost for Adults: **Free**
Cost for Children: **Free**
Tickets available from:
Not required
Routes by Car:
M6 Follow signs to Thorn Cross
Train/Other:
Warrington Bank Quay
Venue: **Appleton Thorn**
Facilities (Parking):
Parking around Village and by the school.
Facilities (Disabled):
Ceremony and school are accessible to disabled
What's On:
Bawming ceremony at the tree in the centre of the village. Dance and song, school fete, sing "Bawming Song" parade, fete, rides, games, afternoon teas.
Historical Background:
The Thorn was planted by Adam de Dutton, a Crusader in the 12th century. Bawming or decorating a tree was once widespread but now only Appleton Thorn holds this ceremony
Media/Public Comments:
BBC TV's "Tracks" featured Bawming of the Thorn

Brampton Live 98

Type of Festival:
Folk, Roots, World Music
Contact: **Mick North**
Address:
**Carlisle Arts Council Arts Unit
Tullie House
Carlisle Street
Carlisle
Cumbria
CA3 8TP**

Tel. No: **01228 34781**
Fax No: **01228 810249**
Date(s) of Festival:
17th - 19th July 1998
Times of Festival:
17th: 7.30pm
18th: 1.30 - 4.30 and 8pm -11pm
19th: 12.30 - 4.30 and 8pm -11pm
Cost for Adults:
Full weekend pass £32 (TBC) Saturday-Sunday pass £26, day pass £13
Cost for Children: **Under 11s free**
Special discounts:
Concessions for OAPs, UB40 and students
Routes by Car:
Brampton 10 miles east of Carlisle, just off A69 Carlisle - Newcastle Rd
Venue:
William   Howard   Centre, Longstown Road, Brampton.
Facilities (Parking):
Plenty of Parking. Free camping with access to good showers/washing facilities. Also bars, mobile catering and cafeteria
Facilities (Disabled):
Spaces for disabled drivers. Access for wheelchair users. Adapted WCs. Access to the outdoor performing areas and marquee is possible but more difficult on grass
What's On:
Wide range of music and dance by top performers from all over the world. Various dance, song and instrumental workshops. Creative activities for children
Historical Background:
The event started in 1995 and has grown steadily to become the biggest of its kind in the northern region

Holker Garden Festival
Type of Festival:
Gardening and Countryside
Contact: **Mrs C Johnson**
Address:
The Show Office
Holker Hall and Gardens
Cark-in-Cartmel
Grange over Sands
Cumbria LA117PL
Tel. No: **015395 58838**
Fax No: **015395 58776**
Date(s) of Festival:
29th - 31st May 1998
Times of Festival:
29th-30th: 10am - 6pm
31st: 10am - 5.30pm
Cost for Adults: **£7**
Cost for Children:
Under 12s free 12-16 £3
Special discounts:
Groups of 20+ £5 each, children £2.50, OAPs £5.50. Advanced ticket price adults £6, OAPs £5, children £2.50
Tickets available from:
Show Office/Tourist Information
Routes by Car:
M6 Junction 36. Signed from A590
Train/Other:
Cark-in-Cartmel Station. Free Bus service runs up to the Hall and Gardens daily
Venue:
Holker Hall and Gardens, Cark-in-Cartmel
Facilities (Parking):
Grass parking, toilets, full catering on field
Facilities (Disabled):
Car park adjacent to the show ground
What's On:
Horticultural displays, traditional and modern crafts, festival gar-

dens, floral art, WI displays, Holker world class gardens, trade stands, good food and wine, Gardeners QuestionTime, floral art demonstration, advice centres, children's play area

Historical Background:
Developed to celebrate all that is good in the garden and countryside and also as an adjunct to the world class 25 acre garden which is a National Award Holder

Media/Public Comments:
"The Best and Friendliest event we have attended"
"The Chelsea of the North" "This is the best organised event we have been to, you could give lessons"

General Information:
The Festival is a wonderful mix of fabulous displays and advice in a wonderful setting. Lots to see and do, many people attend on more than one day. Traditional crafts persons at work as well as modern crafts persons.

Cockermouth Festival

Type of Festival:
Art, Theatre, Music
Contact: **Mr A Betram**
Address:
Cockermouth Town Council
Town Hall
Cockermouth
Cumbria
Tel. No: **01900 822634**
(Tourist Information Office)
Fax No: **01900 822603**
Date(s) of Festival:
28th June - 31st July 1998
Times of Festival: **Various**
Tickets available from:
Tourist information Office
Routes by Car:

Junction 40 off the M6 A66
Workington to Cockermouth
Train/Other:
Via Carlisle/Penrith. Bus links via
Carlisle/Penrith
Venue: **Cockermouth**
Facilities (Parking):
Ample parking town
What's On:
Approximately 70 events. Art, theatre, music, exhibitions, demonstrations, children's shows, etc. Visit Wordsworth's birthplace, Mineral Museum, Printers Museum, Toy and Model Museum, brewery tours, Lakeland sheep and wool centre, Cumwest exhibition etc
Historical Background:
Started approximately 20 years ago by Civic Trust, now coordinated by Town Council
Media/Public Comments:
Always well received in the Press
General Information:
The festival is a pulling together of numerous events organised by the Town Council, local Arts organisations, theatre groups and other music societies

Coniston Water Festival

Type of Festival: **Village Event**
Contact:
Ian Stancliffe (WF Committee)
Address:
Campbell House
Coniston
Cumbria
LA21 8EF
Tel. No: **01539 441707**
Date(s) of Festival:
23rd - 31st May 1998
Times of Festival: **Various**
Cost for Adults:

Various. Some free events
Routes by Car:
A590 at Greenodd or via Ambleside
Train/Other:
Ulverston Railway Station
Venue: **Coniston Water**
What's On:
Sailing, fell running, bowling, tennis, cricket, pony trekking, lake cruises, mountain biking. Various exhibitions (National Trust/Donald Campbell etc)

Wasdale Beer Festival

Type of Festival: **Beer**
Contact:
Howard Christie, Landlord
Address:
The Wasdale Head Inn
Wasdale Head
Gosforth
Cumbria
CA20 1EX
Tel. No: **019467 26229**
Fax No: **019467 26334**
Date(s) of Festival:
4th - 6th September 1998
Times of Festival:
Friday/Saturday 11am - 11pm Sunday 12noon - 10.30pm
Cost for Adults: **Free**
Cost for Children: **Free**
Tickets available from:
Not required
Routes by Car:
From M6 Junction 43. A595 to Gosforth then 9 miles or M6 Junction 36 A590/A595 to Gosforth then 9 miles
Train/Other:
Seascale Station then 11 miles by taxi. Or train to Ravenglass, miniature steam train (La'al Ratty -Boot). From Keswick take the Borrowdale Bus to Seatoller, then

walk 6 miles over mountain pass.
Venue:
Wasdale Head Inn, Gosforth
What's On:
England's highest mountain, deepest lake and smallest church. Good selection of Cumbrian ales. Also rock climbing, walking, hiking, ceilidh band.
Historical Background:
The Inn is at a Crossroads, at one time notorious for smuggling activity. Within the Inn there is a collection of photos/memorabilia taken by the "Keswick Bros" who recorded the birth and development of British rock climbing which was centred upon the Wasdale. Entertainment both Friday and Saturday nights
General Information:
A larger Festival than the Cumbrian Festival, features ales from all over the British Isles from the Orkney islands, right down to the Channel Islands

The La'al Cumbrian Beer Festival

Type of Festival: **Beer**
Contact:
Howard Christie, Landlord
Address:
The Wasdale Head Inn
Wasdale Head
Gosforth
Cumbria
CA20 1EX
Tel. No: **019467 26229**
Fax No: **019467 26334**
Date(s) of Festival:
29th - 30th May 1998
Times of Festival: **11am - 11pm**
Cost for Adults:
B&B £39 including VAT; apart-

ments £78 (2 persons)
Special discounts:
B&B £5 reduction for more than 2 nights Apartments £10 reduction for 2nd night thereon
Routes by Car:
From M6 Junction 43. A595 to Gosforth then 9 miles or M6 Junction 36 A590/A595 to Gosforth then 9 miles
Train/Other:
Seascale Station then 11 miles by taxi. Train to Ravenglass, miniature steam train "La'al Ratty"   From Keswick take the Borrowdale Bus to Seatoller, then walk 6 miles over mountain pass.
Venue:
The Wasdale Head Inn, Gosforth
Facilities (Parking):
Ample parking. Campsites opposite hotel
Facilities (Disabled):
Reasonable disabled access
What's On:
England's highest mountain, deepest lake and smallest church. Good selection of Cumbrian ales. Rock climbing, walking, hiking, ceilidh band
Historical Background:
The Inn is at a crossroads, at one time notorious for smuggling activity. Within the Inn there is a collection of photos/memorabilia taken by the "Keswick Bros" who recorded the birth and development of British rock climbing which was centred upon the Wasdale
Media/Public Comments:
"Once again Sinners congregate in Wasdale" The Parish Magazine "Absolutely no conversions" Scientology Today "Great Booze-Up" Local Rugby Club News

Grasmere Lakeland Sports and Show

Type of Festival:
Traditional Sports and Skills
Contact:
Dr Chris Lane - Show Director
Address:
**Grasmere Sports Committee Ltd
Slack Cottage
High Wray
Ambleside
Cumbria
LA22 0JQ**
Tel. No: **015394 32127**
Fax No: **015394 32127**
Date(s) of Festival:
23rd August 1998
Times of Festival: **9am - 5pm**
Cost for Adults: **£4**
Cost for Children: **Under 14s free**
Special discounts: **Free parking**
Routes by Car: **A592 from M6**
Train/Other:
To Windermere Station, then 8 miles by bus or taxi
Venue: **Grasmere**
Facilities (Parking):
Parking for 500 cars
What's On:
Cumberland and Westmorland wrestling, hound trails, mountain bike races, fell and guides races, displays of walling, tree felling, crafts, antiques,trade stands, band competitions, tug of war etc
Historical Background:
Founded in Viking times. It has been in its present form for 250 years
Media/Public Comments:
**"The Grasmere Sports is the Cumbrian equivalent of Ascot, being the high point of the County summer season"
The Telegraph**

General Information:
Wrestlers come from Iceland, Greenland, Spain, Italy and France (all countries of Viking influence)

The Wordsworth Summer Conference

Type of Festival: **Literature**
Contact: **Mrs Sylvia Wordsworth**
Address:
The Wordsworth Trust
Dove Cottage
Grasmere
Cumbria
LA22 9SH
Tel. No:
01539 435594 (day)
01539 435651 (evening)
Fax No: **015394 35748**
Date(s) of Festival:
1st - 15th August 1998
Times of Festival: **Residential**
Cost for Adults:
Apply for residential costs; which include lectures £5
Routes by Car:
The Trust is located south of Grasmere village on the main A591 Kendal-Keswick Road
Train/Other:
Windermere Railway Station Hourly bus service (555).
In summer open top bus Windermere- Grasmere every 20 mins
Venue:
Prince of Wales Hotel, Grasmere
Facilities (Parking):
Residentially based at the Prince of Wales Hotel in Grasmere.
Car/coach parking next to tea rooms/additional parking Grasmere village car park 250yds
Facilities (Disabled):
With assistance

What's On:
Talks and discussions about books, authors, artists and collectors. Take part in practical workshops and surgeries on printing, bookbinding and restoring works of art.
Historical Background:
Wordsworth Trust was founded in 1891 to secure Dove Cottage "for the eternal possession of all those who love English poetry all over the world." Set in the heart of the Lake District, Dove Cottage was the home to Wordsworth when he wrote his greatest works
General Information:
The award winning museum displays the Trust's unique collection of manuscripts, books and paintings interpreting the life and works of Wordsworth. An excellent shops sells books, gifts and crafts. Dove Cottage Tea Rooms provides veggie meals and snacks

The Weekend Book Festival

Type of Festival: **Art and Literature**
Contact: **Mrs Sylvia Wordsworth**
Address:
The Wordsworth Trust
Dove Cottage
Grasmere
Cumbria
LA22 9SH
Tel. No:
01539 435544 (day)
01539 435651 (evening)
Fax No: **01539 435748**
Date(s) of Festival:
22nd - 24th January 1999
Times of Festival: **Residential**
Cost for Adults:
Apply for residential costs: Lectures £5

Tickets available from:
The Wordsworth Trust (see above)
Routes by Car:
The Trust is located south of Grasmere village on the main A591 Kendal-Keswick Road
Train/Other:
Windermere Railway Station. Hourly bus service (555). In summer open top bus (W1) Windermere-Grasmere every 20mins
Venue:
Dove Cottage, Grasmere and Prince of Wales Hotel, Grasmere
Facilities (Parking):
Residentially based at the Prince of Wales Hotel in Grasmere. Car/ coach parking next to tea rooms. Additional parking Grasmere village car park 250yds
Facilities (Disabled):
With assistance
What's On:
Talks and discussions about books, authors, artists and collectors. Take part in practical workshops and surgeries on printing, bookbinding and restoring works of art.
Historical Background:
Wordsworth Trust was founded in 1891 to secure Dove Cottage "for the eternal possession of all those who love English poetry all over the world." Set in the heart of the Lake District, Dove Cottage was the home to Wordsworth when he wrote his greatest work
Media/Public Comments:
"A fun weekend for art and book lovers"
General Information:
The award winning museum displays the Trust's unique collection of manuscripts, books and paint- ings interpreting the life and works of Wordsworth. An excellent shops sells books, gifts and crafts. Dove Cottage Tea Rooms provides veggie meals and snacks.

The Grizedale International Piano Festival

Type of Festival: **Classical Piano**
Contact: **David Penn**
Address:
The Grizedale Society
Theatre in the Forest
Grizedale
Hawkshead
Ambleside
Cumbria
LA22 0QJ
Tel. No: **01229 860291**
Fax No: **01229 860050**
Date(s) of Festival:
21st - 23rd May 1999
Times of Festival:
8pm start. Gallery in Forest 10am - 4pm
Cost for Adults:
£12. Free admission to the Gallery in Forest
Cost for Children: **£8**
Special discounts:
Special series ticket - £32
Tickets available from: **See above**
Routes by Car:
Leave M6 at Junction 36, take A590 - signs Barrow. Signs Grizedale, Forest Park
Train/Other:
Windermere Station then Taxi (Grizedale is not on a bus route). From Hawkshead village, taxi is necessary
Venue: **Grizedale Forest Park**
Facilities (Parking):

Parking available. Café, Visitors Centre and shop
Facilities (Disabled):
Disabled parking available
What's On:
Evening: the very best in piano music from around the world
Daytime: over 80 site-related sculptures on many miles of forest track. All forest walks are freely available.
Historical Background:
The Grizedale International Festival goes back almost 30 years. It is always at Whit Bank Holiday.
General Information:
Features: 22nd May - Katya Apekisheva (Israel), 23rd May - artist to be announced, 24th May - Christof Berner (Austrian)

Jennings Keswick Jazz Festival

Type of Festival: **Music**
Contact: **Paul Sherwin**
Address:
Carnegie Theatre
Finkle Street
Workington
CA14 2BD
Tel. No: **01900 602122**
Fax No: **01900 67143**
Date(s) of Festival:
21st - 23rd May 1999
Times of Festival:
12 noon -11pm daily
Cost for Adults:
£37.50 weekend (1998) prices for 1999 to be confirmed
Tickets available from:
01900 602122
Routes by Car:
M6 Junction 40 (Penrith) and then A66 westbound to Keswick

Train/Other:
To Penrith on West Cost Main Line then connecting X5 bus service.
By air from USA to Manchester or Glasgow; from Europe to Newcastle
Venue:
Various Venues in Keswick and surrounding areas
Facilities (Parking):
Continuous Jazz bus services links all venues and are free to ticket holders
What's On:
More than 80 separate events of non stop traditional jazz featuring Britain's leading bands and guests from the USA and Europe. Colourful New Orleans-style street parade on the Saturday morning and a morning jazz service and an early evening "Songs of Praise"
Historical Background:
8th annual event
General Information:
Keswick is a picturesque small town in the heart of England's Lake District

Kirkby Lonsdale Victorian Fair

Type of Festival: **Victorian**
Contact:
Tourist Information Centre
Address:
24 Main Street
Kirkby Lonsdale
Cumbria
LA6 2AE
Tel. No: **01524 271437**
Fax No: **01524 271437**
Date(s) of Festival:
5th - 6th September 1998
Times of Festival: **10am - 5.30pm**

Cost for Adults: **Free**
Cost for Children: **Free**
Tickets available from:
Tourist Information (see above)
Routes by Car:
Leave M6 Junction 36 onto A65 signposted Kirkby Lonsdale and Skipton. Parking signs in 6 miles
Train/Other:
To Lancaster or Oxenholme then bus to Kirkby Lonsdale
Venue: **Kirky Lonsdale**
Facilities (Parking):
£5 per car for parking. Free mini bus from school car park. Local accommodation must be booked well in advance
What's On:
Demonstration of Victorian crafts, entertainment acts, morris teams, Barbershop singers, brass bands, stiltwalkers, street theatre, vintage cars, farriers competition. Traditional children rises, traditional side shows, Victorian costume competitions etc
Historical Background:
Started in 1981 and is now one of the most popular northern events attracting in excess of 20,000 over the weekend
Media/Public Comments:
"First class show." Many people return year after year
General Information:
The money raised from the car parking is used to pay for all the street entertainment and the residue goes to local organisations who help to manage the weekend

Potfest '98

Type of Festival: **Pottery**
Contact: **Geoff Cox**
Address:

Stoddahgate Barn
Penruddock
Penrith
Cumbria
CA11 0RY
Tel. No: **017684 83820**
Date(s) of Festival:
7th - 9th August 1998
Times of Festival: **Various**
Cost for Adults: **£2**
Cost for Children: **Free**
Special discounts: **OAPs £1.50**
Tickets available from: **On the door**
Routes by Car:
Junction 40 off the M6
Train/Other: **Penrith Station**
Venue: **Skirgill Mart, Penrith**
Facilities (Parking):
Free parking, bar, restaurants etc
What's On:
200 potters selling their work at the biggest Potters market in the UK

Ulverston Charter Festival

Type of Festival: **Traditional**
Contact: **David Haley**
Address:
Ulverston Town Council
Ulverston Town Hall
Ulverston
Cumbria
LA12 7AR
Tel. No: **01229 585778**
Fax No: **01229 586240**
Date(s) of Festival:
5th - 19th September 1998
Routes by Car:
A590 from Junction 36 off the M6
Train/Other:
Ulverston Railway Station
Venue: **Ulverston Town Centre**
What's On:
2 weeks of events reflecting the character of this South Lakes Mar-

ket Town. A celebration of sports, arts, trade and cultural events.
Historical Background:
Celebration of Royal Charter, granted by Edward I in 1280

Ulverston Comedy Festival

Type of Festival: **Comedy**
Contact: **David Haley**
Address:
Ulverston Town Council
Ulverston Town Hall
Ulverston
Cumbria   LA12 7AR
Tel. No: **01229 585778**
Fax No: **01229 586240**
Date(s) of Festival:
12th - 13th June 1998
Routes by Car:
A590 from Junction 36 off M6
Train/Other:
Ulverston railway station
Venue:
Various venues within Ulverston including Market Street
What's On:
Indoor and outdoor comedy acts and events from Europe and UK
Historical Background:
Celebration of Stan Laurel's birthday. Born in Ulverson 16th June 1890

Ulverston Beer Festival

Type of Festival: **Beer (CAMRA)**
Contact: **Graham Donning**
Address:
Hewitts Close
Great Urswick
Ulverston
Cumbria LA12 0SQ
Tel. No:
01229 842833 (day)
01229 587429 (evening)

Date(s) of Festival:
Thursday-Saturday 1st weekend in September
Times of Festival:
Thursday evening 7pm -11pm
Friday and Saturday noon -11pm
Cost for Adults:
£1.50 after 7pm. Free before 7pm.
Cost for Children: **Free**
Special discounts:
CAMRA Members free entry
Tickets available from: **On the door**
Venue: **Coronation Hall, Ulverston**
What's On:
Drink different ales originating throughout the British Isles. Ulverston is becoming a "Festival Town" with Charter, Comedy, Banner and Flag Festivals as well as Beer Festivals

Rushbearing

Type of Festival: **Traditional**
Contact:
St Mary and St Michael Churches
Address:
Great Urswick
Ulverston
Cumbria
LA12 0SH
Date(s) of Festival:
27th September 1998
Times of Festival:
Procession leaves Urswick Recreation Hall at 1pm
Cost for Adults: **Free**
Cost for Children: **Free**
Tickets available from:
Not required
Venue:
Great Urswick Recreational Hall
What's On:
Procession through village led by band and then a church service. There is a Rushbearing Queen

Historical Background:
Rushbearing originally served the purpose of transporting rushes to church for use as floor covering in the winter. Each year the old rushes were cleared out and new rushes were taken by cart.

DERBYSHIRE

The World Toe Wrestling Championships

Type of Festival: **Sports**
Contact: **George Burgess**
Address:
Ye Olde Royal Oak Inn
Wetton
Ashbourne
Derbyshire
Tel. No: **01335 310287**
Date(s) of Festival: **6th June 1998**
Times of Festival: **12.30 onwards**
Cost for Adults: **Free**
Cost for Children: **Free**
Tickets available from:
Not Required
Routes by Car:
From A52 Asbourne - Leek Road

or A515 Ashbourne - Buxton
Venue:
Ye Olde Royal Oak Inn, Wetton, Ashbourne, Derbyshire
Facilities (Parking):
Ample parking at the Inn and in the village
What's On:
Toe Wrestling Championships, Warslow Silver Band. Take part or just watch. Eat and drink
Historical Background:
Invented by pub regulars in 1976. 1994 saw launch of world championships. National sport of Santa Maria De Redonda
Media/Public Comments:
"Wrestlers fight toe and nail to defeet the opposition!"
The Daily Telegraph
1998: Featured in the Guinness Book of Records
General Information:
1997: Request to British Olympic Association for Olympic Recognition. Japanese hold first National Championships in Aomori City on licence from Ye Olde Royal Oak, Wetton

Belper Folk Festival

Type of Festival: **Folk Music**
Contact: **Tim Burkinshaw**
Address:
Belper Folk Festival
c/o 86 Watson Street
Derby
Derbyshire
DE1 3SP
Tel. No: **01332 367446**
E-mail: **belperfolk@aol.com**
Date(s) of Festival:
3rd -5th July 1998
Times of Festival:
3rd: 8pm-11pm

4th: 10am-10.30pm
5th: 10am-6pm
Cost for Adults: **£10**
Cost for Children:
Half price. Under 8s free (if accompanied by adult)
Tickets available from:
By post from above address
Routes by Car:
Belper is 8 miles north of Derby on the A6
Train/Other:
Belper Station (branch line Derby-Matlock)
Venue:
River Gardens, Matlock Road
Facilities (Parking): **Easy parking**
Facilities (Disabled):
Disabled parking
What's On:
Belper is twinned with Pawtucket, Rhode Island, USA and will celebrate Independence Day with an American theme. Apalachian clog, blues, Cajun, barbershop, Sacred Harp, line dancing plus American food and bar plus a full range of craft stalls
Historical Background:
Samuel Slater, apprentice to Sir Richard Arkwright, stole the secret of cotton spinning and emigrated to the USA where he walked until he found a valley which looked like the Derwent Valley in Belper. This was Pawtucket, Rhode Island

Buxton Country Music Festival

Type of Festival: **Country Music**
Contact: **Mr Frank Hambleton**
Address:
Spa Town CMC
10 Welbeck Avenue

Buxton
Derbyshire
SK17 9HB
Tel. No: **01298 70194;**
0850 996534 (mobile)
Fax No: **01298 70194**
Date(s) of Festival:
12th - 13th September 1998
Times of Festival: **Various**
Cost for Adults:
Saturday £6 in advance (£7 on the door). Sunday £8 in advance (£9 on the door)
Cost for Children:
Under 14s free with an adult
Special discounts:
All weekend special £13. 10% discount for UB40s, OAPs, students provided paid in advance
Tickets available from:
01298 70194 (see above)
Routes by Car: **A6 then A515**
Train/Other:
Buxton railway station is only 300 yards away. Bus station close by
Venue: **Buxton**
Facilities (Parking): **Large car park. Pavilions Gardens Park Cafeteria, restaurant and bars**
Facilities (Disabled):
Disabled facilities available
What's On:
Country music trade stands, clothes. Large dance floor, line dancing, concerts, Ann Breen and her band, Texas Gun and Gordon Lemondine, The Haley Sisters and Tony Haley, Possum Country and Jim Ryder
Historical Background:
14th year and still growing.
Media/Public Comments:
"Best Bands in the UK"
"All indoor Festival"
"Excellent facilities"

Buxton Festival

Type of Festival: **Opera**
Contact: **Jane Davies**
Address:
I Crescent View
Hall Bank
Buxton
Derbyshire
SK17 6EN
Tel. No: **01298 70395**
Fax No: **01298 72289**
Date(s) of Festival:
16th - 26th July 1998
Cost for Adults: **£5 - £35**
Cost for Children:
Half price to all events outside the
Opera House
Special discounts:
Groups 10+ 10% discount. Discounts for OAPs, UB40s and students on some events
Tickets available from:
Box Office: 01298 72190
Routes by Car:
From Manchester follow the A6 to Buxton. From Sheffield follow signs to Bakewell, then A6. From M1 head for Matlock, then Bakewell then Buxton. From Macclesfield take the A537 to Buxton. From Derby A52 to Ashbourne then A515 to Buxton. From Congleton A54
Train/Other:
Inter-city from Euston to Stockport and Manchester and then connecting service to Buxton. Last train from Buxton - Manchester 10.56 Monday - Saturday, 10.25 on Sunday. National Express coach services to Buxton contact 0171 730 0202 or Birmingham 0121 622 4373

Venue: **Buxton**
Facilities (Parking):
Buxton Town Centre
Facilities (Disabled):
Opera House - there are 3 spaces only and 2 transfers, no toilet facilities. All other venues please call Festival Office: 01298 70395
What's On:
Nightly performances at the Opera House, lunchtime recitals, afternoon concerts, festivals, masses and a programme of walks. Thriving fringe and jazz festivals run concurrently. Visit Macclesfield Folk Museum, Pooles Cavern, Quarry Bank Mill.
Historical Background:
Now in its 20th year, this annual classical music festival focuses on opera and the glorious Edwardian Opera House in the centre of this charming Peak District spa town.
General Information:
Experience the custom of Well Dressing in Buxton 8th -14th July. Thought to have originated in pagan times Well Dressing is unique to Derbyshire. Well Dressing is the art of decorating springs and wells with pictures made from growing things.

Castleton Ancient Garland Ceremony

Type of Festival: **Traditional**
Contact: **Mrs V A Turner**
Address:
The Walk
Hope Valley
Castleton
Derbyshire
S33 8WP

Tel. No: **01433 620571**
Fax No: **01433 620519**
Date(s) of Festival:
29th May 1999
Times of Festival:
6.30pm to approximately 9pm
Cost for Adults: **Free**
Cost for Children: **Free**
Tickets available from:
Not required
Routes by Car:
A625 from Sheffield, A6 and A625 from Manchester
Train/Other:
Sheffield or Manchester to Hope Station
Venue: **Castleton**
Facilities (Parking):
Parking on council car park or village streets
Facilities (Disabled):
Access for disabled
What's On:
Garland ceremony which takes place on only one evening in the year. Procession of the Garland King and Consort on horseback. The king wearing the Garland, followed by Castleton silverband and little girls in white dresses covered in flowers
Historical Background:
Ancient fertility rite incorporating the restoration of Charles II and Oak Apple Day. At one time the custom was thought to commemorate a royal flight from Republican enemies (the flow - bearer is known as the King) but it is now considered to be a Pagan ceremony

Dove Holes International Beer and Jazz Festival

Type of Festival:
New Orleans Jazz
Contact: **Roger T Marshall**
Address:
Housesteads
Dove Holes
Buxton
Derbyshire
SK17 8BG
Date(s) of Festival:
3rd - 5th July 1998
Times of Festival:
Friday evening, all day Saturday and Sunday
Cost for Adults:
£20 for weekend ticket
Tickets available from:
R T Marshall (see above)
Routes by Car: **On main A6**
Train/Other:
Regular services from Manchester
Venue: **Halstead**
Facilities (Parking):
Ample parking on hard standing. Campsite with facilities for vans and tents. All day Refreshments and food
Facilities (Disabled):
Access for disabled people
What's On:
Over 20 real ales, 7 jazz bands, Grand Parade, cricket, CD stall etc
Historical Background:
1998 sees the 7th Festival. Associated with Dove Jazz Club which organises events approximately once a month. The money raised goes to local charities.
Media/Public Comments:
"Small friendly Festival with the big names" Jazz Times

National Festival of Transport

Type of Festival: **Transport**
Contact: **Lesley Wyld**
Address:
The National Tramway Museum
Crich
Matlock
Derbyshire   DE4 5DP
Tel. No: **01773 852565**
Fax No: **01773 852326**
Date(s) of Festival:
30th - 31st August 1998
Times of Festival:
Sunday 10am -10.30pm
Monday 10am - 6.30pm
Cost for Adults: **£5.90**
Cost for Children: **£3**
Special discounts:
OAPs £5.10 and discounts for groups
Tickets available from:
Tramway Museum
Train/Other:
Whatstandwell Railway Station
Venue: **Tramway Museum**
Facilities (Parking):
Free car and coach parking. Tea Rooms, picnic areas, free camping for exhibitors
Facilities (Disabled):
Access for disabled people
What's On:
Unlimited vintage tram rises, exhibition hall, video theatre, shops, transport trade stands, large classic vehicle displays, model exhibition
Historical Background:
Established over 30 years ago to recapture the period atmosphere of all kinds of classic transport
General Information:
Exhibitors of classic vehicles welcome with free camping available

Stainsby Folk Festival

Type of Festival: **Folk Music, Dance**
Contact: **John Gillibrand**
Address:
Stainsby Folk Group
46 John Street
Chesterfield
Derbyshire
Tel. No: **01246 559036**
Date(s) of Festival:
17th - 19th July 1998
Times of Festival:
17th: 12noon - midnight
18th -19th: 10am - midnight
Cost for Adults:
Before 1st July - 3 days for £27, thereafter £32. Day tickets are available
Cost for Children:
Under 16s free (accompanied by adult)
Special discounts:
Pre-1st July price available to UB40s at the gate
Routes by Car:
Close to Junction 29 off M1 motorway near to Bolsover Castle, Hardwick Hall and Chesterfield
Train/Other:
Chesterfield Railway Station. Bus Chesterfield-Nottingham No 737
Venue:
Brunts Farm Greenfield Site, Stainsby and the Old School House (5 mins from Brunts Farm)
Facilities (Parking):
Free parking, free camping. Bar and food available
Facilities (Disabled):
Access for disabled
What's On:
Concerts, dancing, crafts, children's entertainment, workshops, singers competition, informal music and song sessions

Historical Background:
One of the few remaining green field site folk festivals
Media/Public Comments:
"A friendly family festival with something to suit all age groups"

DEVON

Arlington Folk Festival

Type of Festival: **Folk Music**
Contact:
James Stout/David Clinch
Address:
Arlington Court
Barnstaple
Devon
EX31 4LP
Tel. No: **01271 850296 (day)**
01271 850449 (evenings)
Fax No: **01271 850711**
Date(s) of Festival:
15th August 1998
Times of Festival:
12 noon - 11.30pm
Cost for Adults: **£6**
Cost for Children: **Under 14s free**
Special discounts:
Adult advance tickets: £4
Tickets available from: **On the gate**

Routes by Car:
8 miles North of Barnstaple on A39 (Lynton Road)
Train/Other: **Barnstaple Station**
Venue: **Arlington Court**
Facilities (Parking):
Ample free parking
What's On:
15 bands, artists on two stages, workshops in dance, music, crafts, children's entertainment including story tellers, magicians, jugglers, craft market
General Information:
Set in the beautiful National Trust Estate of Arlington Court. Offering a broad selection of folk styles including The Equation, Waulk Elektrik, Makvirag (Hungarian) Isaac Guillory (Cuban), Sacred Turf and many more, evening ceilidh with the Oggle Band

Port of Brixham Trawler Race

Type of Festival: **Traditional**
Contact: **Mrs C M Beasley**
Address:
Whaddon
Crownhill Crescent
Galmpton
Brixham
Devon
TQ5 0PS
Tel. No: **01803 846182 or 882325**
Fax No: **01803 882725**
Date(s) of Festival: **20th June 1998**
Times of Festival: **10am onwards**
Cost for Adults: **Free**
Cost for Children: **Free**
Tickets available from:
Not required: Programme £1 (obligatory)

Train/Other:
Paignton then bus to Brixham
Venue: **Fish Quay, Brixham**
Facilities (Parking):
Ample parking in central car park
Facilities (Disabled):
No difficulty for disabled people
What's On:
Trawler race, music, demonstrations, charity stalls, children's rides, film show, model boat race, Navy boat in attendance
Historical Background:
This race between trawlers has been running since the days when trawlers had sails

Brixham Heritage Festival

Type of Festival: **Music**
Contact:
Mr J Routledge - Chairman
Address:
48 Prospect Road
Brixham
Devon
Tel. No: **01803 855262**
Date(s) of Festival:
22nd - 30th May 1999
Times of Festival:
2pm - 9pm daily except firework displays which end at 9.50pm
Cost for Adults:
90% events free. Some events £5 - £13
Tickets available from: **On the door**
Routes by Car:
Via Paignton or Torquay
Train/Other:
To Newton Abbott then bus to Brixham Ferry direct from Torquay
Venue:
Open air in Brixham and Brixham Harbour

Facilities (Parking):
Car parking in Town Centre
What's On:
Live music, car rally, classic boat rallies, children's entertainment, firework display on the pier with synchronised music, photography exhibition, Punch and Judy shows, Scottish country dancing, Gloucestershire Youth Jazz Orchestra, barbecues
Historical Background:
Re-creation of the Whitsun Fair
Media/Public Comments:
Excellent coverage from newspapers and Radio Devon. General public seem to be very pleased with the event

The Hunting of the Earl of Rone

Type of Festival: **Traditional**
Contact: **Pat and Paul Hartley**
Address:
Claremount
Victoria Street
Coombe Martin
Devon
EX34 0JR
Tel. No: **01271 882524**
Date(s) of Festival:
21st - 24th May 1999
Times of Festival: **Various**
Cost for Adults: **Free**
Cost for Children: **Free**
Tickets available from:
Not required
Routes by Car:
Coombe Martin lies between Ilfracombe and Lynton on A399, on the north coast of Exmoor
Venue:
Streets of the village Coombe Martin
Facilities (Parking): **Public Car Park**

What's On:
Villagers parade with Grenadiers and a be-ribboned Hobby Horse led by a Fool in a Smock. Spectacle includes drummers, musicians and a masked person in a sack cloth riding back to front on a donkey - the Earl of Rone. He is regularly shot, revived and finally cast into the sea

Historical Background:
The Earl of Rone (originally Earl of Tyrone) fled to Ireland to escape punishment for being a traitor. He was shipwrecked in the Bristol Channel, survived, and landed between Ilfracombe and Coombe Martin. Soldiers chased him and upon arresting him executed him

General Information:
In 1837 the Hunting of the Earl of Rone was banned by a local bylaw because of "licentiousness and drunken behaviour". Coombe Martin is a wonderful centre for exploring Exmoor, North Devon and South Devon

Coombe Martin Carnival Week

Type of Festival: **Traditional**
Contact: **Paul Bowden**
Address:
3 Brookside Villas
Rosea Bridge Lane
Coombe Martin
Devon
EX34 0LU
Tel. No: **01271 882671**
Date(s) of Festival:
8th - 15th August 1998
Times of Festival: **Various**
Cost for Adults: **Free**
Cost for Children: **Free**

Tickets available from:
Not required
Routes by Car:
Coombe Martin is on the A399 between Ilfracombe and Lynton
Train/Other:
Barnstaple Railway Station
Venue: **Coombe Martin**
Facilities (Parking):
Main Street closed around time of procession. Car parks in the village
What's On:
Procession Wednesday evening. Various events each day

Ways with Words

Type of Festival: **Literature**
Contact: **Stephen Bristow**
Address:
Droridge Farm
Dartington
Totnes
Devon
TQ9 6JQ
Tel. No: **01803 867373**
Fax No: **01803 863688**
Date(s) of Festival:
8th - 15th July 1998
Times of Festival: **10am - 10pm**
Cost for Adults: **From £4**
Special discounts:
Early booking discounts available
Tickets available from:
Droridge Farm (see above)
Routes by Car:
M5 south to Exeter, A38 and A384 to Totnes then follow AA signs
Train/Other:
Totnes mainline station from London, Paddington
Venue:
Dartington Hall, Dartington village
Facilities (Parking): **Ample parking**
Facilities (Disabled):
Wheelchair access to main venues

What's On:

Over 150 writers will be giving talks, lectures, readings, holding workshops and taking part in discussions. Fiction, non-fiction and poetry are covered, plus special theme days on Psychology and Science

Historical Background:

Festival has run for the past 7 years. Privately owned run in association with the Independent on Sunday. Dartington Hall's history runs through many centuries

Media/Public Comments:

"I am so grateful for the opportunities I have been given to expand my reading and thinking each year and in a context of sheer enjoyment"

"I felt the lifting of the skies as we left was a symbol of the mood"

"An invigorating enjoyable week..."

General Information:

Set in the rolling hills of the South Devon countryside the special atmosphere of Dartington Hall captivates visitors. The medieval buildings around the courtyard, the extensive gardens and woodland and River Dart provide a magical environment.

Dawlish Folk Festival

Type of Festival:

Folk Music, Song and Dance

Contact: **Lynne Brown**

Address:

7 Mayflower Close
Dawlish
Devon
EX7 0BC

Tel. No: **01626 863016**

Date(s) of Festival:

4th - 6th September 1998

Times of Festival:

Friday evening - Sunday evening

Cost for Adults:

Season Tickets: £18

Cost for Children: **£9**

Special discounts:

£3 reduction for OAPs, UB40s and students

Tickets available from:

Lynne Brown (see above)

Routes by Car: **A361**

Train/Other:

Intercity to Dawlish and bus from Exeter and Torquay

Venue: **Various Venues in Dawlish**

Facilities (Parking):

Camping available at festival site

What's On:

Concerts with Ian Carr, Karen Tweed, Jimmy Crowley, Old Rope String Band, etc. Dances with the Committee Band, Tango Band, and Racing Demon. Concerts in pubs, singalong sessions, workshops etc. Dawlish Obby Oss Procession and lots more

Historical Background:

3rd year of Festival

Media/Public Comments:

"A friendly festival by the sea"

The Exeter Festival

Type of Festival:

Performing and Visual Arts

Contact: **Lesley Maynard**

Address:

Room 4.44, Civic Centre
Paris Street
Exeter
Devon
QI IJN

Tel. No: **01392 265200**

Fax No: **01392 265366**

Date(s) of Festival:

3rd - 19th July 1998
Times of Festival:
Daily at varying times
Cost for Adults: **Various**
Cost for Children: **Various**
Special discounts:
Standby prices, if available
Train/Other:
Exeter St Davids Railway Station
Venue:
Various venues within Exeter including University Great Hall, Northcott Theatre, Barnfield Theatre.
Facilities (Parking):
Good City parking. Parking facilities at the venues
What's On:
Classical cathedral concerts by candlelight, open air jazz, open air "Last Night at the Proms" style finale, theatre, comedy, craft fair and community events
Historical Background:
Has been in existence since 1979 and is professionally run by Exeter City Council
Media/Public Comments:
Festival held in high regard for its quality profile and breadth of choice. Well supported by the public and by the media in general

Honiton Festival

Type of Festival:
Music and Visual Arts
Contact:
Chris Smith - Public Relations
Address:
Tuck Mill Cottage
Payhembury
Honiton
Devon
EX14 0HF
Tel. No: **01404 841376**

Fax No: **01404 841732**
Date(s) of Festival:
8th - 23rd May 1998
Times of Festival:
Various, during the day and evenings
Cost for Adults: **Various**
Tickets available from:
Booking Office, Westravel, 11 New Street, Honiton
Tel: 01404 44191
Routes by Car:
The town is on the A30 approximately 2 hours from the M25
Train/Other:
Honiton is on the main Waterloo-Exeter line. There are regular weekday bus services between Honiton and the following: Axminster, Ottery St Mary and Exeter (No 380), Herryock and Taunton (No 20), Sidmouth (No 340) and Tiverton (No 376). Tel: 01392 382800
Venue:
Honiton, Colyton and Ottery St Mary
Facilities (Parking): **Good parking**
Facilities (Disabled):
Good disabled access
What's On:
Mozart Concerto Flute and Harp, Elizaveta Kopelman playing Chopin, Katona Twins, Tallis Chamber Choir, Jazz Trilogy Plus, Julian Lloyd Webber, John Lenehan, Mary Nelson and many more plus street art, Spanish art exhibition, art forum, Gilbert and Sullivan
Historical Background:
A bi-annual event which started 10 years ago staging high quality prestige music and visual art

Tapeley Park Folk and Blues Music Festival

Type of Festival: **Music**
Contact:
Brian Worsley, The Yeo Suite
Address:
Barum House
The Square
Barnstaple
Devon
EX32 8LS
Tel. No: **01271 324005**
Fax No: **01271 324005**
Date(s) of Festival:
25th - 26th July 1998
Times of Festival:
12 noon -11.30pm (11pm on Sunday)
Cost for Adults:
£15 weekend, day £8.50
Cost for Children: **Under 14s free**
Special discounts:
Advance Ticket: Weekend £12 Day £7
Tickets available from:
Queens Theatre, Barnstaple: 01271 324242
Routes by Car:
B3233 Barnstaple to Bideford Road just outside Inston
Venue:
Tapeley Park Gardens, Inston, nr Bideford
Facilities (Parking):
Free parking. Camping available Tel: 01271 860269
Facilities (Disabled):
Disabled toilets
What's On:
Ralph McTell, Jacques McShee's Pentagle, John Renbourn, Wizz Jones, Dorris Henderson, John Joyce, Mac McGann, Geoff Bradford, Cliff Arngier, Elaine Samuels and Kindred Spirit, Marc Woodward's Bluemands, The Oggle Band, Gareth Hedges, George Nixs, Junction 7 . . .
Historical Background:
This is the 4th Folk and Blues Music Festival in aid of Victim Support, North Devon
General Information:
North Devon's annual open air Folk and Blues Festival is becoming a focal point for performers from all over the country

Lynton Jazz Weekend

Type of Festival:
Jazz (Traditional, Dixie)
Contact: **Nick Holt**
Address:
9 Forches Avenue
Barnstaple
Devon
EX32 8ED
Tel. No: **01271 372064**
Fax No: **01271 372064**
Date(s) of Festival:
16th -18th October 1998
Times of Festival:
Friday night, Saturday lunch, Saturday night, Sunday lunch. Jam session with Simon Banks Saturday afternoon.
Cost for Adults:
£85 including accommodation. 2 nights B&B, evening meal and admission to all concerts. Arrive Friday for dinner at 6.30pm, the first show begins at 8.30pm
Tickets available from:
Nick Holt (see above)
Routes by Car:
Situated between Minehead and Ilfracombe on the North Devon coast
Venue: **Town Hall, Lynton**
Facilities (Parking):

Ample parking. Bar supplying real ales, tea, coffee and food.

What's On:

Jam session with Simon Banks on Saturday afternoon. Artists including. Chris Watford's Dallas Dandies, Boulevard Django, Papajars All Stars, Alice's Wonderland Band and more

Historical Background:

25th anniversary of the Festival and attended by top bands from all over the UK

Media/Public Comments:

"The best small to medium size festival ever" Daily Mirror

General Information:

Lynton is situated in the Exmoor National Park, the area is known as "little Switzerland", so in between music sessions there are some lovely walks to go on.

Pecorama Steam and Model Festival

Type of Festival: **Steam and Model**
Contact: **Mark Ridgers**
Address:
Pecorama
Beer
Devon
EX12 3NA
Tel. No: **01297 21542**
Fax No: **01297 20229**
Date(s) of Festival:
13th - 14th June 1998
Times of Festival: **10am - 5.30pm**
Cost for Adults: **£3.50**
Cost for Children: **£2**
Special discounts:
OAPs £3.20. Group discounts on application. One helper per one disabled free of charge
Routes by Car:
A3052 East from Exeter, West from Lyme Regis, leave at Beer turning B3174

Train/Other:

Nearest Railway Station is Axminster on the Waterloo/Exeter Line of SW Trains
Venue: **Beer Heights, Pecorama**
Facilities (Parking):
Ample visitor parking. Full catering facilities including a beer tent
Facilities (Disabled):
Designated disabled spaces, toilet facilities for the disabled.

What's On:

Visiting locomotives on the Beer Heights Light Railway, traction engines from models to full size, model railway exhibition, model engineering exhibition, vintage and classic car displays, live entertainment from ethnic folk dancers, children's play areas etc

Historical Background:

Commenced in 1995 with the intent of promoting interest in steam railways, railway modelling and model engineering in particular and also in steam heritage generally

General Information:

The Festival is unusual in that it is based around a permanent railway attraction, the mile long 7¼" gauge Beer Heights Light Railway at Pecorama. Visitors to the festival enjoy all the other facilities at no extra charge.

Sidmouth International Festival

Type of Festival: **Music and Dance**
Contact: **Sidmouth International**
Address:
P O Box 296
Aylesbury

Buckinghamshire
HP19 3TL
Tel. No: **01296 433669**
Fax No: **01296 392300**
Date(s) of Festival:
31st July - 7th August 1998
Cost for Adults: **£3**
Cost for Children: **Free**
Special discounts: **Free**
Tickets available from:
Box Office: 01296 433669
Routes by Car:
Junction 30 off M5 then A3052
Train/Other:
Exeter or Honiton then bus to Sidmouth
Bus Hotline: 01392 427711
Venue:
Various venues in Sidmouth
Facilities (Parking):
Arena Car park - 5000 cars
Facilities (Disabled):
Access for disabled (wheelchairs included) at most venues. Stewards to assist with any specific needs
What's On:
650 events over 8 days. International music and dance spectaculars, concerts, ceilidhs, workshops, processions, craft fair, children's festival
Media/Public Comments:
"The best of family fun" Express Echo

Tiverton Spring Festival

Type of Festival:
Arts, Crafts, Music
Contact: **Mrs Jane French**
Address:
48 Belmont Street
Tiverton
Devon

EX16 6AS
Tel. No: **01884 258952**
Date(s) of Festival:
8th - 16th May 1999
Times of Festival: **Various**
Cost for Adults: **Various**
Tickets available from:
Tourist information:
01884 255827
Venue:
Various venues within Tiverton and surrounding areas
What's On:
Operas, orchestral, street entertainment, drama, lectures, sports events, music and dancing, rock concerts, morris dancers, treasure hunts, exhibitions and much more
Historical Background:
Festival started in 1995 to bring together the talents of Tiverton and to enjoy light and classical music

English Riveria Dance Festival

Type of Festival: **Ballroom Dancing**
Contact: **Philip Wylie**
Address:
73 Hoylake Crescent
Ickenham
Middlesex
Tel. No: **01895 632143**
Date(s) of Festival:
22nd May - 6th June 1998
Times of Festival: **All day**
Cost for Adults: **Various**
Cost for Children: **Various**
Tickets available from:
Philip Wylie (see above)
Train/Other: **Torquay Station**
Venue:
Torquay Town Hall and Victoria Hotel Torquay, Devon
What's On:
Modern ballroom, Latin American,

disco, rock 'n' roll, sequence
Historical Background:
16th year of Festival

DORSET

Bournemouth Musicmakers Festival

Type of Festival: **Music**
Contact: **Paul Buck**
Address:
Bournemouth Tourism
Westover Road
Bournemouth
Dorset
BH1 2BU
Tel. No: **01202 451702**
Fax No: **01202 451743**
Web site:
www.bournemouth.co.uk./
musicmakers
Date(s) of Festival:
20th June - 4th July 1998
Times of Festival: **Various**
Cost for Adults: **Free**
Cost for Children: **Free**
Tickets available from:
Not required
Venue:
Various venues within Bournemouth including The Bournemouth Winter Gardens

What's On:
Amateur bands, choirs and orchestras from around the world. 65 free events in and around the town

Marblers and Stonecutters Day

Type of Festival: **Traditional**
Contact:
Swanage Tourist Information
Address:
Corfe Castle Village
Dorset
Tel. No: **01929 422885**
Date(s) of Festival:
Shrove Tuesday 1999
Times of Festival: **Starts at 12 noon**
Cost for Adults: **Free**
Cost for Children: **Free**
Tickets available from:
Not required
Routes by Car:
Village is on the A351 between Wareham and Swanage
Venue:
Starts at The Fox Inn, Corfe Castle village
Facilities (Parking): **Village parking**
What's On:
At noon St Andrews Church's Pancake bell summons the company from The Fox Inn to the Village Hall. After a meeting a football is kicked along the Old Road to Ower Quay, each participant carrying a pint of beer and a loaf of bread
Historical Background:
The event originated as a ritual to preserve the ancient right of way used in the shipping of marbles
Dorchester Teddy Bear Fairs
Type of Festival: **Teddy Bear**
Contact: **Tim Batty**
Address:
High West Street
Dorchester

Dorset
Tel. No: **01305 269741**
Fax No: **01305 268885**
Date(s) of Festival:
25th October 1998
Times of Festival: **10am - 4.30pm**
Cost for Adults: **£2.50**
Cost for Children: **£1**
Tickets available from: **On the door**
Routes by Car:
Just off the A35 at the eastern end of Dorchester bypass
Train/Other:
Use either Dorchester South or Dorchester West. The fair is just over 1 mile away
Venue:
Kingston Maurward House, Nr Dorchester, Dorset
Facilities (Parking):
Unlimited free parking
Facilities (Disabled):
Access and toilet for the disabled
What's On:
Thousands of Teddy Bears on show and for sale from exhibitors from all over the country

Hengistbury Head Kite Festival

Type of Festival: **Kite Festival**
Contact: **Chris Saunders**
Address:
Town Hall
Bournemouth
Dorset
Tel. No: **01202 451195**
Fax No: **01202 451013**
Date(s) of Festival:
16th August 1998
Times of Festival: **10.30am - 4pm**
Cost for Adults: **Free**
Cost for Children: **Free**
Tickets available from:

Not required
Routes by Car:
A338 into Bournemouth, follow signs for Hengistbury Head
Venue: **Hengistbury Head**
Facilities (Parking):
Pay and display car park
What's On:
Man-lifting kites, kite displays, kite stalls, clowns, puppet shows. Enjoy a day flying kites and even take your teddy bear parachuting
Historical Background:
Formed approximately 10 years ago to encourage family visitors to the town

Lyme Regis Jazz Festival

Type of Festival: **Traditional Jazz**
Contact: **Wendy Shields**
Address:
Jurassic Jazz
21A Broad Street
Lyme Regis
Dorset
DT7 3OE
Tel. No: **01297 445216**
Fax No: **01297 445703**
Date(s) of Festival:
3rd - 5th July 1998
Times of Festival:
From 3.30pm Friday to Sunday evening
Cost for Adults:
Full weekend £30; Friday Stroller £10; Saturday Stroller £16, Sunday Stroller £6 (not Marine Theatre)
Tickets available from:
Ticket Info: 01297 442138
Train/Other: **Axminster Station**
Venue:
Various venues in Lyme Regis
Facilities (Parking):

Town Centre parking

What's On:

Featuring: John Barnes/Pete Strange All Stars, Gerry Brown and The Mission Hall Band, Teign Valley Jazzmen, The Blue Note Jazz Band, Chris Walker Quintet, Roy Pelletts Hot Four, Arcadia Jazz Band, Chescoes Good Time Jazz and many more

Historical Background:

The festival has been running since 1991 and is very popular

Media/Public Comments:

"Jazz from the Pearl of Dorset"

Poole Quay Summer Festival

Type of Festival:

Music, Crafts, Family Fun

Contact:

Graham Shaw - Marketing

Address:

Poole Tourism Centre
The Quay
Poole
Dorset
BH15 IHE

Tel. No: **01202 253131**

Fax No: **01202 684531**

Date(s) of Festival:

Thursday evenings during July and August

Times of Festival: **6pm - 10pm**

Cost for Adults: **Free**

Cost for Children: **Free**

Tickets available from:

Not required

Routes by Car:

A350 (Blandford), A31/A349 (Ringwood), A35 Bournemouth

Train/Other:

London - Weymouth Line. Poole Station half a mile

Venue: **On the Quay, Poole**

Facilities (Parking):

Quay car park (Old Orchard multi-storey) and Hill Street (multi-storey) and Baiter surface parking

Facilities (Disabled):

Parking facilities available

What's On:

Live music, water based displays, traditional crafts, buskers, fashion shows, steam engines, fair organ, dance displays, (morris dancing, line dancing) fireworks finale. Childrens fair rides, face painting, competitions with prizes

Historical Background:

Started in 1997 in the month of July only. Extended into August for 1998

General Information:

The purpose of the events is to encourage family fun on the Quay. During the summer for the benefit of residents and visitors

Poole Cockle Festival

Type of Festival:

Music, Dance, Market

Contact: **Mr R J Kellaway**

Address:

The Blue Boar
29 Market Close
Poole
Dorset
BH15 INE

Tel. No: **01202 682247**

Fax No: **01202 661875**

Date(s) of Festival:

1st - 3rd May 1999

Times of Festival: **9am - midnight**

Cost for Adults:

Free (except occasional guest acts)

Cost for Children: **Free**

Tickets available from:

Not required

Routes by Car:

Poole Town Centre

Train/Other:

London - Weymouth Line. Poole Station in Town Centre. Cycle routes from Wimbourne, Bournemouth, Upton etc. By sea from Cherbourg and Channel Islands

Venue:

Around the Guildhall Market Street, Old Town Poole

Facilities (Parking):

Town Centre is well served with car parks

Facilities (Disabled):

Disabled access to venues

What's On:

Music (folk, blues, rock, country) in old Town pubs, "Holiday Market" (revival of traditional Spring Market), Civil War displays, Witness displays, diving demonstrations using hard hat equipment, maypole and folk dancing, children's entertainment

Historical Background:

This is the first Poole Cockle Festival. Its joint purpose is to instigate a Folk Festival for Poole and to celebrate the various aspect of the town's history and customs.

General Information:

Festival is taking place in and around the licensed premises of Poole Old Town. The seaport of Poole is the largest natural harbour in the world, boasting (last count) some 32 pubs, clubs and wine bars all within a 20 minute circular walk!

Possum Fez Week

Type of Festival: **Traditional**

Contact: **Liz Draper**

Address:

2 Winters Lane
Portesham
Dorset

Tel. No: **01305 871316**

Date(s) of Festival:

29th July - 2nd August 1998

Times of Festival: **Various**

Cost for Adults:

Some events free, others charged separately

Cost for Children: **Half price**

Tickets available from:

The venues within the village

Routes by Car:

Portesham Village is situated on B3157 Weymouth-Bridport Road

Train/Other:

Nearest Stations Weymouth and Dorchester (7 miles)

Venue: **Portesham Village**

Facilities (Parking):

Free Parking. BBQ and refreshments on the Green. Cream teas in the Methodist Hall

Facilities (Disabled):

Most venues have access for disabled

What's On:

Village Crier competition, concerts, children's sports, model boat race, barn dance, Scarecrow Scrummidge, folk dancing, street fair, craft show, whist drive, dancing, street stalls, ends with "Songs of Praise" on Sunday in the garden of a public house

Historical Background:

A very old Dorset Festival which ended in 1913 because of the War,

revived in 1992 to raise money for the village. Thomas Hardy came to live in Portesham as a child and had a great love for the village. He used the village in his "Under the Greenwood Tree"

Media/Public Comments:
"Most people enjoy the feeling of belonging to a village which is having fun"

General Information:
Visitors are welcome to join the locals on guided walks. Hear tales of sailors and smuggling, the sea and ships. Look at the old houses and discover their secrets. The walk ends at 8.30pm at the Kings Arms Public House

Military and Veterans Festival

Type of Festival: **Traditional**
Contact: **Steve Davies**
Address:
Weymouth Tourist Information
The Esplanade
Weymouth
Dorset
Tel. No: **01305 785747**
Fax No: **01305 761654**
Date(s) of Festival:
13th - 19th June 1998
Times of Festival: **Daily**
Cost for Adults: **Free**
Cost for Children: **Free**
Tickets available from:
Not required
Routes by Car:
Major road access from M27, M3, M5
Train/Other:
Weymouth Railway Station

Venue: **Weymouth Town Centre**
Facilities (Parking):
Full range of on site facilities
Facilities (Disabled):
Disabled parking and access available
What's On:
Parade on Sunday 14th, marching military bands, historic military vehicles, outdoor band performance, charity stalls, concerts, wartime music hall.
Historical Background:
Weymouth and Portland are steeped in military tradition. Host of major D-Day VE and VJ commemoration and celebrations. Now in its 3rd year
Media/Public Comments:
"Resort stands Proud"
"Over 50,000 attend festival"
"Britain's biggest seafront parade"
General Information:
Find lost comrades and meet new friends by utilising the Vet-Line Database

Weymouth Jazz in June 1998

Type of Festival: **Music**
Contact: **Julia Sargent**
Address:
Brewers Quay
Hope Square
Weymouth
Dorset
Tel. No: **01305 777622**
Fax No: **01305 761680**
Date(s) of Festival:
10th - 14th June 1998
Times of Festival: **Various**
Cost for Adults: **Free**
Cost for Children: **Free**

Tickets available from:
Not required
Routes by Car:
Follow RAC signs or brown signs to Brewers Quay/Timewalk signs to car parks
Train/Other:
Weymouth Railway Station
Venue:
Brewers Quay, Hope Square, Weymouth
Facilities (Parking):
Parking available at Brewers Quay and within Weymouth Town Centre. Numerous catering facilities close by
What's On:
Five fabulous days of free jazz featuring a host of talent including Humphrey Lyttelton, Helen Shapiro, Blue Magnolia Jazz Orchestra, Tommy Burton, Pete Allen, The Beachcombers etc. Live indoor and outdoor entertainment
Historical Background:
Festival now in its 4th year. 1998 event sponsored by Greenalls, Coca Cola and KP

Weymouth Oyster Festival

Type of Festival:
Traditional and Music
Contact: **Steve Davies**
Address:
Weymouth Tourist Information
The Esplanade
Weymouth
Dorset
Tel. No: **01305 785747**
Fax No: **01305 761654**
Date(s) of Festival: **30th May 1999**
Times of Festival: **10am - 4pm**
Cost for Adults: **Free**

Cost for Children: **Free**
Tickets available from:
Not required
Routes by Car:
Major road access from M5, M3, M27
Train/Other:
Weymouth Railway Station
Facilities (Parking):
Full range of on site facilities
Facilities (Disabled):
Disabled amenities
What's On:
Oyster market, oyster displays and competitions, full programme of live music, shire horses, street entertainment, fancy dress, fair, face painting, oyster trail, oyster trail challenge
Historical Background:
Weymouth enjoys 17th century harbour and seafaring tradition with successful working and leisure based on the fishing fleet, oysters are a local favourite
Media/Public Comments:
Oysters galore and much more - a great fun filled family festival in a venue full of character

Weymouth International Beach Kite Festival

Type of Festival: **Sports**
Contact: **Steve Davies**
Address:
Weymouth Tourist Information
The Esplanade
Weymouth
Dorset
Tel. No: **01305 772444**
Fax No: **01305 761654**
Date(s) of Festival:
1st - 3rd May 1999

Times of Festival: **10am - 6pm**
Cost for Adults: **Free**
Cost for Children: **Free**
Tickets available from:
Not required
Routes by Car:
Major Road access from M27, M3, M5
Train/Other:
Weymouth Railway Station
Venue: **Weymouth Promenade**
Facilities (Parking):
Full range of on site facilities
Facilities (Disabled):
Disabled parking available
What's On:
Packed programme of kite displays, international firework festival, stunts, kite stalls, funfair, competitions, kite workshops, kite stall village (kit bits and pieces and lots of friendly advice)
Media/Public Comments:
"An outstanding aerial extravaganza"
"A Kaleidoscope of colour and adventure"

Weymouth International Firework Displays

Type of Festival: **Traditional**
Contact: **Steve Davies**
Address:
Weymouth Tourist Information
The Esplanade
Weymouth
Dorset
Tel. No: **01305 785747**
Fax No: **01305 761654**
Date(s) of Festival:
3rd, 10th, 19th, 24th, 31st August 1998
Times of Festival: **Free**

Cost for Adults: **Free**
Tickets available from:
Not required
Routes by Car:
Major Road access from M27, M5, M3
Train/Other:
Weymouth Railway Station
Venue: **Weymouth Promenade**
Facilities (Parking):
Full range of on site facilities
Facilities (Disabled):
Parking and access for disabled
What's On:
Internationally famed fireworks fired from a special floating pontoon in Weymouth Bay. Spectacular views from Weymouth Esplanade
Historical Background:
Over 20 years of firework displays has given Weymouth a great tradition
General Information:
Famous "highlight" of Weymouth Summer Season

Weymouth International Maritime Modelling

Type of Festival: **Sports, Traditional**
Contact: **Steve Davies**
Address:
Weymouth Tourist Office
The Esplanade
Weymouth
Dorset
Tel. No: **01305 785747**
Fax No: **01305 761654**
Date(s) of Festival:
18th - 19th July 1998
Times of Festival:
10am - 5pm daily and illuminated night sail on 18th at 9.30pm
Cost for Adults: **Free**

Cost for Children: **Free**
Tickets available from:
Events Office
Routes by Car:
Major road access from M5, M3, M27
Train/Other:
Weymouth Railway Station
Venue:
Weymouth's Harbour area
Facilities (Parking):
Full range of on site amenities
Facilities (Disabled):
Disabled parking and access for disabled in catering establishments
What's On:
Over 1,000 operational models and displays, battleships (live battles), Tall Ships, yacht racing, steam powered, electric speedboats, tug towing, novelty class displays and trawlers. "Try a boat" trade stalls, workshops
Historical Background:
Fourth highly successful international Maritime Modelling Festival
General Information:
Britain's best model boat exhibition situated in the heart of Weymouth's breathtaking 17th century harbour

Wimborne Folk Festival

Type of Festival:
Folk Dance and Music
Contact: **Brian Bishop**
Address:
32 Shillito Road
Parkstone
Poole
Dorset
BH12 2BW
Tel. No: **01202 743465**
Fax No: **01202 718488**

Date(s) of Festival:
12th - 14th June 1998
Times of Festival:
12th: 8am until late. 13th and 14th: 10am until late.
Cost for Adults:
Outdoor events free of charge
Routes by Car:
Wimborne is on A31 approach east or west A350 from north
Train/Other:
To Poole or Bournemouth. Then by Wilts and Dorset bus company
Venue: **Wimbourne**
Facilities (Parking):
Plenty of car parking amenities
Facilities (Disabled):
No problems for wheelchairs as the streets are level.
What's On:
Traditional music and dance including 1200 dancers and musicians from all over the UK and Europe. Opening procession, fair, stalls, concerts, ceilidhs, workshops, street theatre, face painting, juggling, musical workshops
Historical Background:
Founded in 1980 as a direct result of the Queen's Silver Jubilee celebrations when the potential of this historic Minster town was realised for this event. The event has continued to follow the format set in its early days viz Traditional Music and Dance
Media/Public Comments:
"Bells a'jingling as folk have fun in the sun" Local News
"Weekend of folk, fun and strawberries" Echo
"USA meets Ireland in an English summer" Evening Echo
"Much more than Morris" Evening Echo

DURHAM

Allensford Show

Type of Festival:
Music and Entertainment
Contact:
Sue Fox - Leisure Services
Address:
Derwentside District Council
Civic Centre
Medomsley Road
Consett
Durham
DH8 5JA
Tel. No: **01207 218431**
Fax No: **01207 218310**
Date(s) of Festival:
29th - 31st August 1998
Times of Festival:
11am - 5pm daily
Cost for Adults: **Free**
Cost for Children: **Free**
Routes by Car:
A68 through Co Durham. 1 mile north of Consett
Train/Other: **Durham/Newcastle**
Venue: **Allensford Park, Consett**
Facilities (Parking):
£2 per car on site. Refreshment tents
Facilities (Disabled):

Parking and toilet facilities for disabled available. Good access
What's On:
Staged entertainment displays, exhibitions, music, theatre, dance, trade stalls, craft marquee, children's activity tent, fairground rides. The festival culminates in the Allensford Rock 'n' Roots Festival on the Bank Holiday Monday
Saturday: Country and Western, Sunday: Family Day
Monday: Rock 'n' Roots
Historical Background:
The festival grew out of an open air church service held on the Sunday of the Bank Holiday weekend.
Media/Public Comments:
"Excellent family days out"
"Something for everyone"
General Information:
Beautiful sheltered riverside setting in the Derwent valley which is popular with the day visitor. Ideal tourist location with all year round appeal. Show attracts 12,000 people yearly

The Teesdale Thrash

Type of Festival:
Folk Music, Morris Dancing
Contact: **Roy Tranter**
Address:
Teesdale Thrash Committee
49 Victorian Road
Barnard Castle
Durham
DL12 8MR
Tel. No: **01833 638288**
Date(s) of Festival:
30th April - 3rd May 1999 (TBC)
Times of Festival:
8pm on 30th - noon on 3rd
Cost for Adults:
£5 ceilidh/concert

Cost for Children:
£2.50 ceilidh/concert; £1 workshops
Tickets available from:
Festival Office, Withim Hall or R Tranter (see above)
Routes by Car: **A1, A66, M6, A66**
Train/Other:
Darlington No 75 bus to Barnard Castle
Venue:
Various venues within Barnard Castle
Facilities (Parking):
General parking in town
Facilities (Disabled):
Disabled access to Withim Hall on request
What's On:
Dance parade, street dancing, craft fair, circus-style entertainment for children, singaround/ sessions, ceilidh, folk club, bouncy castles, evening folk concert, workshops, dance parade, dancing at Bowes Museum
Historical Background:
11th anniversary started as a Mayday weekend celebration
Media/Public Comments:
"Small friendly festival"
General Information:
Ceilidh band "All Blacked Up", folk concert, Nez Lowe and the Bad Pennies, The Doonan Family and Nebula

Dog Agility Festival
Type of Festival: **Animal**
Contact: **Jacki Winstanley**
Address:
**Publicity Officer
The North of England Open Air Museum
Beamish**

**Durham
DH9 0RG**
Tel. No: **01207 231811**
Fax No: **01207 290933**
Date(s) of Festival:
8th and 9th May 1999
Cost for Adults:
£8 admission charge to museum. Event free
Cost for Children:
£5 admission charge to museum
Special discounts:
OAPs £5 admission charge to museum
Tickets available from:
North of England Open Air Museum (see above)
Routes by Car:
Follow the A1(M) to Junction 63. (Chester-le-Street) exit, then A693 towards Stanley (4 miles)
Train/Other:
Durham City or Newcastle Central Service buses from Newcastle upon Tyne, Durham and Sunderland
Venue: **Beamish**
Facilities (Parking):
Free parking for 2000 cars and 40 coaches, tea room, souvenir shops and picnic areas
Facilities (Disabled):
Not ideal for wheelchair-bound disabled visitors
What's On:
Watch 400 of the country's top agility dogs in action against the clock. Featuring jumps, see saws, tunnels etc
Media/Public Comments:
As seen on TV

The Festival of the Horse at Beamish

Type of Festival: **Equestrian Sports**

Contact: **Jacki Winstanley**

Address:
**Publicity Officer
The North of England Open Air Museum
Beamish
Durham
DH9 0RG**

Tel. No: **01207 231811**

Fax No: **01207 290933**

Date(s) of Festival:
25th - 26th July 1998

Times of Festival: **10am - 5pm**

Cost for Adults:
£8 (includes admission charge to the museum)

Cost for Children: **£5**

Special discounts:
OAPs £5. Group rates for parties of 20+

Tickets available from:**The Museum**

Routes by Car:
Follow the A1(M) to Junction 63. (Chester–le-Street) exit, then A693 towards Stanley (4 miles)

Train/Other:
Durham City or Newcastle Central Stations. Service buses from Newcastle upon Tyne, Durham and Sunderland

Venue: **Beamish**

Facilities (Parking):
Free parking for 2000 cars and 40 coaches, tea room, souvenir shops and picnic areas

Facilities (Disabled):
Not ideal for wheelchair-bound disabled visitors

What's On:
Show jumping competition, horse driving, demonstrations of dressage and vaulting. Northern Horseball Championships. Horseball is a new and very competitive team sport

Historical Background:
Organised in 1997 as part of the celebrations for the Royal Silver Wedding Anniversary. Proved to be popular with both visitors and competitors.

General Information:
Visit Beamish Open Air Museum, which vividly illustrates life in the North of England in the early 1800s and 1900s in the Town, Colliery Village, Home Farm, Railway Station and Pockerley Manor

Billingham International Folklore Festival

Type of Festival:
World Folk Music and Dance

Contact: **Carol Croft**

Address:
**Stockton Borough Council
72 Church Road
Gloucester House
Stockton-on-Tees
Durham
TS18 1YB**

Tel. No: **01642 393907**

Fax No: **01642 393906**

Date(s) of Festival:
15th - 22nd August 1998

Times of Festival:
All day and evening

Cost for Adults: **Various**

Cost for Children: **Various**

Special discounts:
Discounts for OAPs

Tickets available from: **The Gate**

Routes by Car:
A19 to Billingham

Train/Other: **Billingham Station**

Venue: **Billingham**
Facilities (Parking):
Free Town Centre parking
What's On:
International folk music and dance, outdoor stage, evening theatre concerts
Historical Background:
1998 is the festival's 34th year
Media/Public Comments:
"Feast of festival fun"
"World comes to Teeside"
General Information:
This year's groups are from: Russia, France, Germany, Sweden, Bulgaria, Brazil (TBC) and England

Durham Winter Beer Festival

Type of Festival: **Beer**
Contact: **Jim McCaffery**
Address:
Durham CAMRA
7 Hillcrest
Gilesgate
Durham City
Durham
DH1 1RB
Tel. No: **0191 386 8149**
Date(s) of Festival:
18th - 20th February 1999
Times of Festival:
18th 5pm - 11pm; 19th and 20th 11am - 11pm
Cost for Adults: **£1.50**
Tickets available from:
The door or contact above
Venue:
Catholic Chaplaincy, Old Elvet, Durham City
Facilities (Disabled):
Disabled access limited. Prior notification required
What's On:

Over 35 different real ales from north of Britain usually winter ales (can be strong) and all from microbreweries
Historical Background:
13th Winter Real Ale Festival

Durham Beer Festival

Type of Festival: **Beer**
Contact: **Jim McCaffery**
Address:
Durham CAMRA
7 Hillcrest Gilesgate
Durham City
Durham
DH1 1RB
Tel. No: **0191 3868149**
Date(s) of Festival:
3rd - 5th September 1998
Times of Festival:
3rd: 5pm - 11pm
4th and 5th: 11am - 11pm
Cost for Adults: **£1.50**
Cost for Children: **Free**
Tickets available from:
The door or contact above
Venue:
Dunelm House, Elvet, Durham
Facilities (Disabled):
Disabled access with early notification
What's On:
135 real ales and ciders from all over Britain particularly from microbreweries and live music. Drink and listen and dance to live bands
Historical Background:
23rd Festival

Stanley Blues Festival

Type of Festival: **Music**
Contact:
Martin Weston - Leisure Services
Address:
**Derwentside District Council
Civic Centre
Medomsby Road
Consett
Durham
DH8 5JA**
Tel. No: **01207 218431**
Fax No: **01207 218310**
Date(s) of Festival:
9th August 1998
Times of Festival: **12 noon - 5pm**
Cost for Adults: **TBC**
Routes by Car:
**A1 to Chester-le-Street then A693
to Stanley**
Train/Other: **Durham/Newcastle**
Venue:
Staged in marquee in Stanley
Facilities (Parking):
**Parking available. Refreshment
Tents**
What's On:
**Open air Blues Festival staged in a
marquee with peripheral activity
for children. Children's entertain-
ment and activity. Listen to good
music provided by some of the best
blues bands in the North East**
Historical Background:
**This Festival ran alongside Stanley
Fun Day for a couple of years, then
evolved into a stand alone event.**
Media/Public Comments:
**"Developing Show of regional im-
portance"**
General Information:
**Blues Festival with great atmos-
phere with 4500 people currently
attending. Got to be there to know
how good it is**

Stockton International Riverside Festival

Type of Festival:
**Street Theatre, Music, Comedy
Dance**
Contact: **Graham Reeves**
Address:
**Stockton Borough Council
72 Church Road,
Gloucester House
Stockton-on-Tees
Durham
T318 1YB**
Tel. No: **01642 393911 or
K Maculae: 01642 393964**
Fax No: **01642 393906.**
Web site:
http://www.Festival.co.uk
Date(s) of Festival:
24th July - 2nd August 1998
Times of Festival: **Various**
Cost for Adults:
Some charge for selected shows
Tickets available from:
**Dovecote Arts Centre:
01642 611625**
Routes by Car:
**From A1(M) north take A19 to
Teeside then A66 to Stockton**
Train/Other:
**GNER to Thorny, Darlington or
Middlesborough. Teeside Interna-
tional Airport**
Venue:
Various venues in Town Centre
Facilities (Parking):
Town Centre parking
Facilities (Disabled):
**Access for disabled. Pre-book disa-
bled seats**
What's On:
**International street entertainers,
pyrotechnics, eye opening acrobat-
ics, famous bands, well-known**

comedians, a finale not to be missed. Dance, sing-a-long, music, craft stalls, bars and restaurants, street theatre

Historical Background:
Started in 1988 to promote Stockton with a small number of entertainers and music. Grown to be internationally recognised as the largest street theatre festival with attendance of more than 250,000 people over 4 days

Media/Public Comments:
"Sparks really fly at pulsating pyrotechnic finale"
"Dance to Afro Caribbean funk, hippo, dub, trance, techno, soul, India, mod, reggae and even 70's"
"Much too much to see, hear, do and feel in 4 days"

Sunderland International Kite Festival

Type of Festival:
Kite Flying and Art Event
Contact: Pauline Taylor
Address:
City Library and Arts Centre
Fawcett Street
Sunderland
Durham
SR1 1RE
Tel. No: 0191 514 1235
Fax No: 0191 514 8444
Date(s) of Festival:
4th - 5th July 1998
Times of Festival: 11am - 5pm
Cost for Adults: Free
Cost for Children: Free
Tickets available from: Not required
Routes by Car:
Site situated on the A195 just south of the A1(M) intersection.

Train/Other:
A regular bus service operates from a variety of sites
Venue:
Northern area playing fields, Dist12, Washington, Tyne and Wear
Facilities (Parking):
Parking is available at the local school, £1 per car
Facilities (Disabled):
Disabled parking is available at the Northumbria Centre and a free bus service operates from the Northumbria Centre to the site
What's On:
Displays of kite flying by specialists from around the world, international programme of music and street theatre, arts and craft fair selling a range of work at affordable prices, children's activities and a range of international food available
Historical Background:
The festival was set up 13 years ago and operates annually attracting 70,000 people
Media/Public Comments:
"A great day out for all the family"

ESSEX

The Benfleet Beer Festival

Type of Festival: **Beer**
Contact: **Sue Bayles**
Address:
**Castlepoint Borough Council
Kiln Road
Benfleet
Essex
SS7 1TF**
Tel. No: **01268 882475**
Fax No: **01268 882464**
Date(s) of Festival:
20th - 24th April 1999
Times of Festival:
**Lunchtime sessions: 11am-3pm
Evenings: 6pm-11/11.30pm**
Cost for Adults:
**£1 entry fee, £5 entertainment
(this includes price of commemo-
rative glass)**
Cost for Children: **Over 18s only**
Routes by Car:
**A13 London Road-Kiln Road/A127
- A130 London Road-Kiln Road.
Runnymede Hall is behind
Castlepoint Council Offices on Kiln
Road**
Train/Other: **Benfleet Station**
Venue: **Runnymede Hall, Benfleet**

Facilities (Parking):
**Large car park. Tasty meals and
snacks available**
Facilities (Disabled):
**Access for disabled including toi-
let facilities**
What's On:
**Over 41 British real ales and bot-
tled beers from around the world
to try. Experts from CAMRA will
be on hand to advise and discuss
the merits of each beer. Special entertainment evenings on Thursday
and Saturday evenings**
Media/Public Comments:
**"The beer will be flowing and musi-
cians and comedians will be
entertaining at the 7th Annual Castle Point Beer Festival" Evening Echo**
General Information:
**Limited tickets available for Thurs-
day and Saturdays evenings.
Themed Festival "Around the
World" with entertainment, food
and drink available from around
the world**

BP Arts Festival

Type of Festival:
Art, Music, Dance, Drama,
Contact: **Sue Bayles**
Address:
**Castle Point Borough Council
Kiln Road
Benfleet
Essex
SS7 1TF**
Tel. No: **01268 882475**
Fax No: **01268 882464**
Date(s) of Festival:
19th - 26th September 1998
Times of Festival:
**Varying times throughout the
week**
Cost for Adults: **Mostly Free**

Cost for Children: **Mostly Free**
Routes by Car:
A13 London Road-Kiln Road/A127
A130 London Road-Kiln Road.
Train/Other: **Benfleet Station**
Venue: **Benfleet**
What's On:
Street entertainment, displays, exhibitions of static art, drama, dance, music, Shakespeare etc. Opportunity to participate in and enjoy the arts
Historical Background:
First ever in Castle Point
General Information:
Sponsored by BP and supported by the eastern Arts Board. A launchpad for raising the profile and developing the arts in Castle Point

Festival Brentwood

Type of Festival:
Music, Dance, Drama, Arts
Contact: **Andy Wilson**
Address:
Tourist Information Office
High Street
Brentwood
Essex
Tel. No: **01277 201111**
Fax No: **01277 202375**
Date(s) of Festival:
29th August - 20th September 1998
Times of Festival: **Various**
Cost for Adults: **Various**
Tickets available from:
Tourist Information Office (see above)
Routes by Car:
M25 Junction 28 or A12 or A128
Train/Other:
Liverpool Street Line
Venue: **Various within Brentwood**
Facilities (Parking): **Town parking**

What's On:
Flower festivals, international Blues Festival, shows, lectures, street entertainment and much more
Media/Public Comments:
"Goes from strength to strength"

New Hall Vineyards English Wine Festival

Type of Festival: **Wine**
Contact: **P W Greenwood**
Address:
New Hall Vineyards
Chelmsford Road
Purleigh
Chelmsford
Essex
CM3 6PN
Tel. No: **01621 828343**
Fax No: **01621 828343**
Date(s) of Festival:
22nd - 23rd August 1998
Times of Festival:
10.30am - 5.30pm
Cost for Adults: **£4**
Cost for Children: **Under 16s free**
Tickets available from: **The door**
Routes by Car:
A12/A414 to Purleigh B1010
Train/Other:
Chelmsford or South Woodham Ferrers
Venue: **New Hall Vineyards**
Facilities (Parking):
1,000 - 1,500 cars and 30 coaches. Food hall and cream teas
What's On:
Over 35 stands, craft fair, wine tasting, art exhibition with over 300 paintings, jazz band, Colchester oyster sea food stall, vintage tractors. Trailer rides around 90 acre vineyard. Vineyard and press house tours. Children's play area,

theatre, minstrels
Historical Background:
23rd annual festival
Media/Public Comments:
"Great family fun day out"

V98

Type of Festival: **Music**
Contact: **Bob Angus**
Address:
Maztec Ltd
491a Holloway Road
London
N19 4DD
Tel. No: **0171 272 2442**
Fax No: **0171 263 2434**
Date(s) of Festival:
22nd - 23rd August 1998
Times of Festival:
Open noon - 11pm
Cost for Adults:
£30 per day; £64 weekend with camping; £55 without camping
Cost for Children:
Under 5s free. Must be accompanied by adult
Booking arrangements:
Please make cheques payable to: SG Box Office. Send to V98, P O Box 2052, London W1A 1HH. Add £1.50 booking fee for day tickets; £2.50 for weekend. Also can be purchased from Virgin megastores (no booking fee) Hotline: 0870 165 5555
Tickets available from:
Ticketmaster: 0171 344 4444
Star Green: 0171 784 8932
Way Ahead: 0171 403 3331
Credit Hotline: 0171 287 0932
Train/Other:
BR Information: 0345 484 950. Chelmsford via Liverpool Street. Late return service to London available. Coach information:

01159 129 222; 0990 329889
Venue: **Hylands Park, Chelmsford**
Facilities (Parking):
Parking on site. Public transport recommended
Facilities (Disabled):
Car park for disabled, a special viewing platform on both outdoor stages and toilets for the disabled. No separate tickets are required. Stewards on site briefed on care and facilities for the disabled
What's On:
The Verve, The Seahorses, Texas, Robbie Williams, Green Day, The Charlatans, Richard Ashcroft, Space, Iggy Pop, James and Chumbawamba, Underworld, Fun Lovin' Criminals, Lightning Seeds ...
Historical Background:
Festival is now in its 3rd year. Winner Live Magazine "European Festival of Year Award" two years running aiming for number three. V98 is sponsored by Virgin Cola and Budweiser
Media/Public Comments:
"Radio One is proud to announce that for the first time ever, they are the broadcast partner for V98. Broadcasting live to the nation over the weekend, they will update the public on all the latest line-up details" BBC Radio 1
General Information:
North and South Unite at V98. The double header Festival takes place on two sites at the same time. 55,000 from the North and 55,000 from the South will be united in spirit as V98 brings Indie, dance and pop music to Temple Newsam in Leeds and Chelmsford

Chelmsford Cathedral Festival

Type of Festival: **Music**
Contact: **Mrs Hilary Simmonds**
Address:
The Festival Office
"Guy Harlings"
New Street
Chelmsford
Essex
CM1 1AT
Tel. No: **01245 359890**
Fax No: **01245 280456**
Date(s) of Festival:
12th - 22nd May 1999
Times of Festival: **Mostly 8pm**
Cost for Adults: **Various**
Tickets available from:
Box Office, Civic Centre, Fairfield: 01245 606505
Routes by Car:
A12 from Colchester, A12 from Brentwood
Train/Other:
Chelmsford Station
Venue: **Chelmsford Cathedral**
Facilities (Parking):
There are public car parks in Waterloo Lane and Victoria Road. High Street is pedestrianised. Certain amount of kerbside parking in Waterloo Lane. Public toilets - Market Rd, opposite Chancellor Hall
What's On:
Classical and jazz concerts, film, poetry, talks, dance, street music and theatre, lectures, midday music box, organ recitals, fringe lectures, fringe performances, exhibitions and more
Historical Background:
The festival started in 1984. It was soon realised that the cathedral had good acoustic quality and has been home to the festival ever since
Media/Public Comments:
"One of the Top Forty Festivals in Britain" The Independent
General Information:
Relax at "Guy Harlings", the Georgian fronted listed building opposite the cathedral: lunch and supper served, licensed bar, marquee in garden serving real ale and bar snacks (open after evening concerts)

Colchester History Fayre

Type of Festival: **Historical**
Contact: **Derek Drew**
Address:
Colchester History Fayre
19 South Street
Colchester
Essex
Tel. No: **01206 563400**
Fax No: **01206 563400**
Date(s) of Festival:
13th - 14th June 1998
Times of Festival:
Saturday and Sunday 10am - 5.30pm
Cost for Adults:
£3. Castle Park is free
Cost for Children: **£2**
Special discounts:
Family tickets (2 adults and 2 children) £8
Tickets available from:
Visitor Information Centre: 01206 282920
Venue: **Colchester**
Facilities (Parking):
Car parks in the Town Centre. Food stalls, drink stalls, beer tent
What's On:

English War Society parade in costume. Cavalier and Roundhead battle re-enactment, period entertainment and market, falconry, music, theatre and dance. Cavalry, arena displays, strolling players . . .
Historical Background:
Commemoration of English Civil War. 1998 is the 350th anniversary of the start of the siege on 13th June 1648
General Information:
Guided tours of Castle

Saffron Walden Folk Festival

Type of Festival:
Folk Music and Dance
Contact: **Hawksmoor Arts**
Address:
109 Radwinter Road
Saffron Walden
Essex
CB11 3HY
Tel. No: **01799 528046**
Fax No: **01799 528046**
Web site:
http: //ds.dial.pipex.com hawksmoor/swff.htm
E-mail: **swff@dial.pipex.com**
Date(s) of Festival:
23rd - 25th October 1998
Times of Festival:
Friday 6pm - Sunday 6pm
Cost for Adults:
Individual events £7, £35 for the season
Cost for Children:
Under 14s free (space permitting)
Tickets available from:
Hawksmoor Arts (see above). Credit card bookings accepted
Routes by Car:
M11 Junction

Train/Other:
Audley End station on the Liverpool Street-Cambridge line (2 miles from the City Centre)
Venue:
Town Hall, Saffron Walden
Facilities (Disabled):
Disabled access to main venues, but smaller venues maybe difficult. Phone for full details
What's On:
Lots of festival events plus the attraction of one of England's most beautiful Medieval towns. Two mazes and prize-winning museum. Also concerts, dances workshops, pub sessions, morris dancing
Historical Background:
Now in its 6th year, this festival has a reputation for the quality of its acts and friendly atmosphere
Media/Public Comments:
"Sell out success"
"Festival a treat for everyone" Saffron Walden Weekly News

Victorian Christmas

Type of Festival: **Seasonal**
Contact: **Lisa Tidder**
Address:
Southend Borough Council
P O Box 6
Southend on Sea
Essex
SS2 6ER
Tel. No: **01702 215166/69**
Fax No: **01702 215465**
Date(s) of Festival:
28th - 29th November 1998
Times of Festival: **11am - 4pm**
Cost for Adults: **Free**
Cost for Children: **Free**
Special discounts: **Free**
Tickets available from:
Not required

Routes by Car:
A127/A13 to Southend Town Centre
Train/Other:
Fenchurch Street to Southend Central or Liverpool Street to Southend Victoria
Venue: **Southend Town Centre**
What's On:
Costumed characters, music, jugglers, jesters, clowns, stiltwalkers, Dickensian market.
Historical Background:
Proceeds to Fairhavens

Southend Annual Jazz Festival

Type of Festival: **Music**
Contact: **Lisa Tidder**
Address:
Southend Borough Council
PO Box 6
Southend on Sea
Essex
SS2 6ER
Tel. No: **01702 215166/69**
Fax No: **01702 215465**
Date(s) of Festival:
28th July - 2nd August 1998
Times of Festival: **Various**
Cost for Adults:
Some events are free, some ticketed
Routes by Car:
A13/A127 then follow signs to the event
Train/Other:
Fenchurch Street to Southend Central or Liverpool Street to Southend Victoria
Venue:
Various venues within Southend
What's On:
A number of jazz musicians at a variety of venues around the town
Historical Background:
This is the 7th Festival

Southend Water Festival

Type of Festival: **Water Sports**
Contact: **Lisa Tidder**
Address:
Southend Borough Council
P O Box 6
Southend on Sea
Essex
SS2 6ER
Tel. No: **01702 215166/69**
Fax No: **01702 215465**
Date(s) of Festival:
13th -14th June 1998
Times of Festival: **12 noon - 5pm**
Cost for Adults: **Free**
Cost for Children: **Free**
Special discounts: **Free**
Tickets available from:
Not required
Routes by Car:
A127/A13 to Southend Seafront
Train/Other:
Fenchurch Street London to Westcliffe or Southend Central or Liverpool Street London to Southend Victoria Station
Venue: **Southend Seafront**
Facilities (Parking):
Parking in Town Centre and parks
What's On:
Offshore circuit power boat racing. UK skiff Grand Prix, Dragon Boat racing, yacht racing, children's entertainment, exhibition areas. Open air concert featuring top pop artists together with radio presenters
Media/Public Comments:
On the Sunday Essex FM are hold-

ing an open air pop concert "Essex FM Big Beach Bash" from 6pm - 9pm, featuring top pop artists together with Essex FM Presenters

LTS Rail
Southend Airshow

Type of Festival: **Aircraft Display**
Contact: **Lisa Tidder**
Address:
Southend Borough Council
P O Box 6
Southend on Sea
Essex
SS2 6ER
Tel. No: **01702 215166/69**
or 01702 390333 (Airshow)
Fax No: **01702 215465**
Date(s) of Festival:
24th - 25th May 1998
Times of Festival:
24th: 12 noon - 8pm
25th: 10am - 6pm
Flying 2pm - 5.30pm both days
Cost for Adults: **Free**
Cost for Children: **Free**
Tickets available from: **Not required**
Routes by Car:
A13/A127 to Southend Town Centre
Train/Other:
Fenchurch Street/Liverpool Street-Chalkwell/Leigh/Westcliffe or Southend
Venue:
Western Esplanade, Southend Seafront
Facilities (Parking):
Town parking.
Facilities (Disabled):
Limited disabled parking along seafront
What's On:
Breathtaking flying programme on

both days with many ground attractions including arena events, exhibition area, market craft fair and military ground displays. Firework spectacular on Sunday evening at approximately 9.30pm
Historical Background:
Festival is in its 13th year and is Europe's largest free airshow staged against a backdrop of the Thames Estuary

Thaxted Festival

Type of Festival:
Classical Music and Jazz
Contact: **G Stainer**
Address:
Thaxted Festival Ticket Office
Clarence House
Thaxted
Essex
CM6 2PJ
Tel. No: **01371 831421**
Fax No: **01371 831421**
Date(s) of Festival:
19th June - 12th July 1998
Times of Festival: **7.30pm**
Cost for Adults: **Various**
Special discounts:
Normal concessions
Tickets available from:
Ticket Office (see above)
Routes by Car:
B184 from either Dunmon or Saffron Walden
Venue:
Thaxted Guildhall, Church, Windmill
Facilities (Parking):
Parking available
Facilities (Disabled):
Access for the disabled
What's On:
Concerts, recitals, and a wide variety of classical music and jazz

Historical Background:
Founded in 1916 by Gustav Holst
Media/Public Comments:
"Excellent festival"
"Thaxted is the ideal venue and the Church of course is quite magnificent"
General Information:
Enjoy one of the most beautiful small towns in England

GLOUCESTERSHIRE

Waterways Weekend, Bristol

Type of Festival: **Waterways Event**
Contact: **Jo Ashwell**
Address:
Richmond Event Management Ltd
59 Prince Street
Bristol
Gloucestershire
BS1 4QH
Tel. No: **0117 9276614**
Fax No: **0117 9221497**
Date(s) of Festival:
27th - 28th June 1998
Times of Festival:
27th: 10am - 10pm
28th: 12 noon - 6pm

Cost for Adults: **Free**
Cost for Children: **Free**
Tickets available from:
Not required
Routes by Car:
Off the motorways, follow the signs to Bristol City Centre
Train/Other:
Bristol Templemeads (short walk to harbour). Ferry (0117 9273416).
Bus (0117 9553231)
Venue: **Bristol's historic harbour**
Facilities (Parking):
Parking at Canons Marsh car park plus City Centre car parks.
There will be food, drink and a Real Ale Bar.
Facilities (Disabled):
Disabled parking available for Orange Badge Holders
What's On:
See the arrival of over 150 canal and waterways vessels from all over the country. Among the main attractions will be live music, funfair, water-based activities, street entertainment, firework display, exhibitions, craft stalls, boat competitions.
Historical Background:
Anglo-Welsh and British waterways sponsoring the pilot event.
General Information:
Bristol Industrial Museum - special exhibits, i.e. the Mayflower (the world's oldest working tug) and Pyronaut will be on display. Mayflower spent her working life on the Gloucester and Sharpness Canal while the Pyronaut provided fire cover for the harbour.

Unipart Bristol Balloon Fiesta

Type of Festival:
Hot Air Balloon Fiesta
Contact:
Susan Armstrong Brown
Address:
Bristol Balloon Fiestas Ltd
St Johns Street
Bedminster
Bristol
Gloucestershire
BS3 4NH
Tel. No: **0117 953 5884**
Fax No: **0117 953 5606**
Date(s) of Festival:
6th - 9th August 1998
Times of Festival:
6th: 2pm - 10pm
7th - 9th: 6am - 8pm
Cost for Adults: **Free**
Cost for Children: **Free**
Tickets available from:
Not required
Routes by Car:
On B3128 4 miles from Junction 19 off the M5
Train/Other:
Bristol Templemeads close by
Venue:
Ashton Court Estate, Long Ashton
Facilities (Parking):
£4 per car. Catering and refreshment stands
Facilities (Disabled):
Disabled parking and Toilets
What's On:
Evening concerts, night glow and fireworks, early morning balloon launches, arena events, village green events, trade stands and entertainment, Red Arrows display, jousting, jazz, funfairs, fieldguns, live entertainment
Historical Background:
The fiesta was started by the Chamber of Commerce in conjunction with local balloonists in 1979 with just 27 balloons. It has now grown into the largest Balloon meet in Europe and one of the top outdoor events in the UK
Media/Public Comments:
"Voted best event in Bristol" Evening Post
"The Fiesta has rightly earned its best event tag"
"Balloon Fiesta is world class"
"The Fiesta is Bristol's biggest annual event and is a showpiece for the City of Bristol and Bristol business"
General Information:
To celebrate the 20th anniversary and the 10th year of Unipart sponsorship, the Fiesta is lifting off with a new "Special Shapes Rodeo" on the first evening where some of the most weird and wonderful balloons will take to the skies.

Bristol Volksfest

Type of Festival:
Music and Automotive
Contact:
Adrian Ashby
Address:
204 Lawrence Hill
Bristol
Gloucestershire
Tel. No: **0117 9559559**
Fax No: **0117 9540044**
Date(s) of Festival:
7th June 1998

Times of Festival:
10am - 5pm
Cost for Adults: **£4**
Cost for Children: **Under 12s free**
Special discounts: **None**
Tickets available from: **At the gate**
Routes by Car:
1 mile south on A38 from Junction 16 M5
Venue:
St Brendans Rugby Grounds, Filton
Facilities (Parking):
Free parking, refreshments and food
What's On:
Local bands, local DJs, community entertainers, cult fashion, surf wear VW air-cooled motor show, Show 'n' Shine line ups, trade stands, autojumble, Gladiator-style pugel stick fighting, car cruise around Bristol.
Historical Background:
6th year of alternative car show with cult vibes and music. Cool ice equipment etc
Media/Public Comments:
"The Bristol Volksfest has joined the ranks of national events - why not cruise on down and join in."

Bristol Sound '98

Type of Festival:
Music
Contact:
Jo Ashwell/Anthony Braine
Address:
59 Prince Street
Bristol
Gloucestershire, BS1 4QH
Tel. No:
0117 9276614 (J Ashwell)
0117 9779917 (A Braine)

Fax No:
0117 9221497 (J Ashwell)
0117 9779917 (A Braine)
Date(s) of Festival:
10th - 17th October 1998
Times of Festival: **Various**
Cost for Adults: **Various**
Tickets available from:
Various venues in Bristol
Routes by Car:
Junction 19 off M4, then M32 Junction 16,17 off M5, A4 from Bath
Train/Other:
Bristol Templemeads
Venue:
Various venues in Bristol City Centre
Facilities (Parking):
City Centre parking. Various according to venue
What's On:
A week of music in a network of venues over Bristol. To include all types of music plus a free Music Industry seminar Programme. (The 1998 event has not yet been programmed)
Historical Background:
Third year of the Festival which followed on from Radio One's Sound City in Bristol in 1995. 1997 had been a good year for Bristol's music with major label album releases from Roni Size and Reprazent, Portishead, Way Out West and others.
Media/Public Comments:
"As well as being entertaining public festival, Bristol Sound is also about the music business and the business of music"
"If you are involved in dance music in any way, you cannot afford to miss this event"

Cheltenham Festival of Christmas Lights

Type of Festival: **Christmas**
Contact: **Sue Bird**
Address:
Cheltenham Borough Council
Imperial Square
Cheltenham
Gloucestershire   GL50 1QA
Tel. No: **01242 521621**
Fax No: **01242 573902**
Date(s) of Festival:
28th Nov 98 - 6th Jan 99
Times of Festival:
Switch on at 6pm (TBC)
Cost for Adults: **Free**
Cost for Children: **Free**
Tickets available from:
Public No: 01242 522878
Train/Other:
Cheltenham Spa railway station is 20 mins walk from the Promenade. National Express buses arrive at the Royal Well Bus Station (parallel to the Promenade).
Venue: **Cheltenham Promenade**
Facilities (Parking):
Use Town Centre Car parks or the Park and Ride Services
What's On:
Live entertainment during the day, children's workshops, family discos followed by Santa Claus switching on the lights. Watch the procession as it passes along the streets of Cheltenham.
Historical Background:
Cheltenham has become famous for its spectacular Christmas lights display. People travel from all over to see the lights and do their Christmas shopping in style.
Media/Public Comments:
"The Town was buzzing all day long" The Clarion

Cheltenham Festival of Literature

Type of Festival: **Literature**
Contact: **Judith Garrett**
Address:
Cheltenham Arts Festival Ltd
Town Hall
Imperial Square
Cheltenham
Gloucestershire
GL50 1QA
Tel. No: **01242 521621**
Fax No: **01242 256457**
Date(s) of Festival:
9th - 18th October 1998
Times of Festival:
10am - midnight
Cost for Adults: **TBC**
Cost for Children: **TBC**
Special discounts:
Concessions mainly £1 off. Available to under 25s, students, UB40s, disabled, Friends of the Festival.
Tickets available from:
01242 264280
Routes by Car:
Junction 11 off M5/approximately 40 miles west of Oxford on A40
Train/Other:
Regular services to most towns/cities - Regular trains from London Paddington.
Venue:
Cheltenham Town Hall and Everyman Theatre
Facilities (Parking):
Many public car parks in Cheltenham
Facilities (Disabled):
Disabled access to Town Hall and Everyman Theatre
What's On:
A wide range of events including talks and lectures, poetry readings,

novelists in conversation, exhibitions, large bookshop, discussions, talks, debates, workshops. Celebration of Shakespeare, exploration of song writing, poetry, language of rock 'n' roll

Historical Background:
Began in 1949 by writer John Moore. The first purely literary festival of its kind. This festival has over the past decade developed from an essentially local event into the largest most popular in Europe.

Media/Public Comments:
"The mother of all literary festivals" The Times
"The Festival of Literature is fast approaching and as usual I'm in a dilemma about what to see... No one could possibly say that (it) doesn't offer something for every taste." Wilts and Glos. Standard

General Information:
The 1997 festival was the biggest yet with over 300 authors taking part in nearly 250 events. This years' event will be celebrating revolution in all its forms; literary, social, historical, from the demos of 1968 to Europe's "Year of Revolutions" in 1848

Cheltenham International Jazz

Festival
Type of Festival: **Modern Jazz**
Contact: **Jim Smith**
Address:
Cheltenham Arts Festivals Ltd
The Mews
Mitcheldean
Gloucestershire
GL17 0SL
Tel. No: **01594 544446**

Fax No: **01594 544448**
Date(s) of Festival:
9th - 11th April 1999
Times of Festival: **All day**
Cost for Adults: **£5 - £18**
Cost for Children:
25% discount on standby
Special discounts:
25% on all tickets - standby only
Tickets available from:
Box Office: 01242 227979
Routes by Car: **A40 or M5**
Venue: **Everyman Theatre**
Facilities (Parking): **Parking Limited**
Facilities (Disabled):
Parking and access for the disabled available.
What's On:
Modern jazz from around the world including funk, salsa, Drum 'n' Bass, wide range of jazz from Be-Bop to Avante Garde European. Also many events in the town including great prizes to be won, lots to eat and drink and free events
Historical Background:
Founded in 1996 and has become internationally recognised
Media/Public Comments:
"Cheltenham Jazz Festival has become perhaps the leading English event of its kind" The Independent
General Information:
Wonderful setting at the gateway to the Cotswolds. Beautiful Regency Town. For brochure ring Hotline: 01242 237377

Sequence Dance Festivals at Cheltenham Town Hall

Type of Festival:
Sequence Dancing
Contact:
Gary Fleetwood, Tricia Fleetwood

and Tim Hulse
Address:
Town Hall
Cheltenham Borough Council
Imperial Square
Cheltenham
Gloucestershire
G150 1QA
Tel. No:
01793 522232 (Gary/Tricia)
Date(s) of Festival:
4th - 6th September 1998
Cost for Adults: **£20**
Tickets available from:
01793 522232 or
Box Office: 01242 227979
Routes by Car:
Junction 11 off M5/approximately
40 miles west of Oxford on A40
Train/Other:
Regular services to most towns
and cities, regular trains to Lon-
don Paddington
Venue: **Cheltenham Town Hall.**
Facilities (Parking):
Public car parks in Cheltenham
Facilities (Disabled):
Disabled access to Town Hall
What's On:
Dance the weekend away. Join
your hosts, Gary and Patricia for
a weekend of instruction, practice
and enjoyable sequence dancing to
live music in good company - an
ideal opportunity to meet old
friends and make new ones

The Cirencester Festival

Type of Festival: **Music, Arts**
Contact: **Roger Jenkins**
Address:
Manor Cottage
School Lane
Meysey Hampton

Cirencester
Gloucestershire
GL7 5JS
Tel. No: **01285 851355**
Fax No: **01285 850182**
Date(s) of Festival:
13th June - 5th July 1998
Times of Festival: **Various**
Cost for Adults:
Varies with each event. Some
event are free.
Tickets available from:
Roger Jenkins (see above).
Venue:
Various venues in Cirencester:
Market Place, Sundial Theatre,
Brewery Arts, parish church, Corn
Hall, Regal Cinema, Woolmarket,
Manor House, Phoenix Centre,
Cirencester Library, Harnhill
Manor, Abbey grounds, Poulton
House etc
Facilities (Parking):
Town Centre parking. Parking
available at all venues
Facilities (Disabled):
Access for disabled at all venues.
What's On:
Open air Shakespeare, concerts,
films, Flamenco, comedy, vintage
Traditional/New Orleans jazz, art
exhibitions, Spanish and South
American music, organ recitals,
drama, Gilbert and Sullivan, bal-
let, open air music day - blues,
rock, roots band etc
Media/Public Comments:
"This years' festival will have a
Spanish theme and propose to un-
derwrite a larger range of artistic
events than in 1997; classical mu-
sic and opera will be augmented
by a series of popular events which
we hope will attract the crowds"
General Information:

Grand opening fiesta, live music, street performers, circus acts, buskers, stalls, face painters, open air café

Didmarton Festival of Bluegrass Music

Type of Festival: **Music**
Contact:
Didmarton Festival of Bluegrass Music
Address:
38 Nutgrove Avenue
Bristol
Gloucestershire
BS3 4QF
Tel. No: **0117 963 1446**
Date(s) of Festival:
4th - 6th September 1998
Times of Festival:
7pm on 4th - 5pm on 6th
Cost for Adults:
On the gate weekend ticket £25
Cost for Children:
Under 10s free, 10-16yrs £11
Special discounts:
BBMA members £20 (proof required). Advance weekend ticket (before 21/8) £22
Tickets available from:
Festival Office (see above)
Routes by Car:
Holford Arms, Knockdown on A4333 between Didmarton and Tetbury (M4/M5 motorways)
Train/Other:
Bath Spa or Chippenham
Venue:
The Holford Arms, Didmarton, Gloucestershire
Facilities (Parking):
Parking available, campsite, food, bar
Facilities (Disabled):
Wheelchair accessibility

What's On:
The Bluegrass Patriots (USA), The Down Boys, The Hillbilly Boogiemen (Holland), The Daily Planet, A Band Like Alice, Bill Smarme and The Business, The Next Band, Jane on Thunder, The Bluegrass Bros, Blackjack, club tent, workshops, dance etc
Historical Background:
10th and last festival. It has grown from 200 to 800 people.
Media/Public Comments:
"Bloody Good"
General Information:
Camping included in price of weekend ticket. No "camping only".

Gloucester Cricket Festival

Type of Festival: **Sports**
Contact: **Colin Sexton**
Address:
Gloucestershire Cricket Club
Neville Road
Bristol
Gloucestershire
BS7 9EJ
Tel. No: **01179 245216**
Fax No: **01179 241193**
Date(s) of Festival:
21st - 24th May 1998
Times of Festival:
Thursday, Friday, Saturday starts at 11am; Sunday start at 2pm
Cost for Adults:
Thursday, Friday, Saturday: £7 Sunday: £9
Cost for Children:
Under 16s 4 days £2; 1 day £2
Special discounts:
OAPs and Leisure Discount Card holders 4 days £4. 1day £5.
Tickets available from:
On the day or contact GCC (see

above).

Routes by Car:
From the north exit Junction I I off M5, south exit Junction 12 off M5.
Train/Other:
Gloucester Station. National Express
Venue:
The King's School, Archdeacon Way, off St Oswalds Rd, Gloucester
What's On:
Gloucestershire versus Yorkshire cricket

Gloucester Christmas Celebration

Type of Festival:
Traditional and Music
Contact: **Lesley Pritchard**
Address:
**Gloucester City Council
Herbert Warehouse
The Docks
Gloucester
Gloucestershire
GL1 2EQ**
Tel. No: **01452 396620**
Fax No: **01452 396622**
Date(s) of Festival:
15th November - 25th December 1998
Times of Festival:
Christmas launch event on 15th November 12 noon - 6pm. Events Thursday evenings 5pm - 9pm and Sundays 11am - 4pm
Routes by Car:
From the north Junction11 off M5, South Junction 12 M5
Train/Other:
Gloucester Station. National Express from London, Manchester, Birmingham, Bristol and Cardiff
Venue: **Gloucester Town Centre**
What's On:

Cartoon celebrities at Christmas launch event, clowns and music. Street entertainment (Thursday evenings and Sundays) until Christmas

Gloucester Festival

Type of Festival: **Music, Sport, Arts**
Contact: **Lesley Pritchard**
Address:
**Gloucester City Council
Herbert Warehouse
The Docks
Gloucester
Gloucestershire
GL1 2EQ**
Tel. No: **01452 396620**
Fax No: **01452 396622**
Date(s) of Festival:
25th July - 8th August 1998
Times of Festival: **All day**
Cost for Adults: **Most events free**
Cost for Children: **Most events free**
Special discounts:
Gloucester Leisure Discount Card holders
Routes by Car:
From the north Junction 11 off M5, south Junction 12 M5
Train/Other:
Gloucester Station served by trains from London, Midlands, the South West and South Wales. National Express from London, Manchester, Birmingham, Bristol and Cardiff
Venue: **Gloucester**
Facilities (Parking):
Parking available on most sites
Facilities (Disabled):
Access for the disabled
What's On:
Carnival procession, Docks Folks Roots Weekend, Blues Trail, country fayre, Funtasia USA theme day, street entertainers, films, open air theatre at English Heritage sites,

Asian music and dance event, fire-works display
Historical Background:
56th year of a festival which origi-nally started as a "holiday at home" event for the people of Gloucester

Gloucester Three Choirs Festival

Type of Festival: **Music**
Contact: **Anthony Boden**
Address:
Community House
College Green
Gloucester
Gloucestershire
GLI 2LZ
Tel. No: **01452 529819**
Fax No: **01452 502854**
Date(s) of Festival:
15th - 22nd August 1998
Cost for Adults:
Prices range from £4 - £29
Special discounts:
Concessions available for students and UB40s
Routes by Car: **Exit 11 from M5**
Train/Other: **Gloucester Station**
Venue:
Gloucester Cathedral, Tewksbury Abbey, Prinknesh Abbey, Blaisdon Hall etc
Facilities (Disabled):
Information sheets are available for disabled people
What's On:
54 events, full programme.
Historical Background:
The oldest music festival of its type in Europe having started in the early years of the eighteenth century
General Information:
Booking form available from the 9th March 1998

The Gloucestershire Festival

Type of Festival:
Music, Community, Sports, Heritage
Contact: **The Event Unit**
Address:
Gloucester City Council
Herbert Warehouse
The Docks
Gloucester
Gloucestershire
GLI 2EQ
Tel. No: **01452 396620**
Fax No: **01452 396622**
Date(s) of Festival:
25th July - 8th August 1998
Cost for Adults:
Various. Many events free
Special discounts:
Concessions available
Tickets available from:
Information Hotline:
01452 396666
Routes by Car:
Junction 11 M5, follow tourist signs
Train/Other: **Gloucester Station**
Venue: **Gloucester City Centre**
Facilities (Parking):
City Centre parking
Facilities (Disabled):
Access for disabled
What's On:
Carnival procession, fireworks dis-play, outdoor exhibitions, arena events, country fayre, children's events, indoor exhibitions, dance , music, theatre, street entertain-ment and more...
Historical Background:
The festival is now in its 56th year
Media/Public Comments:
Good public response and turnout

Guiting Festival of
Music and the Arts
Type of Festival: **Music and Art**
Contact: **Virginia Sandbach**
Address:
Stoneley
Cutsdean
Cheltenham
Gloucestershire
GL54 5RX
Tel. No: **01386 584408**
Fax No: **01386 584673**
Date(s) of Festival:
25th July - 1st August 1998
Times of Festival:
7.45pm every evening and 11.30am lunch time concert on 26th July
Cost for Adults: **£7.50**
Cost for Children: **£7.50**
Tickets available from:
Geraldine Wishon:
01242 603912
Train/Other:
Cheltenham, Kingham, Moreton-in-Marsh
Venue:
Village Hall, Guiting Power, Nr Cheltenham
Facilities (Parking): **Car park**
Facilities (Disabled):
Ramps for disabled
What's On:
Concert Royale, Music for Eight, Tanya Sarkisova Piano Trio, Peter and Zoltan Katona (Guitars) Sorrel Quartet, David Kennedy and Rianka Bouwmeester, Sweet Soul Sisters, Elizaveta Kopelman and Jacqueline Dankworth
Historical Background:
Originally called "Off the Beaten Track" has grown and developed in its 28th year into a festival of considerable stature

Media/Public Comments:
"The festival is growing in size and popularity and goes from strength to strength" Gloucestershire Echo

Randwick WAP
Type of Festival: **Traditional**
Contact: **Mr and Mrs S Giles**
Address:
2 Humphreys End
Randwick
Gloucestershire
GL6 6EW
Tel. No: **01453 766782**
Date(s) of Festival: **8th May 1999**
Times of Festival: **1pm - 5pm**
Cost for Adults: **Free**
Cost for Children: **Free**
Tickets available from:
Not required
Train/Other: **Stroud Station**
Venue:
Randwick Village, Lanes and Playing Field
Facilities (Parking):
On field next to playing field. Car parking £1.50
Facilities (Disabled):
Hilly, so access for disabled may be difficult.
What's On:
Colourful procession with Mayor and Queen carried shoulder high. Cheese rolling, mayor ducking, morris dancing, traditional music, varied entertainment, dog show, dog display and stalls
Historical Background:
Dates back to the Middle Ages, possibly a celebration after the church was built. The celebration was revived in 1972 by the Rev. Nial Morrison after being stopped in 1892 due to rowdiness!

Stowe on the Wold Annual Antiques And Fine Arts Festival

Type of Festival:
Antiques and Fine Art
Contact: **Alan J Rose**
Address:
**The Old Stocks Hotel
The Square
Stowe on the Wold
Gloucestershire
GL54 1AF**
Tel. No: **01451 830666**
Fax No: **01451 870014**
Date(s) of Festival:
1st - 5th February 1999
Cost for Adults:
Subject to individual hotel rates. However individual lectures can be booked by day. Visitors - £10 per lecture
Tickets available from:
The Old Stocks Hotel (see above), Grapevine Hotel: 01451 830344, Fosse Manor: 01451 830354, Unicorn Hotel: 01451 830257
Routes by Car:
Easy reach of Cheltenham, Stratford upon Avon, Broadway, Cirencester, Warwick, Gloucester. Major Motorway network (M40)
Train/Other:
Nearest train station Moreton in Marsh
Venue: **Hotels, antique dealers and galleries within Stowe on the Wold.**
Facilities (Parking):
Hotel parking and town parking
What's On:
Residents staying at each hotel will have the opportunity to listen to lectures of their choice. Many antique dealers and art galleries will have their own exhibitions and late openings. Listen and speak to the experts

Historical Background:
1999 heralds the 4th year of this successful festival. The town plays host to 70 antique dealers, fine art galleries and bookshops and an envied reputation for fair trading
Media/Public Comments:
Extensive media coverage both at home and in North America. Media and the travel industry have hailed the festival as a major event on the international antiques calendar
General Information:
One of the finest unspoilt towns in the heart of the Cotswolds, the town has a distinctive character. The last encounter of the Civil War was fought in and around Stowe in March 1646 when Sir Jacob Astley surrendered to Cromwell's Army

Stroud International Brick and Rolling Pin Throwers

Type of Festival: **Sporting**
Contact: **Mrs Eunice Guy**
Address:
**The Cot
Middle Road
Thrupp
Stroud
Gloucestershire
GL5 2DR**
Tel. No: **01453 882039**
Date(s) of Festival: **18th July 1998**
Times of Festival:
In the afternoon
Cost for Adults: **Free**
Cost for Children: **Free**
Tickets available from:
Not required
Routes by Car:
Stroud, then follow signs to Stratford Park Leisure Centre, then to top field.

Train/Other:
Stroud Railway Station. 1 mile from Stratford Leisure Centre
Venue:
Stratford Park Leisure Centre
Facilities (Parking): **Free parking**
What's On:
The event takes place in the park of the Leisure Centre. Within the Leisure Centre there are the usual activities such as swimming, tennis, indoor sports most of which are chargeable
Historical Background:
Brick throwing started in 1960 between Stroud, Gloucestershire and Stroud, Oklahoma, USA. In 1961 Stroud, NSW Australia and Stroud, Ontario, Canada joined. In 1962 women also joined in from the 4 countries throwing Australian produced rolling pins.
Media/Public Comments:
Good coverage given to event by BBC and HTV, several national radio "phone-ins", national and local newspapers and several magazines
General Information:
Teams of 6 playing in their respective countries on the 3rd Saturday in July. The results are sent to the UK for the working out of International Results Table

Stroud Fringe Festival of Performing Arts

Type of Festival:
Roots Music and the Arts
Contact: **Sue Bearder**
Address:
Stroud Fringe Festival of Performing Arts Ltd
18 Woodstock Avenue
Tetbury
Gloucestershire

GL8 8NG
Tel. No:
01453 832370/01453 827717
Fax No: **01453 832370**
Date(s) of Festival:
11th - 13th September 1998
10th - 12th September 1999
Times of Festival: **8pm - 11pm**
Cost for Adults:
£25 (before 1st August) £28 (after)
Cost for Children:
Ages 8-17 £12 (before 1st August) £14 (after)
Special discounts:
OAP, UB40s, students: £23 (before 1st August)
Tickets available from:
01453 832370/01453 827717 (from 22nd May). Tickets available at door
Routes by Car:
M5 Junction 13. M4 Junction 15
Train/Other:
Stroud Station (London to Cheltenham Line)
Venue: **Stroud**
Facilities (Parking):
Town Centre Parking. Camping available.
Facilities (Disabled): **Available.**
What's On:
Concerts, bands, street entertainment, (dance from around the world on central stage), poetry, theatre, grand procession, art exhibitions, market and crafts, workshops in dance and music, full children's programme
Historical Background:
Now in its third year the festival is the largest event in Stroud's calendar with something for everyone
Media/Public Comments:
"With festivals like this around Sidmouth had better watch out!" Folkwrite

Hailes Music Festival

Type of Festival: **Classical Music**
Contact:
Bernard Partridge (Director)
Address:
Hailes Music Festival
Hailes House
Hailes
Winchcombe
Gloucestershire
GL54 5PB
Tel. No: **01242 602379**
Date(s) of Festival:
4th - 27th July 1998
Cost for Adults: **£7.50 - £11.50**
Cost for Children:
Under 12s half price
Tickets available from:
Box Office: 01242 602379
Routes by Car:
10 miles North East of Cheltenham
Train/Other: **Cheltenham Station**
Venue:
Various venues including Hailes Abbey, Hailes Barn, Winchcombe Village, Broadway, Bowton on the Water, Stow on the Wold
Facilities (Parking):
Available for every event
Facilities (Disabled):
Access for disabled people
What's On:
Situated in the heart of the Cotswold Hills enjoy outside pursuits such as riding, walking etc on the Cotswold Way
General Information:
Distinguished musicians have appeared at this festival including William Bennett, Hugh Bean, Keith Harvey, Alan Schiller and the English Heritage Singers

HAMPSHIRE

Basingstoke Kite Festival

Type of Festival: **Kite**
Contact: **Alan Cosgrove (Kite entry/specifics only)**
Address:
Loddon Valley Kite Flyers
18 Loggon Road
Basingstoke
Hampshire
RG21 3PH
Tel. No: **01256 421800**
Date(s) of Festival:
6th - 7th June 1998
Times of Festival: **10am - 5pm**
Cost for Adults: **Free**
Cost for Children: **Free**
Tickets available from:
Tourist Information:
01256 817618
Train/Other:
15 min bus ride from Basingstoke Station; 10 min taxi
Venue:
Down Grange playing fields. Follow AA signs
Facilities (Parking): **On site parking**
What's On:
Kite displays and competitions and

demonstrations. **Children's workshop and traders**
General Information:
Biggest Kite Festival in the region

Basingstoke Festival of Transport

Type of Festival:
Vintage, Veteran, Classic Cars
Contact: **Tom Mansbridge**
Address:
The Garage
Cliddesden Road
Cliddesden
Basingstoke
Hampshire
Tel. No: **01256 322376**
Date(s) of Festival: **9th May 1999**
Times of Festival: **11am - 5pm**
Cost for Adults: **Free**
Cost for Children: **Free**
Tickets available from:
Tourist Information:
01256 817618
Routes by Car:
A33 from Reading to Black Dam Roundabout/A339 Newbury/Junction 6 M3
Train/Other:
10 min walk from Basingstoke station up through the town
Venue:
Basingstoke Memorial Park
Facilities (Parking):
On site. Follow signs.
Facilities (Disabled):
Disabled Parking (see stewards)
What's On:
Display of cars, buses, commercials, service, upright pump engines, arena acts
Historical Background:
Thorneycroft used to build cars and commercials in Basingstoke

General Information:
Largest collection of this type of vehicle in the region

Balloons Over Basingstoke

Type of Festival:
Hot Air Ballooning
Contact: **Chris Powell**
Address:
Basingstoke Borough Council
Civic Offices
London Road
Basingstoke
Hampshire
RG21 4AH
Tel. No: **01256 845682**
Date(s) of Festival:
27th - 28th June 1998
Times of Festival:
Saturday: 6am - 11pm
Sunday: 6am - 8pm
Cost for Adults: **Free**
Cost for Children: **Free**
Tickets available from:
Tourist Information:
01256 817618
Routes by Car:
Follow AA signs and head for Town Centre
Train/Other: **10 mins from station**
Venue:
War Memorial Park, Basingstoke
Facilities (Parking):
£2 per car on site. Refreshments on site
Facilities (Disabled):
Disabled parking available (see stewards)
What's On:
Mass balloon launches, Nightglow, laser show, arena acts, balloon tethering, funfair, children's acts
Historical Background:

There has been a Balloon Festival in Basingstoke for the last 10 years. Second only in size to Southampton Balloon Festival in the Central Southern Region

Bedhampton Festival

Type of Festival:
Art, Music, History, Drama
Contact: **Judith Worley**
Address: **Bidbury House**
Bidbury Lane
Bedhampton
Hampshire
PO9 3JG
Tel. No: **01705 483217**
Fax No: **01705 454233**
E-mail:
bidbury@ compuserve.com
Date(s) of Festival:
18th - 25 July 1998
Times of Festival: **Various**
Cost for Adults:
£16 season ticket (booked in advance) or separate costs for each event
Tickets available from:
J Worley (see above)
Routes by Car:
A3(M) from London, take exit 5 or A27 (South Coast route), follow signs
Train/Other:
Bedhampton Station. Served by bus nos: 21, 22, 23, 63, 673A, 36 and 145
Venue:
Bidbury House, St Thomas Church, Pond House (Bedhampton village)
What's On:
Sculpture exhibition and classical music recital, gardens trail, drama, jazz concert, evening walk on the history and architecture of Bedhampton. Talk on local history

Bishops Waltham Festival

Type of Festival:
Music and Drama
Contact:
J A Whetham
Festival Secretary
Address:
Yew Trees
Lower Lane
Bishops Waltham
Hampshire
SO32 1AS
Tel. No: **01489 893197**
Date(s) of Festival:
6th - 14th June 1998
Times of Festival:
Events start: 7pm/8pm. Access to grounds for picnics at 5pm
Cost for Adults: **Various**
Cost for Children:
Discounts available
Special discounts:
Discounts for Early Bird, groups and OAPs
Tickets available from:
Bath Travel: 01489 896428, HW Veck and Sons, High Street/by post to above
Routes by Car:
B2177 from Winchester or Fareham. B3035 from Botley
Train/Other:
The nearest station is Hedge End or Eastleigh
Venue:
The Palace Grounds, Bishops Waltham
Facilities (Parking):
Ample car parking
Facilities (Disabled):
Disabled parking and access for disabled
What's On:

6th: Folk Night, 7th: Jazz at the Palace, 8th: Simfonietta, 9th: Ludwig Beatles, 11th: Botley Choral Society concert, 13th: Carnival fete and Macbeth

Historical Background:
Third year of Festival. The aim is to build community spirit by providing high quality events at affordable prices

General Information:
Events attract 1,000 -1,500 people. The Palace grounds offer a superb site for picnics close to the centre of the village. There are other activities for children on Saturday 6th, Sunday 7th, and carnival fashion show on the 10th June

Gosport Easter Festival

Type of Festival: **Music**
Contact: **Mr Peter Chegwyn**
Address:
51 Russell Street
Gosport
Hampshire
PO12 3JD
Tel. No: **01705 528017**
Fax No: **01705 528017**
Date(s) of Festival:
1st - 5th April 1999
Times of Festival:
Daytime and evenings at varying times
Cost for Adults: **Various**.
Tickets available from:
Festival Box Office:
01705 522944
Routes by Car:
Between Portsmouth and Southampton the South Coast just opposite the Isle of Wight. M27 Junction 11
Train/Other:
Portsmouth Harbour station (Lon-
don Waterloo, Cardiff, Bristol and Reading) then take the ferry across the harbour to Gosport, then bus or taxi**
Venue:
Thorngate Halls, Bury Road
Facilities (Parking):
Free parking, free camping. Plenty of cheap B&Bs within yards of the venue. Also there are plenty of more luxurious hotels on the seafront
Facilities (Disabled):
Easy access for disabled
What's On:
Ceilidhs, Celtic folklore, dance tuition, Romany songs, masterclasses, meet the bands, guest slots, informal sessions, Celtic rock 'n' roots, comedy, concerts, dances, workshops, sessions plus unique late night Festival Club
Historical Background:
Launched in 1992, the festival has expanded every year. It is now recognised as England's premier Celtic Music Festival.
Media/Public Comments:
"Simply brilliant . . . Miss it at your peril" Portsmouth Evening News

Havant Arts Festival

Type of Festival:
Music, Dance, Theatre, Visual Arts, Street Arts
Contact:
Joe Sumsion
Arts Development Officer
Address:
Havant Borough Council
Civic Offices
Havant
Hampshire
PO9 2AX
Tel. No: **01705 446434/480113**

Fax No: **01705 446156**
Date(s) of Festival:
1st - 30th May 1998
Times of Festival: **Various**
Cost for Adults:
Various. Many events are free
Special discounts:
Concessions available
Tickets available from:
**Tourist Information Office:
01705 480024**
Routes by Car:
Access from A27 between Chichester and Southsea/Portsmouth.
Train/Other:
Served well by train (London Waterloo or London Victoria) to Havant Station.
Venue:
Various venues within Havant town and surrounding areas
Facilities (Parking):
Parking available at most venues
Facilities (Disabled):
Ring Tourist Information Office for details (see above)
What's On:
Theatre, Shakespeare, photography exhibition, woodcarving and sculpture exhibition, classical, rock, jazz, pop music, Gilbert and Sullivan, poetry, film and craft events, poetry and "Garbage Music" workshops, 4 part harmony workshops, barn dance, line dancing. . .
Historical Background:
This is the first Festival of its kind in Havant. Once a leading leather glove and parchment making centre, Havant evolved around an ancient network of springs and an old Roman crossroads which linked

Arundel to Winchester and Hayling Island to Rowlands Castle
General Information:
Havant is a thriving market town, characterised by its fine Georgian buildings and narrow weaving footpaths called "the Twittens". Visit Chichester (13 miles), Portsmouth (5 miles) and Arundel (20 miles)

Hi There!

Type of Festival:
Music, Community, Educational
Contact: **Mark Ringwood**
Address:
**Hi-Peractive
23 Station Road
Hayling Island
Hampshire
PO11 0EA**
Tel. No: **01705 461934**
Fax No: **01705 461935**
Date(s) of Festival:
16th July - 5th August 1998
Times of Festival: **Various**
Cost for Adults:
Price varies, some events free
Tickets available from:
**Havant Tourist Office:
01705 480024**
Routes by Car:
A3023 from A27 West
Train/Other:
Bicycle routes down Hayling Billy link
Venue:
Various venues on Hayling Island
Facilities (Parking):
Parking at most venues
Facilities (Disabled):
Disabled facilities at most venues
What's On:
Concerts, art exhibitions, street

theatre, Japanese kite flying, display lectures, music from Canada, Africa, Palestine, India, Trinidad, USA. Also Cybercafe, tree dressing, juggling, circus skills workshops, wine making, clay modelling . . .

Historical Background:
Started in 1997 with aid of a National Lottery Grant. Set to become one of the biggest Festivals on the south coast by 2007.

Media/Public Comments:
"Very positive, long overdue, provides much needed artistic stimulation, and about time something like this happened on Hayling"

General Information:
Hayling Island is a traditional family seaside resort. Much of the foreshore remains untamed and Hayling Island is essentially rural in appearance

Summer Arts Across Portsmouth

Type of Festival:
Music, Art, Dance, Street Theatre
Contact: **Nigel Gossop**
Address:
City Arts
Leisure Service
Civic Offices
Guildhall Square
Portsmouth
Hampshire
PO1 2AD
Tel. No: **01705 834182**
Fax No: **01705 834904**
Date(s) of Festival:
Mid-May - mid-September 1998

Times of Festival: **Various**
Cost for Adults:
Most events are free
Routes by Car:
Portsmouth is off the A27
Train/Other:
Portsmouth & Southsea station
Venue:
Events are at various venues within the city
Facilities (Parking):
Most venues have nearby parking and are fully accessible
Facilities (Disabled):
Access for disabled
What's On:
Bandstand, street theatre, children's theatre, newly commissioned art work and performances, workshops and activities for children, dance and literature events
Media/Public Comments:
"Fantastic - there is much going on - and it's brilliant that it's free"

International Festival of the Sea

Type of Festival:
Celebration of the Sea
Contact: **Royal Naval Flagship**
Address:
HM Naval Base
PP16
Building 1/78
The Parade
Portsmouth
Hampshire
PO1 3NH
Tel. No: **0870 9091998**
Tour Operators: 0171 9303000
E- mail: **Seafest**
@aol.com\www.Portsmouth.co.uk

Date(s) of Festival:
28th - 31st August 1998
Times of Festival: **TBC**
Cost for Adults: **£16 day ticket**
Cost for Children: **£10 (Ages 4-16)**
Special discounts:
UB40s, OAPs, students: £12.50
Tickets available from:
Hotline: 0870 9091998
Routes by Car:
M275 to Portsmouth. Follow signs to Historic Ships.
Train/Other:
Portsmouth Harbour Stations (2 mins walk from entrance to festival)
Venue: **Portsmouth**
Facilities (Parking):
Park and Ride System will operate
What's On:
Tall ships, warships, helicopters, high speed launches, Naval display teams, Royal Marine combat units, fireworks, exhibits, travel through the "Time Tunnel" into 21st Century. Try your hand at ancient maritime skills and crafts, learn about marine life
Historical Background:
The international pilot festival took place in 1996. The Festival attracted more than 350,000 visitors and 37 million TV viewers nationwide
General Information:
There are also musicians, buskers, and entertainers. Enjoy interactive computer displays, auctions and waterside races

The Hampshire Teddy Bear Festival

Type of Festival: **Teddy Bear**
Contact: **World Heritage Fairs**
Address:

Botley Grange Hotel
Hedge End
Southampton
Hampshire
Tel. No: **Tim Batty: 01305 269741**
Fax No: **01305 268885**
Date(s) of Festival:
7th June 1998 and
27th September 1998
Times of Festival: **10am - 4.30pm**
Cost for Adults: **£2.50**
Cost for Children: **£1**
Special discounts: **None**
Tickets available from: **On the door**
Routes by Car:
Nr Junction 7 off the M27
Venue: **Botley Grange Hotel**
Facilities (Parking): **Free parking**
Facilities (Disabled):
Access for disabled
What's On:
Thousands of Teddy Bears to see, old and new, large and small. Teddy Bear lovers paradise
General Information:
Tim Batty's address should you wish to contact is: 25 High West Street, Dorchester, Dorset

The Balloon and Flower Festival

Type of Festival:
Flower and Balloon
Contact:
Southampton City Council
Address:
Special Events Unit
4th floor
Frobisher House
Nelson Gate
Southampton
Hampshire
SO15 1GX
Tel. No: **01703 832525**

Fax No: **01703 832929**
E-mail: **gbv6jhar@ibmmail.com**
Date(s) of Festival:
4th - 5th July 1998
Cost for Adults: **Free**
Cost for Children: **Free**
Tickets available from:
Not required
Routes by Car:
Common is on the A33. Follow the AA signs
Venue: **Southampton Common**
Facilities (Parking):
Festival Car park on Southampton Common: car £3; minibus £10; coach £20
What's On:
Evening only on Friday 3rd July - "Night Glow". Saturday/Sunday morning and afternoon: hot air balloon launches, floral displays (Royal Southampton Horticultural Society), large trade village featuring arts, crafts, gifts fair, funfair, children's play zone.
Historical Background:
1998 is the festival's 10th Anniversary

Southampton Over 50's Festival

Type of Festival: **Various**
Contact: **Norma Campbell**
Address:
**17 Avondale Court
Highfield Lane
Portswood
Southampton
Hampshire
SO17 1PE**
Tel. No: **01703 361879**
Date(s) of Festival:
20th - 30th August 1998
Times of Festival: **Various**

Cost for Adults: **Various**
Special discounts:
Discounts for Leisure Card holders
Tickets available from:
Box Office: 01703 632601
Routes by Car: **Off the M27**
Venue:
Various venues within Southampton e.g: Guildhall, Civic Centre, Mayor's Parlour and Southampton Sports Centre
Facilities (Parking):
Good town parking
Facilities (Disabled):
Most events have facilities for disabled
What's On:
Bowling, dancing, swimming, photography, crafts, pizza making in Italian restaurants. Blue Funnel Cruise and tea dance, Festival Ball, behind the scenes tour of the Mayflower, coach trips, archaeological finds. Whist drive, river cruises . . .
Historical Background:
The festival was started by an Ex-Mayor of Southampton, Mr Fred Goater, over 10 years ago. It was then a 3 day event. As it became popular it was taken on by the Special Events Unit, Southampton City Council who ran it until 3 years ago
Media/Public Comments:
"Age doesn't matter!"
General Information:
The Southampton Over 50's Festival is pleased to welcome Julian Clegg, Assistant Editor of BBC Radio Solent. Julian was seen on TV last year when he presented the Sussex edition of the "South Today" feature series

Creamfields

Type of Festival: **Music**
Contact: **Mean Fiddler/Cream**
Address:
**Information Line
Mean Fiddler
22-28a High Street
London
NW10 4LX**
Tel. No: **0181 963 0940**
Fax No: **0181 961 5743**
Date(s) of Festival:
1st - 2nd May 1999 (TBC)
Times of Festival: **1pm - 6am**
Cost for Adults: **£37.50 in advance**
Tickets available from:
0171 344 0044 or 0541 504444
Routes by Car:
M25, A3, A31 follow signs: from M3, Junction 10
Train/Other:
National Express are operating direct coach services to the site from various parts of the country call: 0990 80 80 80. The site is NOT within walking distance of Winchester station, so use bus shuttle from station
Venue:
The Bowl, Matterley Estate, near Winchester, Hampshire
Facilities (Parking):
Ample parking. Food, trade stands
Facilities (Disabled):
What's On:
9 Arenas showcasing over 100 of the worlds leading DJs and dance acts covering the whole spectrum of club life: techno, trance, house, drum 'n' bass, hip hop, big beat
Historical Background:
The festival started 10 years ago. Liverpool Club Cream in conjunction with Mean Fiddler will unveil Britain's only one day Dance Festival
Media/Public Comments:
**"This is the festival that managed to convince the world's greatest Rap act Run DMC to reform and play live for their first British date in 10 years"
Broadcast live on BBC Radio 1
"This is the bomb . . . presenting the big ones . . ."**

Winchester Folk Festival

Type of Festival:
Folk, Music, Dance and Song
Contact: **Anne Sutherland**
Address:
**Winchester Folk Festival Committee
44 Peverells Wood Avenue
Chandlers Ford
Hampshire
SO53 2BW**
Tel. No: **01703 270292**
E-Mail: **winch-ff@tcp.co.uk**
Date(s) of Festival:
23rd - 25th April 1999
Times of Festival:
Events start at 8pm on Friday the 24th and end evening of Sunday 26th April
Cost for Adults:
Season tickets (before 31/3) £20 season tickets (after 31/3) £25 concert/ceilidh £6 (Friday) £8 (Saturday)
Cost for Children:
Under 10s free; under 16s season tickets £10,
Tickets available from:
Winchester Folk Festival

Routes by Car:
M3 Southbound, leave at Winchester Junction, follow signs to City Centre
Train/Other:
Winchester Railway station. Ferry to Southampton or Portsmouth. Southampton International Airport at Eastleigh, nr Southampton off the M27
Venue: **Winchester**
Facilities (Parking):
Short stay car park behind Winchester Guildhall, long stay car park at Chesil Street. Refreshments from North Pole Café etc
What's On:
Dance displays and dance concert, family ceilidh, pub sessions and singarounds, tea dances, workshops, children's events, traditional hymn sing, evening concerts, indoor camping
Historical Background:
Festival was started 24 years ago by local folk enthusiasts. Changed from a mainly dance festival to a more all round festival with something for all the family
Media/Public Comments:
"Bells and Bows bring music to city streets, Winchester Folk Festival attracts hundreds of visitors"
General Information:
Performers include: Woodpecker Band, Les Barker, Capriole (Belgium), Risky Business, Brian Peters and Gordon Tyrrel Bedlam, Smile, Sundance Band, Sarah-Deere Jones and Mike Eaton, Graham and Eileen Pratt and Tony Rose

HEREFORDSHIRE

Hay Children's Festival of the Arts

Type of Festival:
Arts, Children's Theatre
Contact:
Caroline Wylie - Festival Director
Address:
15 Knowle Avenue
Burley
Leeds
Yorkshire
Tel. No: **0113 230 4661**
Fax No: **0113 230 4661**
Date(s) of Festival:
23rd - 24th May 1998
Times of Festival:
10am - 6pm daily
Cost for Children:
Free to author's events. £4 - £12 per session
Special discounts: **None**
Tickets available from:
12 Fosse Way, Bronllys, Brecon, Powys, LD3 0HX: 01874 712253
Routes by Car:
Hay on Wye is on the A438 between Hereford and Brecon

Train/Other:
Hereford is the nearest station
Venue:
Community Centre, Oxford Road, Hay on Wye
Facilities (Parking):
Parking available
Facilities (Disabled):
Access for disabled people
What's On:
3 day programme of creative educational workshops for children aged 6-12 years eg: video animation, wood carving, enamelling and mosaic. Authors readings, children's theatre and parties, Maisy Mouse, Flower Fairies, Paddington's 40th Party
Historical Background:
The Children's Festival has been running in its present format for 5 years alongside the Hay Festival of Literature
Media/Public Comments:
Sponsored by the Sunday Times
General Information:
The philosophy of the festival is to present a wide variety of creative workshops, authors readings and the best in children's theatre, giving children the opportunity to experience a selection of arts not usually available to them

The Sunday Times Hay Festival

Type of Festival:
Literature and the Arts
Contact: **Coralie Rogers**
Address:
Hay Festival
Hay on Wye
Herefordshire
HR3 5BX

Tel. No: **01497 821217**
Fax No: **01497 821066**
Date(s) of Festival:
22nd May - 30th June 1998
Times of Festival: **10am -10pm daily**
Cost for Adults: **£5 - £10**
Special discounts: **Standby £2**
Tickets available from:
Box Office (see above)
Routes by Car:
M4 from London, Junction 14.
Train/Other:
Hereford is the nearest station
Venue:
Various venues in Hay on Wye
Facilities (Parking):
Parking available
Facilities (Disabled):
Access for disabled people
What's On:
The exchange of ideas, meeting of minds and celebration of art forms from world class literature, classical music, comedy, science and poetry, makes Hay Festival a magical ten days celebrating language in all its forms. In a relaxed and informal atmosphere meet Nobel Prize winners, world class writers and favourite comedians in an easy and convivial setting
Historical Background:
Launched in 1988 to celebrate the best in literature and the spoken word from around the world
Media/Public Comments:
"In my mind it has replaced Christmas" Tony Benn

Herefordshire Photography Festival

Type of Festival: **Photography**
Contact:
Kathryn Parker - Director

Address:

P O Box 54
Hereford
Herefordshire
HR2 9YS

Date(s) of Festival:

18th September-10th October
1998

Times of Festival:

Usually between 10am and 4pm

Cost for Adults:

Many events are free but some are
priced between £3 and £25

Special discounts:

OAPs, UB40s, and students 25%
discount

Tickets available from:

Kathryn Parker (see above)

Routes by Car:

M50 - A49(Ross) A49 Leominster

Train/Other:

Direct trains from London Pad-
dington, Birmingham New Street
and Manchester

Venue:

Various venues throughout Her-
eford City and Herefordshire

Facilities (Parking):

Plenty of parking available near to
the venues.

Facilities (Disabled):

Disabled access varies from venue
to venue

What's On:

A wide variety of photographic ex-
hibitions by some of Europe's
leading practitioners. A choice of
talks, workshops and seminars.
Designed to tempt new amateurs
and long term professionals

Historical Background:

The UK's only annual national Pho-
tography Festival located in a rural
area. Now 11 years old and has a
growing international reputation

Ledbury Poetry Festival

Type of Festival: **Poetry**

Contact: **Bianca Rey-Surman**

Address:

Town Council Offices
Church Street
Ledbury
Herefordshire

Tel. No: **01531 634156**

Fax No: **01531 634156**

Date(s) of Festival:

9th - 19th July 1998

Times of Festival: **Various**

Cost for Adults:

Between £5 and £10

Tickets available from:

Festival Office: 01531 634156

Routes by Car: **A417, M50**

Train/Other: **London Paddington**

Venue: **Various venues in Ledbury**

Facilities (Parking): **3 car parks**

Facilities (Disabled):

Please check with Festival Office

What's On:

Readings, performances, concerts,
exhibitions, discussions, debates
workshops, walks, tours,
masterclasses, limerick competi-
tions, writing competitions. In the
past has played host to Germaine
Greer, Roger McGough, Lavinia
Greenlaw, Timothy West, Ruth
Padel and John Hegley

Historical Background:

Birthplace of John Masefield and
has become the cradle of inspira-
tion of many poets, past and
present. Ledbury's poetry connec-
tions go back to Elizabeth Barrett
Browning, who lived in nearby
Hope End and William Langland
who dreamt up "Piers Ploughman"

Media/Public Comments:

"Highly regarded"
Daily Telegraph

"Oh what a day - what a night, and what a really good festival"   Raw Edge programme

General Information:

Ledbury is a medieval market town with great beauty and character and has become the venue for what is set to be the best poetry celebration in Britain. The festival aims to promote poetry on a broad base with performances

Leominster Fringe Festival

Type of Festival: **Music**

Contact: **B G Scott**

Address:

Banny Tree
Forobridge
Leominster
Herefordshire

Tel. No: **01568 614289**

Date(s) of Festival:

12th - 13th June 1998

Times of Festival:

7.30pm - 1am and 7.30pm - 12 midnight

Cost for Adults: **£10 per day**

Tickets available from:

The Blue Note Cape Bar, 18 West Street, Leominster. 01568 610060

Routes by Car:

A49 to Leominster. The site is on the Junction A49 and Worcester Road

Train/Other: **Leominster Station**

Venue:

Site on Leominster bypass

Facilities (Parking):

Parking and limited camping

What's On:

The Fringe Festival caters for those who like a lighter diet of music than that provided by the mainstream

festival.

Friday 12th June - Edwin Starr
Saturday 13th June - The Manfreds

Historical Background:

The Fringe as its name implies is based around the Leominster Festival. 1998 is its 5th year and third year on dedicated site on the Leominster bypass

Media/Public Comments:

Voted best small festival in 1996

The Big Apple in Much Marcle

Type of Festival:

Countryside, Community

Contact:

Mrs Jackie Denman

Address:

Woodcroft
Putley
Ledbury
Herefordshire
HR8 2RD

Tel. No: **01531 670544**

Date(s) of Festival:

17th - 18th October 1998

Times of Festival: **11am - 5pm**

Cost for Adults:

£5 pass or pay as you go

Cost for Children: **Half price**

Tickets available from: **On the door**

Routes by Car:

A449 Ledbury - Ross-on-Wye passes through Much Marcle

Train/Other:

6 miles from Ledbury Station. Excellent for cyclists

Venue:

Much Marcle Memorial Hall and various other venues in the area

Facilities (Parking):

Parking available at the venues.

Facilities (Disabled):

Wheelchair access to Much Marcle Memorial Hall, other venues restricted
What's On:
Traditional cider making at Wistons Cider Factory. Displays of apple varieties (eg, dessert, culinary, cider fruit) orchards, craft demonstrations, family activities. Also cider tasting, apple tasting, apple teas, apple identification, walks etc
Historical Background:
Initiated in 1989 , the Festival is a non profit making celebration of English Apples and Cider
Media/Public Comments:
"Very friendly community event in delightful countryside. Visitors are made very welcome and our conservation activity is always appreciated"

Blossom Time in Putley

Type of Festival:
Countryside, Community
Contact: **Mrs Jackie Denman**
Address:
Woodcroft
Putley
Ledbury
Herefordshire
HR8 2RD
Tel. No: **01531 670544**
Date(s) of Festival:
2nd - 3rd May 1999
Times of Festival:
Sunday: 2pm - 6pm
Monday: 12 noon - 4pm
Cost for Adults:
Free entry. Pay as you go
Tickets available from: **On the door**
Routes by Car:
A438 Ledbury to Hereford. 6 miles west of Ledbury signposted to

Putley
Train/Other:
6 miles from Ledbury Station. Rail tickets in advance 01531 635988. Excellent for cyclists
Venue:
Putley Village Hall, Parish Church and other venues in the area
Facilities (Parking):
Field parking, refreshments and food i.e. Ploughmans Lunch
Facilities (Disabled):
Access for disabled in Putley Village hall. Other venues no access
What's On:
A large range of local ciders and apple juices, orchards in blossom, Spring Flower Festival in tiny country church. Cider and juice tasting, fruit tree gardening demonstrations and advice, guided walks, family activities
Historical Background:
Initiated in 1989, the festival is a non-profit making celebration of English apples and cider
Media/Public Comments:
"Very friendly community event in delightful countryside. Visitors are made very welcome and our conservation activity is always appreciated"

Ross-on-Wye International Festival

Type of Festival: **Cross Arts**
Contact: **Lee Pugh**
Address:
Ross-on-Wye International Festival Ltd
The Mews
Mitcheldean
Gloucestershire
Tel. No: **01594 544446**

Fax No: **01594 544448**
Date(s) of Festival:
21st - 31st August 1998
Cost for Adults: **£6 - £20**
Cost for Children:
Concessions available
Special discounts:
Concessions available
Routes by Car:
A449 from South Wales, M50 from Midlands, A40 from London
Train/Other:
Nearest train stations Gloucester/ Hereford
Venue:
Various venues in Ross-on-Wye
Facilities (Parking):
Ample car parking. Great restaurants and public houses in and around Ross
Facilities (Disabled):
Good facilities for disabled
What's On:
The very best of national and international music, dance, theatre, opera and comedy
Historical Background:
Founded in 1996 and fast becoming a key festival event on the UK cultural calendar
Media/Public Comments:
"If you enjoy your urban culture in a rural setting, then Ross-on-Wye is the place to be, small cannot only be beautiful but wonderfully varied" The Guardian
General Information:
Ross-on-Wye is a beautiful historic town surrounded by glorious countryside. Beautiful riverside setting. Ross has a good number of unusual and antique shops and a regular market on Thursdays and Saturdays

Ross-on-Wye Real Ale Festival

Type of Festival: **Beer**
Contact:
Kevin Bryant/Michael Lefever
Address:
**The Crown and Sceptre Inn
Market Place
Ross-on-Wye
Herefordshire**
Tel. No: **01989 562765**
Date(s) of Festival: **Every Easter**
Times of Festival: **11am -11pm**
Cost for Adults: **Free**
Tickets available from:
Not required
Routes by Car:
A449 from South Wales, M50 from Midlands, A40 from London
Train/Other:
Nearest train station is Gloucester. Ross-on-Wye is well catered for by National Coach Companies
Venue: **Crown and Sceptre Inn**
Facilities (Parking):
The Public House does not have its own parking but there are several car parks just minutes away
What's On:
There is an extension to 11.45pm on the 10th and 11th April 1998. Live band playing every evening of the festival
Historical Background:
This is the 6th year of the festival
Media/Public Comments:
The Crown and Sceptre was awarded Pub of the Year for Herefordshire 1994 by CAMRA

HERTFORDSHIRE

Elstree Film Festival

Type of Festival: **Film**
Contact:
Paul Welsh
Elstree and Borehamwood Council
Address:
Fairway Hall
Brook Close
Borehamwood
Hertfordshire
WD6 5BT
Tel. No: **0181 207 1382**
Fax No: **0181 953 7645**
Date(s) of Festival: **27th June 1998**
Times of Festival: **7.30pm**
Cost for Adults:
TBC Ticket only event: tickets
must be purchased in advance
Routes by Car: **A1, M25, A41**
Train/Other:
Thameslink Kings Cross to Luton
Venue:
BBC Centre, Clarendon Road,
Borehamwood
Facilities (Parking): **Ample parking**
What's On:
Music from BBC Elstree Concert
Band. Film Clips and meet the ce-
lebrities
Historical Background:

10th annual Elstree Film Evening
previously part of the Elstree Film
Festival which will start again when
a new cinema/theatre opens in 2000

Elstree and Borehamwood Festival

Type of Festival:
Outdoor and Indoor Events
Contact:
Paul Welsh
Elstree and Borehamwood Town
Council
Address:
Fairway Hall
Brook Close
Borehamwood
Hertfordshire
WD6 5BT
Tel. No: **0181 207 1382**
Fax No: **0181 953 7645**
Date(s) of Festival:
20th June - 4th July 1998
Times of Festival: **Various**
Cost for Adults:
Free admission, however some
events chargeable.
Tickets available from: **(see above)**
Routes by Car: **A1, M25, A41**
Train/Other:
Thameslink Kings Cross to Luton
Venue:
Various venues within Boreham-
wood and surrounding area
Facilities (Parking): **Available**
What's On:
Musical events, rambles, lectures,
parade etc. Main event: "Families
Day", arena acts, stalls sideshows,
children's activities.
Historical Background:
This is the 42nd annual Festival de-
signed to entertain and provide a
fund raising platform for local or-
ganisations

Major Country and Western Themed Festival

Type of Festival: **Music and Crafts**

Contact: **Anne Steele**

Address:
**Four Seasons Exhibitions Ltd
23 Brockenhurst Road
Ascot
Berkshire**
Tel. No: **01344 874787**
Fax No: **01344 874673**
Date(s) of Festival:
22nd - 24th May 1999
Times of Festival: **10am - 6pm**
Cost for Adults: **£5**
Cost for Children: **£1. Under 5s free**
Special discounts: OAPs £4. Pre-booking discounts available
Tickets available from:
Four Seasons Exhibitions Ltd. (see above)
Routes by Car:
Junction 5 off M1 - Junction 20 off M25 or use A5
Venue:
Aldenham Country Park, Nr Elstree, Hertfordshire
Facilities (Parking):
Parking £1. Refreshments available and licensed bar
Facilities (Disabled):
Toilet facilities for disabled
What's On:
6 well known bands, entertainment including: rope spinning, cowboys, line dancing, whip cracking, Can-Can girls, Indian village, puppet shows, Hill Billies, clog dancing, the North and South Re-enactment Society, trade stands, crafts and gunfight at the OK Corral
General Information:
2 other similar Festivals at Purley

Playing fields, Croydon, Surrey (13th - 14th June 1998) and Moss End Farm, Warfield, Nr Bracknell (29th – 31st August 1998)

Festival of Gardening

Type of Festival: **Garden**

Contact: **Michael Pickard**

Address:
**Gascoyn Cecil Estates
Hatfield House
Hatfield
Hertfordshire
AL9 5NQ**
Tel. No: **01707 262823**
Fax No: **01707 275719**
Date(s) of Festival:
20th - 21st June 1998
Times of Festival: **10am - 6pm**
Cost for Adults: **£5.40**
Cost for Children: **£2**
Special discounts:
Groups, OAPs £4.80
Tickets available from:
The Curator: 01707 262823
Routes by Car:
21 miles north of London, A1(M) Junction 4, 2 miles, M25 Junction 23, 7 miles
Train/Other:
Hatfield Station opposite main gate (Kings Cross, 23 mins)
Venue: **Hatfield House**
Facilities (Parking):
Convenient coach and car parking
Facilities (Disabled):
Disabled parking available and wheelchair access throughout
What's On:
National flower exhibitors, Festival of Flowers in the house, garden trade stands, arena events, jazz band, floral art/design competition. Gardening lectures, demonstra-tions, tours, "Gardeners Question

Time", visit the house and walk in the park

Historical Background:
Festival's 16th year

Media/Public Comments:
"The festival at Hatfield House is staged in an outstanding garden and combines the atmosphere of flower show, country fair and a garden party" The Gardening Courier and The Times

Hertford Music Festival

Type of Festival: **Music**
Contact:
Adrian Foster
Margaret Walton Lane
Address:
AVF Communications
Castlegate House
36 Castle Street
Hertford
Hertfordshire
SG14 1HH
Tel. No: **01992 503129**
Date(s) of Festival:
26th April - 30th May 1998
Times of Festival: **Various**
Cost for Adults: **Various**
Tickets available from:
Castle Travel: 01992 500020
Routes by Car:
M11 Junction 7. M25 Junction 25 then A10, M1 Junction 7
Train/Other:
Hertford mainline Station
Venue:
Castle Hall, Haileybury College Chapel, The Fairway Suite, Welwyn Garden City, Marriott Hanbury Hotel and Country Club, Friends Meeting House, St Josephs in the Park, The Waggon and Horses, The Playhouse, All Saints Church, St Leonards Church

Facilities (Parking):
Ample parking in Town Centre.
What's On:
Opening ceremony at Hertford Castle, ballet, Gilbert and Sullivan, organ recitals, Jazz at the Fairway, classical guitar, Godspell, concerts, rock prom, Serenata, evening with Kate Hodges, Ely Cathedral Choir, Hertford Symphony Orchestra, Chas and Dave etc
Historical Background:
Started in 1992 the festival's aim was to provide a celebration of the vast musical talent in and around Hertford. It was a project with a difference: "by the community for the community"
Media/Public Comments:
"A well organised festival and great fun"
"It's a wonderful project, bringing local and national performing groups together, giving local people the opportunity to see acts they would not normally be able to see close to home. A must for all music lovers"

Universe '98

(Postponed at time of going to press)
Type of Festival: **Dance**
Contact: **Conal Dodds**
Address:
MCP Promotions Ltd
16 Birmingham Road
Walsall
West Midlands
Tel. No: **0171 229 8866**
Fax No: **01922 725654**
Date(s) of Festival:
23rd - 24th May 1998
Times of Festival:
Saturday: 12 noon - 6am
Sunday: 1pm - 11pm

Cost for Adults:
£60 includes camping and parking (each ticket subject to a max. £4 booking fee)
Tickets available from:
Info Hotline: 0830 444572
Ticketline: 0115912 9129
Ticketmaster: 0990 344 4444 and Virgin Megastores
Venue:
Knebworth House, Nr Stevenage
What's On:
Live Acts featuring celebrity bands, celebrity DJs together with cutting edge comedy, films, poets, story- telling, universe shamen, conspiracy cyber circus, multime- dia and Internet zone, extreme sports, healers, masseurs, virtual white knuckle rides and more
Historical Background:
Founded in 1991. Through count- less battles with the authorities, Universe has had a dream of stag- ing the ultimate festival a million miles away from the staid and ar- chaic rock Festival. This dream has now become a reality with Uni- verse '98
Media/Public Comments:
"A decade on from the now legen- dary first Summer Of Love when the pioneers of what was to be- come the dance explosion first tasted the joy and liberation of partying all night outdoors we are thrilled to announce the coming of age of dance culture"
General Information:
Universe '98 is licensed for 60,000 people and will feature over a 100 DJs together with 50 live acts. The first ever camping dance event, as well as being the biggest and most innovative dance festival ever. The fes- tival will house 8 massive tented orbs.

Ricky Week

Type of Festival: **Mixed**
Contact: **Mrs Barbara Owen**
Address:
23 Copthorne Road
Rickmansworth
Hertfordshire
WD3 4AB
Tel. No: **01923 772325**
Date(s) of Festival:
15th - 22nd May 1999
Times of Festival: **Various**
Cost for Adults: **Various**
Tickets available from: **At the gate**
Routes by Car:
M25 Junction 18 then follow signs to Rickmansworth. A412/A404
Train/Other:
Rickmansworth station
Venue:
Grand Union Canal. Follow signs
Facilities (Parking):
Free town parking
What's On:
Exhibitions, Flower Festival and spring sale, decorated floats, fun- fair, cabaret, lectures, opera, canoeing. Canal Festival, grand fireworks party, coffee mornings, bowls club. Visit the Three Rivers Museum, Sunday at the Lock
Historical Background:
Ricky Week started in 1954 and has been celebrated each year since then. It enables clubs/socie- ties to put on entertainment to boost their funds and membership
General Information:
The Rickmansworth Canal Festival draws large crowds and generally coincides with "Steam trains on the Met" organised by railway company

Rickmansworth Canal Festival

Type of Festival: **Waterways**
Contact:
Christopher Jacques
Rickmansworth Waterways Trust
Address:
Batchworth Lock Canal Centre
99 Church Street
Rickmansworth
Hertfordshire
WD3 1JD
Tel. No: **01923 778382**
Date(s) of Festival:
21st - 22nd May 1999
Times of Festival: **11am - 6pm daily**
Cost for Adults: **£2**
Cost for Children: **£1**
Special discounts: **Family ticket £5**
Tickets available from: **On the gate**
Routes by Car:
M25 Junction 18 to Rickmans-worth then A404
Train/Other:
London Underground. Metropoli-tan Line and Chiltern Railways
Venue:
Grand Union Canal at Batchworth Lock, Rickmansworth
Facilities (Parking):
Free Parking in Aquadrome, cater-ing facilities and refreshments
What's On:
Canal boats moored alongside tow path, boat trips, dragon boats and Canadian canoes, inflatable pirate galleon, trade crafts and charity stalls, musical entertainment, chil-dren's helter skelter, bouncy castles
Historical Background:
1999 is the festival's 7th year. To raise the features of the canal and raise money for restoration

projects such as the restoration of wooden narrow boats
General Information:
The festival coincides with "Steam on the Met". Vintage buses link-ing the station to the lock/canal

St Albans Folk at the Festival

Type of Festival: **Music and Dance**
Contact: **Alan Reimer**
Address:
2 Nursery Gardens
Welwyn Garden City
St Albans
Hertfordshire
AL7 1SF
Tel. No: **01707 336632 (home)**
Date(s) of Festival:
10th - 12th July 1998
Times of Festival: **Various**
Cost for Adults: **Season Ticket £18**
Cost for Children: **No concessions**
Special discounts:
Concessions for individual events
Tickets available from:
Alban Arena Box Office:
01727 844488
Routes by Car:
Junction 21a on M25; Junction 8 on M1
Train/Other:
St Albans is on St Pancras-Bedford line
Venue:
St Albans and surrounding areas
Facilities (Parking):
Each venue has own parking area
Facilities (Disabled):
Limited access for disabled
What's On:
Chiploata 5, Committee Band with Nick Walden, open air concert, Volker Calle and G'orice (Hun-

gary), day of dance, music sessions, workshops on French dance, historical dance
Historical Background:
This event takes place every 2 years

Woodmanstock

Type of Festival:
Folk and Contemporary Music
Contact: **Nick Browne**
Address:
The Woodman public house
30 Chapmore Road
Ware
Hertfordshire
SG12 0HF
Tel. No: **01920 463143**
Date(s) of Festival: **11th July 1998**
Times of Festival: **12 noon - 11pm**
Cost for Adults:
£3 in advance (£5 on the day)
Cost for Children:
£1 in advance (£3 on the day)
Tickets available from:
The Woodman Public House
Routes by Car:
A1(M) to Stevenage, A602 to Ware, B158. A10 to Ware, A602 to Stevenage
Train/Other:
Hertford North, Hertford East or Ware
Venue: **The Woodman public house**
Facilities (Parking): **Free Parking**
What's On:
Wide range of folk and contemporary music mixed with poetry and folk dancing, 2 main stages, mini beer festival, BBQ, Thai food, informal sessions, children's play area, bouncy castles, children's entertainers. Evening ceilidhs
Historical Background:
Festival started 3 years ago and grown in popularity each year.

Now in its 4th successful year.
Media/Public Comments:
"We always like to make time on stage for any visiting musicians - those who play on stage have come back time and time again"

ISLE OF MAN

Vagabonds International Festival of Rugby

Type of Festival: **Sport**
Contact: **Steve Wilson**
Address:
Steve Wilson Sport Ltd
49 St Catherines Close
Douglas
Isle of Man
Tel. No: **01624 673029**
Date(s) of Festival: **Every Easter**
Times of Festival: **10am - 6pm**
Train/Other:
Ferry from Liverpool, Heysham and Dublin
What's On:
Players of all standards come to play. Friendly 15s with a 7s competition

IOM Crown Green Bowling Festivals

Type of Festival: **Sport**
Contact: **Festival Secretary**
Address:
Special Events Unit
Isle of Man Dept. of Tourism
Isle of Man
Tel. No: **01624 644644**
Fax No: **01624 644642**
Date(s) of Festival:
15th - 19th June 1998
7th - 11th September 1998
Times of Festival: **Daily 9am to late**
Cost for Adults: **£7 entry fee**
Tickets available from:
Entry forms available from above address
Train/Other:
Sea or Air (see Travel Agents)
Venue:
Various Greens on the Isle of Man
Facilities (Parking):
Parking at various Greens
What's On:
Meet new friends and enjoy a game of bowls on the tranquil Greens on the beautiful Isle of Man
Historical Background:
Festival started in 1921
Media/Public Comments:
"Excellent"

Isle of Man International Jazz Festival

Type of Festival: **Jazz**
Contact: **Alan Grubb**
Address:
Mount Pleasant
Laxey
Isle of Man
Tel. No: **01624 861095**

Fax No: **01624 862834**
Date(s) of Festival:
28th - 30th August 1998
Times of Festival:
Evenings from 7.45pm - 12.15am
Cost for Adults:
Any evening £10. Three day ticket £26
Tickets available from:
Villa Marina Box Office; Tourist Board; Sea Terminal, Douglas; Ron Gill, Hon Sec : 01624 622530
Routes by Car:
Ferry from Heysham. Sea Cat from Liverpool, Dublin, Belfast. I.O.M. Steam Packet Co: 01624 661661
Train/Other:
Manx Airlines: 0345 626629; Air flights from Liverpool, London, Dublin, Birmingham, Cardiff, Manchester, Aberdeen, Glasgow, Luton, Leeds, Bradford etc
Venue:
Villa Marina, Douglas
Facilities (Parking):
Car Park and street parking
Facilities (Disabled):
Access for wheelchairs
What's On:
Alan Gresty, Brian White Ragtimers, Flyde Coast Jazz Men, Manx Jazz Aces, Harry Allen, Kenny Baker, John Barnes, Les Bolger, Randy Colville, Honor Heffernam, John Harper, Jim Thomson and Roy Williams
Historical Background:
Festival started in 1993 as part of the celebrations of the centenary of the Manx Electric Railway.
Media/Public Comments:
"A friendly festival and opportunities for members of the audience to chat with the musicians" BBC Radio Ulster
General Information:

"I've been to quite a few jazz festivals in my time and often came away feeling disappointed, but not in the case of the IOM Festival. Here the organisers have got it just right, set in three rooms in the Villa Marina Complex, the formula worked very well"

Peel Traditional Boat Weekend

Type of Festival: **Traditional Boats**
Contact: **Mike Clark**
Address:
Peel Traditional Boat Association
Pankina
Croit-E-Quill Road
Lonan
Isle of Man
IM4 7JG
Tel. No: **01624 861127**
04624 495015 (mobile)
Web site:
http: //www.isle-of-man.com/interests/tradboats/index.htm
E- mail: **Mclark@enterprise.net**
Date(s) of Festival:
13th - 14th June 1998
Times of Festival: **10am - midnight**
Cost for Adults: **Free**
Cost for Children: **Free**
Train/Other:
Ferry from Liverpool, Heysham and Dublin
Venue:
All around the harbour at Peel
Facilities (Parking):
Public Transport to and from ferry
Facilities (Disabled):
Festival site mainly flat
What's On:
Traditional sailing and power boats, ship/boat models, fish curing, traditional music and song. If you are an owner of a traditional boat then join in, otherwise soak up the ambience and listen to the music.
Historical Background:
Festival is run by owners of traditional boats for the benefit of other traditional boat owners
Media/Public Comments:
"Fast becoming the best event in the Irish Sea" Classic Boat Magazine

Viking Longboat Races (World Championship)

Type of Festival:
Viking Longboat Rowing
Contact: **Patricia S Sweeney**
Address:
Peel Viking Assoc. Longboat Committee
13 Stanley Road
Peel
Isle of Man
IM5 1NY
Tel. No: **01624 843640**
Fax No: **01624 843640**
Date(s) of Festival: **11th July 1998**
Times of Festival: **Start at 1pm**
Cost for Adults:
Spectators free. Rowers £50 per team (10 in a team). Longhouse and Heritage entrance fee £5
Cost for Children:
Longhouse and Heritage entrance fee £2.50
Routes by Car:
A1 from Douglas, A3 (north route) from Ramsey, A3 (south route) from Castletown
Train/Other:
All Island National Transport
Venue: **Peel**
Facilities (Parking):
Ample parking spaces and facilities

at Heritage Centre

What's On:

Three Viking Longboats racing on a timed basis over a specified course. Usual average 60 teams (each rowing approximately 5mins). Last year biggest entry of over 90 teams. Also children's entertainment, amusements etc. View the Viking Longhouse and Heritage Centre

Historical Background:

In the 1960s a pageant was held but its popularity faded in the 70s. The raiding Viking crews would race their boats to the shore and the racing idea stems from this.

Media/Public Comments:

Good write-ups each year in local press and results are broadcast on local radio

General Information:

Teams from all over the Island (and now teams from N. Ireland) take part. Competing on a handicapped time basis to be World Champions, 1997 World Champions are a mixed crew called "Sod the Woolies"

Mananan International Festival of Music and The Arts

Type of Festival:
Music, Drama, Arts, Jazz
Contact: **Mr John Bethell**
Address:
Erin Arts Centre
Victoria Square
Port Erin
Isle of Man
IM9 6LD
Tel. No: **01624 835858**
Fax No: **01624 836658**

Date(s) of Festival:
19th June - 4th July 1998
Times of Festival: **8pm**
Cost for Adults: **£5 - £12**
Cost for Children: **Some discounts**
Tickets available from:
By post only: see above
Train/Other:
Ferry from Liverpool, Heysham and Dublin
Venue:
Erin Arts Centre, Port Erin
Facilities (Disabled):
Full disabled access
What's On:
Opera, cabaret, choral, theatre, films, puppetry, classical music, jazz, art exhibition . . .
Historical Background:
The festival is in its 24th year

Manx Heritage Flower Festival

Type of Festival: **Floral and Cultural**
Contact: **J Wilkinson - Secretary**
Address:
Sunnymead
Ballafesson
Port Erin
Isle of Man
Tel. No: **01624 832941**
Date(s) of Festival:
5th - 12th July 1998 (always 1st week in July)
Times of Festival: **11am - 8pm**
Cost for Adults:
Free (donations appreciated)
Cost for Children: **Free**
Tickets available from:
Free brochure from Tourist Office: 01624 686766
Routes by Car:
Travel Services, Harris Promenade, Douglas: 01624 661177

Train/Other:
Bus tours: 01624 674301. Specially chartered trains on the Manx Electric Railway to take visitors to an Ecumenical Service at Ramsey Methodist church
Venue:
In 10-20 churches around the Isle of Man
Facilities (Parking):
Parking available at each site. Visitors are welcomed with light refreshments in most churches and more substantial refreshments (buffet lunches, suppers etc) available in 5 churches
What's On:
Unique heritage of the Isle of Man is depicted in flowers with each church choosing its own relevant theme. "Ministry of the World" is the theme for 1998.   Many churches feature live music, 14 evening events, 4 daytime events
Historical Background:
Initiated in 1990 as ecumenical annual celebrations for the decade of Evangelists to generate interest in the history of Christianity and the churches of the Isle of Man.
Media/Public Comments:
"touching and memorable"
"impressive interpretation with a fascinating backdrop."
"an uplifting experience"
"evocative scents and scenes"

Mannin Angling Club Festival '98

Type of Festival:
Fishing (Boat and Shore)
Contact:
Mrs Allen, Mannin Angling Club
Address:
P O Box 6

Port St Mary Post Office
Port St Mary
Isle of Man
IM9 5
Tel. No: **01624 835458**
Date(s) of Festival:
1st - 7th August 1998
Times of Festival: **Various**
Cost for Adults:
£3 per competitor. Charter Boat fees £3 per hour
Cost for Children:
£3 per competitor
Tickets available from:
Mannin Angling Club
Train/Other:
Ferry to Island (tickets available from Isle of Man Steam Packet)
Isle of Man Airlines (see your travel agent)
Venue:
Shore events: on the harbour
Boat events: meet at Port St Mary
What's On:
After the competitions visit various beauty spots on the Island. Visit Peel Castle, Heritage Centres. Enjoy a ride on the steam trains. Disco in Port Erin "Falcon" for younger member
Historical Background:
The festival has been held each year for over 30 years
General Information:
Brochures available from Mannin Angling Club (see above)

Yn Chruinnaght Festival

Type of Festival: **Inter-Celtic Arts**
Contact:
Muriel Atkin - Festival Director
Address:
c/o Town Hall
Ramsey

Isle of Man
Tel. No: **01624 814559**
Date(s) of Festival:
18th - 25th July 1998
Times of Festival:
Daily between 11am - 1am
Cost for Adults:
Daytime events free
Evening events £6
Cost for Children:
Under 16s half price if accompanied by adult
Tickets available from:
Copy Cat, Bourne Place, Ramsey
Tel: 01624 814687 Fax: 815593
Train/Other:
Isle of Man Steam Packet Co.
Tel: 01624 661661. Manx Airlines (from major airports including Heathrow, Birmingham, Manchester, Glasgow, Dublin, Liverpool), Jersey European from Belfast
Venue: **Ramsey, Isle of Man**
Facilities (Parking): **Free parking**
Facilities (Disabled):
Disabled access to marquee
What's On:
Outdoor dance, music displays, food and folk, dance and music workshops, evening concerts, ceilidhs, arts and crafts exhibitions, open classes
Historical Background:
1998 is the 21st Yn Chruinnaght. Began in 1978 as an "Inter-Celtic" festival. Means "the Gathering" in Manx Gallic. There have been many changes over the years, however Yn Chruinnaght will continue to promote the vision of its founder Mona Douglas.
Media/Public Comments:
"In Yn Chruinnaght we celebrate the heritage of Man. We are gathering to celebrate the kinship and the similarities of the Celts"

General Information:
Mleeaney, ta shin cur failt mooar reesht er caarjyn veiih ny cheeraghyn Celtiagh elley.
(This year we give a great welcome once more to friends from the other Celtic countries)

ISLE OF WIGHT

Bembridge Festival

Type of Festival: **Mixed**
Contact: **Mrs Mary Steane**
Address:
Combined Churches of Bembridge
3 Meadow Drive
Bembridge
Isle of Wight
PO35 5XZ
Tel. No: **01983 872177**
Date(s) of Festival:
22nd - 28th May 1998
Times of Festival: **Various**
Cost for Adults: **Free**
Cost for Children: **Free**
Tickets available from:
Not required
Routes by Car:
To Portsmouth, Southampton, or Lymington, then car ferry
Train/Other:
Portsmouth, Southampton passenger ferry

Venue: **Bembridge Isle of Wight**
What's On:
Variety Show, RNLI coffee morning, art exhibition, street fair, needlecraft exhibition, plant sale, bingo, conducted tour of Bembridge marshes, United "Songs of Praise" in Parish Church. Musical evening.
Historical Background:
Founded as Trinity Tide Festival (the Parish Church is dedicated to Holy Trinity)

IOW Heavy Horse Festival

Type of Festival: **Rural**
Contact: **Mr Mrs Legge**
Address:
Brickfields Horsecountry
Binstead
Isle of Wight
Tel. No: **01983 566801/615116**
Fax No: **01983 562649**
Date(s) of Festival:
12th - 15th June 1998
Times of Festival: **10am - 5pm**
Cost for Adults: **£4**
Cost for Children: **£3**
Special discounts:
OAPs, UB40s, students: £3.50
Tickets available from: **On the gate**
Routes by Car:
Half a mile off A3054 near Ryde
Train/Other:
Nearest station Ryde Esplanade then courtesy bus. Wightlink ferries or hover travel from Portsmouth to Ryde
Venue:
Brickfield Horsecountry, Binstead
Facilities (Parking): **Free parking**
Facilities (Disabled):
Access for disabled and disabled toilet facilities

What's On:
Working Shire horses, traditional farming, rural crafts, parades, displays, demonstrations, wagon and tractor, pony rides, pig racing
Historical Background:
Annual event
Media/Public Comments:
Previously covered by Meridian TV and local radio

Cider Making

Type of Festival:
Cider Making and Rural Interests
Contact: **Mr and Mrs Legge**
Address:
Brickfields Horsecountry
Binstead
Isle of Wight
Tel. No: **01983 566801**
Date(s) of Festival:
25th October 1998
Times of Festival: **10am - 5pm**
Cost for Adults: **£4**
Cost for Children: **£3**
Special discounts:
UB40s, OAPs, students £3.50
Tickets available from: **At the gate**
Routes by Car:
Off A3054 (half a mile) near Ryde
Train/Other:
Nearest station, Ryde Esplanade
Venue: **Binstead**
Facilities (Parking): **Free parking**
Facilities (Disabled):
Disabled toilet, ramps etc
What's On:
Cider making by shire horsepower, rural displays, demonstrations, wagon rides, guided tours, children's gymkhana
Media/Public Comments:
Previously covered by BBC

Cowes Week (Skandia Life)

Type of Festival:
Sport - Yachting
Contact: **Capt. Dan Bradby RN**
Address:
18 Bath Road
Cowes
Isle of Wight
PO31 7QN
Tel. No: **01983 295744**
Fax No: **01983 295329**
Date(s) of Festival:
1st - 8th August 1998
Cost for Adults:
Free for spectators. Race entry fee £20 upwards per day
Train/Other:
Ferry or hydrofoil to the island from Southampton/Portsmouth. British Rail (Southampton/Portsmouth)
Venue:
Cowes and surrounding areas
Facilities (Parking):
Park and Ride in the town
What's On:
International yacht racing afloat. Carnival-type atmosphere ashore. Firework spectacular on the Friday night (9.30pm)
Historical Background:
Yachting Regatta since 1892

East Cowes Enterprise Victorian Festival

Type of Festival: **Traditional**
Contact:
Mrs M J Lloyd (Chairman)
Mrs Ebbatson (Secretary)
Address:
E Cowes Enterprise Centre
The York Centre
11 York Avenue

East Cowes
Isle of Wight
Tel. No: **01983 281524**
Date(s) of Festival: **11th July 1998**
Times of Festival: **10am - 4pm**
Cost for Adults: **Free**
Cost for Children: **Free**
Tickets available from:
Not required
Routes by Car:
A3054 from Newport to Ryde to A3021 Main Road to East Cowes
Train/Other: **Red Funnel Ferry**
Venue: **East Cowes**
Facilities (Parking):
Free Parking, refreshments
Facilities (Disabled):
Access for disabled
What's On:
10am arrival of "Queen Victoria" in horse and carriage and escorted by local army cadets. There are stalls, crafts, Punch and Judy, arena events, people dressed in Victorian costume, "It's a Knockout" for children, Antiques Roadshow, sideshows, fortune telling . . .
Historical Background:
First festival held in July 1995 as a great fun day for all the family. Opportunity for local charities and groups to come together and raise funds for each group.
Media/Public Comments:
"Young and old enjoy fair fun"
"I thoroughly enjoyed the atmosphere and the setting and the organisation was great"
IOW County Press
General Information:
Evening, "Old Time Music Hall" held in Town Hall from 7.30pm - 9.30pm approximately. Varied acts including dancing, singing, monologues, belly dancers. Concludes with community singing.

IOW Garlic Festival

Type of Festival: **Themed**
Contact: **Island Partners Ltd**
Address:
Alpine House
13 Alpine Road
Ventnor
Isle of Wight
PO38 1BT
Tel. No: **01983 853411**
Fax No: **01983 856411**
E-mail:
garlicFestival@islandpartners.co.uk
Date(s) of Festival:
22nd - 23rd August 1998
Times of Festival: **10am - 6pm**
Cost for Adults: **£4**
Cost for Children: **Under 15s £1**
Special discounts:
OAPs £3. Advanced sale discount £3.50, £2.50 and £1 respectively
Tickets available from:
IOW Press Shop, Newport: 01983 521333
Routes by Car:
Wightlink Ferry from Portsmouth to Fishbourne. Newport is on the A3056
Train/Other:
London Waterloo to Ryde IOW
Venue:
Many marquees on Greenfield, Fighting Cocks Crossroads
Facilities (Parking): **Free**
Facilities (Disabled):
Special area for disabled drivers
What's On:
Accent on garlic. Garlic flavoured: ice-cream, beer, seafood, mushrooms etc. Royal Logistics Corps catering team tempt garlic lovers with specially created recipes. There is also a Wild West spectacular, birds of prey, Ebony steel band, escapology etc

Historical Background:
The Garlic Marquee, sponsored by Mersley Farms, the UKs only commercial garlic grower, swells with oak-smoked garlic, plaits etc. Island and mainland restaurants highlight their garlic delicacies, health orientated companies expound its virtues
Media/Public Comments:
"Lots of Fun"
General Information:
The unique merchandise and foods produced on the Island is proudly displayed. The arts, crafts and bazaar marquees accommodate the increasing demand for stallholder space from both mainlanders and islanders

KENT

Broadstairs Dickens Festival

Type of Festival:
Historical commemoration
Contact:
Mrs Priscilla Foot
Hon Festival Organiser
Address:
Kingscote
8 Stone Road

Broadstairs
Kent
CT10 1DY
Tel. No: **01843 601364**
Date(s) of Festival:
20th - 27th June 1998
Times of Festival:
1pm on the 20th June - midnight on the 27th June
Cost for Adults:
Some events are free, some are ticketed
Special discounts:
Group discounts on application
Tickets available from:
Booking Kiosk: 01843 861118
Routes by Car:
M2 to London, 15 miles from Canterbury. A28 to Broadstairs
Train/Other:
London Victoria on Connex South East
Venue:
Various venues in Broadstairs
Facilities (Parking):
Car and coach parks in the town
Facilities (Disabled):
Outside events ideal for disabled. Inside events accessible to the disabled
What's On:
Over 60 events. Opening parade, ceremony and entertainment, open air service at Preachers Knoll, Victorian cricket match, duels, Victorian sea bathing, melodramas, croquet, collectors fair, bazaar, fair, street musicians
Historical Background:
Charles Dickens visited Broadstairs many times between 1837 and 1859 where he wrote parts of a number of his books. Broadstairs branch of the International Dickens Society started the festival in 1937 to commemorate the 100th anniversary of his first visit
Media/Public Comments:
The Festival has been featured in National newspapers during the last year and over the years has featured in a variety of magazines
General Information:
The first evening of the festival features Dorothy Tutin and Joan Amis with a musical trio performing "In Victorian Times". There is a Dickens play; "Bleak House" and a Victorian Music Hall. Festival ends with a dance and supper

Celebrity Connections

Type of Festival: **Mixed Arts**
Contact: **Kim Headley**
Address:
Town Clerks Office
Pierremont Hall
Broadstairs
Kent
CT10 1JH
Tel. No: **01843 868718**
Fax No: **01843 866048**
Web Site:
http: //www.broadstairs.gov.uk
Date(s) of Festival:
24th - 31st October 1998
Times of Festival:
10am - 11.30pm approximately
Cost for Adults:
Various. Some free events
Tickets available from:
Broadstairs Town Centre
Routes by Car:
M2 to London, 15 miles from Canterbury. A28 to Broadstairs
Train/Other:
From London Victoria or Charing Cross
Venue:
Various venues in Broadstairs and

St Peter's village
Facilities (Parking):
Car parking Town Centre
Facilities (Disabled):
Most venues have disabled access
What's On:
Exhibitions, seminars, The Hogarth Puppets, film, theatre, shows, concerts, dances, walks special events, children's club, tour of St Peter's village, cookery demonstration, The Fat Owl's Meal, Murder Mystery lunch and lots more
Historical Background:
A new Mixed Arts Festival designed to applaud famous people who have lived in or visited the town. 1998 list features famous people such as Jack Warner (Dixon of Dock Green), John Buchan (The 39 Steps), Annette Mills (Creator of Muffin the Mule) and more
General Information:
The Festival is an initiative of the Broadstairs and St Peter's Town Council

Broadstairs Folk Week

Type of Festival:
Music, Song and Dance
Contact: **Mr Ian Harker**
Address:
Festival Office
Pierremont Hall
Broadstairs
Kent
CT10 1JH
Tel. No: **01843 604080**
Fax No: **01843 866048**
Date(s) of Festival:
6th - 14th August 1998
Times of Festival:
Early morning until very late
Cost for Adults: **Various**

Cost for Children: **Under 5s Free**
Special discounts:
Discounts available on tickets purchased before 31st May
Tickets available from:
Broadstairs Town Centre
Routes by Car:
M2 to London, 15 miles from Canterbury. A28 to Broadstairs
Train/Other:
London Victoria - Broadstairs
Venue: **Broadstairs Town Centre**
Facilities (Parking):
Town Centre parking. Also festival campsite equipped with showers and catering on site is available to season ticket holders only. The site is located approximately 10 mins away from the Town Centre. No animals
Facilities (Disabled):
Wheelchair access is possible at most venues. Advice on specific needs contact the Festival Office
What's On:
Concerts, open air shows, dances, workshops, craft market, children's programme, fireworks, torchlight procession, sides dancing on promenade, music, dance and song from all over the world. Also traditional folk music, ceilidhs, barn dances, dance workshops
Historical Background:
Broadstairs Folk Week is several festivals which overlap. Started in the mid-60s, the foundation was traditional dancing
Media/Public Comments:
"The entire town is the stage - jetty, promenade, bandstand, churches, concert and dance halls, taverns, restaurants and the streets. Folk week is an event for all the family - dance to bands from

all around the world"
General Information:
Broadstairs is blessed with seven sandy beaches and a variety of cafes, restaurants and family venues that offer a unique timeless charm that is hard to define. Very English, very Kentish, but also very near to France and Belgium

Canterbury Festival

Type of Festival: **Arts**
Contact: **Jo Tuffs**
Address:
Christ Church Gate
The Precincts
Canterbury
Kent
CT1 2EE
Tel. No: **01227 472820**
Fax No: **01227 781830**
Date(s) of Festival:
10th - 24th October 1998
Times of Festival:
From 11 am - 11pm daily
Cost for Adults: **Free - £22**
Special discounts:
Concessions available
Tickets available from:
01227 452853
Routes by Car:
M20 or M2 onto A2
Train/Other:
From London Victoria or Charing Cross
Venue:
Various venues within Canterbury, specifically the Cathedral
Facilities (Parking):
Parking in and around City
What's On:
Exhibitions, street entertainment, concerts, readings, lectures, plays, opera, workshops, community projects, street processions. Fes-

tival club in Canterbury Centre hub of successful jazz, folk, blues etc
Historical Background:
Begun in 1929, Canterbury hosts one of England's oldest arts festivals. Famous plays commissioned by the festival include "Murder in the Cathedral" by T S Eliot
Media/Public Comments:
"A very strong programme"
The Times
General Information:
The core of the festival is the series of high quality concerts in Canterbury Cathedral, ranging from full symphonic concerts and choral pieces to more intimate concerts

Kent Festival of Science

Type of Festival: **Science**
Contact: **Rachel Dodgson**
Address:
Canterbury College
New Dover Street
Canterbury
Kent
CT1 3AJ
Tel. No: **01227 811111**
Fax No: **01227 811101**
Date(s) of Festival:
18th - 19th February 1999
Times of Festival: **9.30am - 4.30pm**
Cost for Adults: **Various**
Cost for Children:
Various at reduced price
Special discounts:
Concessions available for groups of 20+
Tickets available from:
Kent Festival of Science, Canterbury College: 01227 811227
Routes by Car: **Off the A2**
Train/Other:

East Canterbury station, Coach Station
Venue: **Canterbury College**
Facilities (Parking):
College parking. Hot and Cold drinks, snacks and cooked meals are available during the day from the College restaurant
Facilities (Disabled):
The area by the main entrance is reserved for disabled visitors. Good disabled access. Stewards will be available to help everyone who attends
What's On:
2 days of lectures and workshops on subjects related to science. Physical theatre, dance and drama workshops, hands on sessions, planetaria, genetics, exhibitions, science fun and lots more
Historical Background:
Sponsored by Pfizer and Glaxo Wellcome - two of the world's leading Pharmaceutical Companies - discovering, developing and marketing innovative medicines
Media/Public Comments:
"Making science fun for all the family"
"Pfizer and Glaxo Wellcome support initiatives which encourage a greater understanding of science and technology and are pleased to sponsor the Kent Festival of Science"
General Information:
Varied programme for visitors of all ages. No advance booking for individual daytime programme items. The daytime programme is the same on both days. Children under 14 must be accompanied by adult

Dartford Festival, Guinness Music Festival

Type of Festival:
Music, Dance, Community
Contact:
Padraig Herlihy
Dartford Festival Committee
Address:
Dartford Borough Council
Home Gardens
Dartford
Kent
DA1 1DR
Tel. No: **01322 343242**
Fax No: **01322 343607**
Date(s) of Festival:
25th - 26th July 1998
Times of Festival:
25th: 12 noon - midnight
26th: 10am - 6pm
Cost for Adults: **Free**
Cost for Children: **Free**
 Tickets available from: **Not required**
Routes by Car:
M25 Junction 2 or 16, A2 Junction with M25
Train/Other:
10 min walk from Dartford Station
Venue: **Central Park, Dartford**
Facilities (Parking):
Town Centre parking
Facilities (Disabled):
Disabled parking on site
What's On:
Procession, Irish Festival, English folk music, rock music, dance, arena displays, charity and commercials stalls. Competitive dog shows, funfair, children's rides, helicopter rides.
General Information:
Dartford Festival incorporates the Guinness Music Festival. Both festivals are sponsored by Guinness

Festival of Dover

Type of Festival:
Mixed Arts, Community
Contact: **Lisa Webb**
Address:
Dover District Council
White Cliffs Business Park
Dover
Kent
CT16 3PD
Tel. No: **01304 872058**
Fax No: **01304 872062**
Date(s) of Festival:
29th May- 5th June 1999
Times of Festival: **Various**
Cost for Adults:
Over 90% events free
Venue:
In and around Dover Town Centre
Facilities (Disabled):
Access for the disabled
What's On:
Arts activities - theme "Coastal Landscapes"(1999 theme is "Echoes of a Era"). Programme of activities aimed at increasing awareness of environmental issues. Street theatre, concerts, open air spectaculars, workshops, art exhibitions, walks, lectures
Historical Background:
1999 heralds the 8th year of the festival
General Information:
Coastal landscapes in association with the White Cliffs Countryside Project

Elham Elizabethan Festival

Type of Festival: **Flower**
Contact: **Mr B J Shepherdson**
Address:
Mount Lodge
Elham

Canterbury
Kent
CT4 6UJ
Tel. No: **01303 840286**
Fax No: **01303 814222**
Date(s) of Festival:
27th - 28th June 1998
Times of Festival: **11am - 4.30pm**
Cost for Adults: **Various**
Routes by Car: **M20 Junction11**
Train/Other:
Folkestone or Canterbury
Venue: **Elham**
Facilities (Parking): **Ample parking**
Facilities (Disabled):
Wheelchair access
What's On:
Village gardens open, flower festival, art exhibition, maypole dancing, various sideshows and stalls
Historical Background:
11th century church of St Mary and other old buildings

Hever Lakeside Theatre

Type of Festival: **Arts**
Contact: **Fran Palmer**
Address:
Hever Lakeside Theatre
Hever Castle
Edenbridge
Kent
TN8 7NG
Tel. No: **01732 864824**
Fax No: **01732 866796**
Date(s) of Festival:
27th June - 30th August 1998
Times of Festival:
Performances start at 8pm. Gates open for picnics by the lake at 6.30pm
Cost for Adults: **£10.50 - £15.50**
Special discounts: **None**

Tickets available from:
Box Office: 01732 866114
Routes by Car:
3 miles south east Edenbridge off the B2026 between Sevenoaks and East Grinstead. Exit Junctions 5 or 6 M25
Train/Other:
London Victoria to Edenbridge Town (3 miles from castle). Taxis available or Hever Station (1 mile walk from castle)
Venue: **Hever Lakeside Theatre**
Facilities (Parking):
Free car and coach parking. Pavilion restaurant and bars
Facilities (Disabled): **Disabled facilities**
What's On:
This annual festival comprises a season of Professional Repertory Theatre (perfomed by the Kent Rep Theatre Co). A concert season of classical music, opera, drama, Gilbert and Sullivan, and guest celebrities including George Melly, Humphrey Lyttelton and Sheila Steafel
General Information:
The Box Office has gone wild with bookings

Kent Beer Festival

Type of Festival: **Beer**
Contact: **Gill Kealy**
Address:
Festival Organiser
42 Orchard Street
Canterbury
Kent
CT2 8AP
Tel. No: **01227 463478**
Fax No: **01227 463478**
Date(s) of Festival:
23rd - 25th July 1998

Times of Festival:
23rd: 6.30pm -11pm,
24th: noon - 4pm & 6.30pm -11pm,
25th: 11.30am - 4.30pm
& 6.30 pm - 11pm
Cost for Adults:
23rd: £1.50, 24th evening £3, lunchtime free. 25th evening/ lunchtime £1.50
Cost for Children: **Free**
Special discounts:
Free entry for CAMRA members except Friday evening. Tickets sold in advance by post. Cheques payable to CAMRA Kent Beer Festival
Tickets available from: **Gill Kealy**
Routes by Car:
2 miles south of Canterbury. RAC signposted from Canterbury
Train/Other:
Canterbury Station (East is best) then walk to Bus Station. Free Shuttle Bus to all sessions from Canterbury Bus Station. Starts 15 mins before each session. Runs every 30 mins on Friday and Saturday evenings
Venue:
Merton Farm, Merton Lane, nr Nackington Village
Facilities (Parking):
Large field for parking
What's On:
Approximately 80 real ales and ciders and Belgian, Dutch and German Beers. Hot and cold food. Souvenir glasses. Live music, all sessions except Friday lunchtime, (jazz, R&B, string quartets etc), children's entertainers Saturday lunchtimes
Historical Background:
This is the 24th Kent Beer Festival

Shepway Festival

Type of Festival: **Aviation**
Contact: **Lisa Holden**
Address:
Shepway District Council
Castle Hill Avenue
Folkestone
Kent
CT20 2QY
Tel. No: **01303 852321**
Fax No: **01303 852502**
Date(s) of Festival:
5th - 6th September 1998
Times of Festival:
5th: 10am - 5pm. 6th: 9am - 6pm
Cost for Adults: **Free**
Cost for Children: **Free**
Tickets available from:
Not required
Routes by Car:
M20 and A20, A259 road from Dover
Train/Other:
Charing Cross to Folkestone
Venue:
On the Leas, Folkestone Promenade, exhibition in Leas Cliff Hall
Facilities (Parking):
Designated car parks
Facilities (Disabled):
Disabled parking area on the 6th only
What's On:
Airshow, ground exhibitions with stands and displays, exhibition in Leas Cliff Hall
Historical Background:
Started in 1990 for Battle of Britain celebrations. Now in its 9th year
Media/Public Comments:
"Extremely good quality event and it's free!"

Finchcocks Festival

Type of Festival: **Music**
Contact: **Mrs Katrina Burnett**
Address:
Finchcocks Musical Museum
Goudhurst
Kent
TN17 1HH
Tel. No: **01580 211702**
Fax No: **01580 211007**
Date(s) of Festival:
September weekends (Fridays, Saturdays and some Sundays)
Times of Festival:
Fridays, Saturdays and some Sundays: 8pm. Saturdays 2.30pm
Cost for Adults: **£7 - £12.50**
Cost for Children: **£6 for some**
Tickets available from: **Finchcocks**
Routes by Car:
Off A262 10 miles from Tunbridge Wells
Train/Other:
Nearest station with taxi Paddock Wood (8 miles)
Venue: **Finchcocks Museum**
Facilities (Parking):
Lots of parking. Catering facilities from light refreshment to formal dinners. Picnics are permitted.
Facilities (Disabled):
Some access for disabled people
What's On:
Concerts on period instruments in famous Finchcocks Museum by leading players. Also ballad play by "Out of the Blue" Theatre Company
Historical Background:
Finchcocks, built 1725, is a fine early Georgian manor house. In 1979 Finchcocks was acquired by Richard Burnett, leading exponent of the early piano and it now houses some 80 historical musical instruments

General Information:
Finchcocks is now a musical centre of international repute. The house with its high ceilings and oak panelling provides the ideal setting for music performed on period instruments

Herne Bay Festival

Type of Festival: **Traditional**
Contact: **Mr John Hawkins**
Address:
Herne Bay Leisure Centre
William Street
Herne Bay
Kent
CT6 5NX
Tel. No: **01227 742690**
Fax No: **01227 742731**
Date(s) of Festival:
1st -16th August 1998
Times of Festival: **Daily**
Cost for Adults: **Free**
Cost for Children: **Free**
Tickets available from:
Not required
Train/Other:
London Victoria-Herne Bay. National Express from London Victoria
Venue: **Herne Bay Seafront**
Facilities (Parking):
Plenty of parking on or near seafront
Facilities (Disabled):
Disabled facilities
What's On:
Festival opening with the Vander Brothers triple wall of death. Fireworks, carnival, kite workshop, majorette workshop, sandcastle competition, mask competition . . .

Hythe Festival Week

Type of Festival:
Music, Sport
Contact: **Mr M Masey**
Address:
Hythe Festival Company
St Marys House
St Marys Road
Hythe
Kent
Tel. No: **01303 268715**
Date(s) of Festival:
4th - 12th July 1998
Times of Festival:
Throughout the day and evenings
Cost for Adults:
Most events free to spectators
Cost for Children: **Free**
Tickets available from:
Not required
Routes by Car:
M20 Junction 11, A20 to A261
Train/Other:
Sandling railway station. Many local bus routes
Venue: **Various venues in Hythe**
Facilities (Parking):
Good car parking available
Facilities (Disabled):
Facilities for disabled at most events
What's On:
Flower and garden show, pop and jazz concerts, cricket match, sailing regatta, street entertainers, parachute display, hovercraft rides, raft race, hot air balloon rides, rowing, fishing, walks, Festival Ball with fireworks, choral and orchestral concerts, etc
General Information:
Ideal week to have a holiday; many hotel and B&B's available within a 5 mile radius.

Apple and Cider Festival

Type of Festival: **Traditional**
Contact: **Amy Austin**
Address:
Museum of Kent Life
Lock Lane
Sandling
Maidstone
Kent
ME14 3AU
Tel. No: **01622 763936**
Fax No: **01622 662024**
Date(s) of Festival:
10th - 11th October 1998
Times of Festival:
Saturday 11am - 6pm
Sunday 11am - 5.30pm
Cost for Adults: **£3.95**
Cost for Children: **£2.25**
Special discounts:
£2.25 for OAPs, UB40s and students. Family ticket £11
Tickets available from:
Museum of Kent Life
Routes by Car:
M20 Junction 6, A229 to Maidstone (1mile)
Train/Other:
Maidstone East (1½ miles from town). M&D Bus, No 155 from Maidstone
Venue: **Museum of Kent Life**
Facilities (Parking):
Free car and coach parking, toilets. Food available
Facilities (Disabled):
Disabled access, parking and toilets
What's On:
Traditional apple press in operation, apple displays, apple tasting, apple bobbing, apples, apple juice for sale, real CAMRA approved ciders, morris dancers

Historical Background:
Celebration of apples and apple growers in Kent. Raising awareness of the different varieties of apples

Beer and Hop Festival

Type of Festival: **Traditional**
Contact: **Amy Austin**
Address:
Museum of Kent Life
Lock Lane
Sandling
Maidstone
Kent
ME14 3AU
Tel. No: **01622 763936**
Fax No: **01622 662024**
Date(s) of Festival:
5th - 6th September 1998
Times of Festival:
Saturday 11am - 8pm
Sunday 11am - 5pm
Cost for Adults: **£3.95**
Cost for Children: **£2.25**
Special discounts:
£2.25 for OAPs, UB40s and students. Family Ticket £11
Tickets available from:
Museum of Kent Life
Routes by Car:
M20 Junction 6, A229 to Maidstone (1mile)
Train/Other:
Maidstone East (1½ miles from town)
Venue:
Special bus service from Maidstone (Saturday only)
Facilities (Parking):
Free car and coach parking, toilets. Food available
Facilities (Disabled):
Disabled access, parking and toilets

What's On:

Oast in operation on both days. Hop drying process, Pearly King and Queen, live music, craft stalls, hop picking (by hand), circus workshops (Saturday only) CAMRA Beer Festival (over 60 real ales for sale)

Historical Background:

11th year. Only place in Britain where hops are still picked by hand and oast used in the traditional way

Balloon and Vintage Car Fiesta

Type of Festival:
Hot Air Ballooning
Contact: **Mr Nicholas Day**
Address:
Marketing and Special Events
Leeds Castle
Maidstone
Kent
ME17 1PL
Tel. No: **01622 765400**
Fax No: **01622 735616**
Date(s) of Festival:
6th - 7th June 1998
Times of Festival:
6am - 7pm (weather dependent)
Cost for Adults:
£6.80 includes entrance to event, park, and gardens. Entrance to castle is extra.
Cost for Children:
Under 15s £4.30
Special discounts:
Students, OAPs £4
Tickets available from:
Leeds Castle Ticket Office
Routes by Car:
B2163 Junction 8 off M20. 1 hour from London

Train/Other:
Connex South East Joint Admission Scheme to Bearsted Station. Coach operators from London. Also National Express Joint Admission Scheme from London Victoria
Venue: **Leeds Castle, Maidstone**
What's On:

Up to 30 special and regular shaped balloons including a fire extinguisher and a pig take to the sky, flying up and over the castle and moat, followed on ground by a fleet of vintage cars. Display of vintage bicycles, aerobatic display of Tiger Moths . . .

Historical Background:

Festival began in 1986 and is now one of the premier hot air balloon events in the country

General Information:

Other attractions are an aviary, grotto and maze, greenhouse and gardens

Festival of English Food and Wine

Type of Festival: **Food and Wine**
Contact: **Mr Nicholas Day**
Address:
Marketing and Special Events Manager
Leeds Castle
Maidstone
Kent
ME17 1PL
Tel. No: **01622 765400**
Fax No: **01622 735616**
Date(s) of Festival:
15th -16th May 1999 (TBC)
Times of Festival:
10am - 5pm last admission
Cost for Adults:
£6.80 (includes entrance to event and park)

Cost for Children:

Under 15s £4.30 (includes entrance to event and park)

Special discounts:

OAPs and students £4 (includes entrance to event and park)

Tickets available from:

Leeds Castle Ticket Office

Routes by Car:

B2163 Junction 8 off M20, 1 hour from London

Train/Other:

Connex South Eastern Joint Admission Scheme to Bearsted Station. Coach operators from London. Also National Express Joint Admission Scheme from Victoria London

Venue: **Leeds Castle, Maidstone**

Facilities (Parking):

Free car and coach parking. Baby changing facilities, restaurants, outside catering

Facilities (Disabled):

Disabled car park, wheelchair hire

What's On:

Produce from farm and field from Kent. Breads, cheeses, sausages, cured meats, fish, honey, chutneys, jams, ice creams. Top quality English wines produced from South East vineyards. Celebrity chefs, talks, demos . . .

Historical Background:

Wine Festival began in 1984 and became the Food and Wine Festival in 1996

General Information:

Punch and Judy shows for the children and outdoor activities on the festival site. Other attractions include aviary, grotto, maze, greenhouse and gardens

Flower Festival

Type of Festival: **Flower**

Contact: **Mr Nicholas Day**

Address:

Marketing and Special Events Manager
Leeds Castle
Maidstone
Kent
ME17 1PL

Tel. No: **01622 765400**

Fax No: **01622 735616**

Date(s) of Festival:

16th -19th September 1998

Times of Festival:

10am - 5pm (last admission to grounds)

Cost for Adults:

£8.80 (includes entrance to castle and park)

Cost for Children:

Under 15s £5.80 (includes entrance to castle and park)

Special discounts:

OAPs, students £6.80 (includes entrance to castle and park)

Tickets available from:

Leeds Castle Ticket Office

Routes by Car:

B2163 Junction 8 off the M20 (1 hour from London)

Train/Other:

Connex South East Joint Admission Scheme to Bearsted Station. Coach operators from London. Also National Express Joint Admission Scheme from London Victoria

Venue: **Leeds Castle, Maidstone**

Facilities (Parking):

Free car and coach parking. Baby changing facilities, restaurants, outside catering

Facilities (Disabled):

Disabled car park, wheelchair hire

What's On:

Displays of beautiful flowers and fruit. Created by the award winning **NFU/Leeds Castle** floristry team throughout the castle. 1998 theme is "The Theatre" and flowers and fruits will be inspired by theatre productions from Shakespeare to Lloyd Webber.
Historical Background:
First festival was in 1976

Whitstable Oyster Festival

Type of Festival: **Traditional**
Contact: **Jeanne Harrison**
Address:
The Gatehouse
Tower Hill
Whitstable
Kent
CT5 2BW
Tel. No: **01227 265666**
Fax No: **01227 265666**
Date(s) of Festival:
25th July - 2nd August 1998
Cost for Adults:
Many events are free
Tickets available from: **Not required**
Train/Other:
London Victoria - Whitstable
Venue: **Whitstable Town**
What's On:
Landing of oysters. Parade all day, petanque, raft race, mud run, Punch and Judy, marching bands, Beat Retreat. Visit art exhibitions, dancing, craft fair, Teddy Bears Picnic, sandcastle competition, dog shows. . .
Media/Public Comments:
"Fun festival for the whole family"
"Unpretentious wonderful family place"

LANCASHIRE

Easter Saturday Springtime Festival Dance

Type of Festival: **Dance**
Contact: **Joe Healey**
Address:
304 Rochdale Road
Britannia
Bacup
Lancashire
OL13 9TW
Tel. No: **01706 874872 (evening)**
01706 854020 (day)
Date(s) of Festival:
3rd April 1999
Times of Festival: **9am - 7pm**
Cost for Adults: **Free**
Cost for Children: **Free**
Tickets available from: **Not required**
Routes by Car:
From Rochdale take A671 to Bacup
Train/Other:
Nearest stations are Manchester Piccadilly or Burnley
Venue: **Bacup**
Facilities (Parking):
Lots of free car parking in and around Bacup

What's On:
Performed by the "Britannia Coconut Dancers" of Bacup. Follow the Coconutters and brass band from boundary to boundary calling in at all the pubs, inns and taverns. Gorgeous costumes, concertinas and Lancashire clogs.
Historical Background:
A pagan springtime fertility dance, the only dance of its kind left in the world and unique to Bacup. The first "Coconutters" were called the Tunstead Mill Group, formed in 1857, from which the Britannia Coconutters are descended.
Media/Public Comments:
"Nutty flavour black magic has world drooling"
"Nutters, fettlers and a good day out"
General Information:
Bacup is a typical cotton mill town mostly preserved by English Heritage. Stone terraces, cobbled streets and stone buildings in Town Centre. The smallest street in the world is in Bacup (see Guinness Book of Records)

Fleetwood Tram Sunday

Type of Festival: **Transport**
Contact: **Mr J W Cowpe**
Address:
Fleetwood Transport Festival Committee
The North Euston Hotel
Fleetwood
Lancashire
FY7 6BN
Tel. No: **01253 876525**
Fax No: **01253 777842**
Date(s) of Festival: **19th July 1998**

Times of Festival: **All day**
Cost for Adults: **Free**
Cost for Children: **Free**
Tickets available from: **Not required**
Routes by Car: **M5, M55, A585**
Train/Other:
Blackpool North or Poulton
Venue: **Fleetwood**
Facilities (Parking):
Plenty of parking available
What's On:
Vintage trams and vintage cars, buses, lorries, bikes. Variety of bands, vintage tram rides, side shows . . .
Historical Background:
This festival is now in its 15th year
Media/Public Comments:
"One of the biggest one-day events in the North West"

Flyde Folk Festival

Type of Festival: **Folk Music**
Contact:
Alan Bell - Festival Director
Address:
55 The Strand
Rossall
Fleetwood
Lancashire
FY7 8NP
Tel. No: **01253 872317**
Fax No: **01253 878382**
Date(s) of Festival:
4th - 6th September 1998
Times of Festival:
From 8am - 11.30pm. Late night show on Friday 4th at 1.30am
Cost for Adults: **Various**
Special discounts:
Discounts available if booked before 15/6/98
Tickets available from:
Festival Secretary (see above)
Routes by Car:

M6 Junction with M55. M55 to first Junction A585. Leave M55 - A585 to Fleetwood follow signs to Seafront/Marine Hall

Train/Other:
Blackpool is the main transport centre for the Flyde Coast. Local bus to Fleetwood

Venue:
Marine Hall, The Esplanade, Sea front, Fleetwood

Facilities (Parking):
Plenty of parking around Marine Hall

Facilities (Disabled):
Good access for disabled in many venues

What's On:
Over 125 events of music, song and dance. Concerts, ceilidhs, workshops, singarounds, pub sessions, craft fair, competitions, children's sessions, Palace of Varieties, meet the artists, dance displays, story telling, poems 'n' pints, clog dancing etc

Historical Background:
Founded 26 years ago by a group of folk enthusiasts to promote local and national interest

Media/Public Comments:
"The quality of the music is outstanding. Great value for money" "On top of the exciting array of artists, musicians and special events, Flyde is known as the friendly festival..."

Lancaster LitFest

Type of Festival: **Literature**
Contact: **Andy Darby - Director**
Address:
Sunday Street Studios
23 -29 Sunday Street
Lancaster
Lancashire
LA1 1EW

Tel. No: **01524 62166**
Fax No: **01524 841216**
Date(s) of Festival:
21st - 25th October 1998
Times of Festival:
Varies with each event
Cost for Adults:
£2.50 - £6.50 per event
Cost for Children:
£1.50 - £4.50 per event
Special discounts:
Concessionary tickets available for UB40s, OAPs and students, special rates for block bookings of 10+
Tickets available from:
Sunday Street Studios and Waterstones/Atticus Book shops
Routes by Car:
Lancaster is off the M6 motorway
Train/Other:
West Coast line - Virgin trains
Venue:
Various venues within Lancaster City Centre
Facilities (Disabled):
Wherever possible LitFest tries to run its events in disabled accessible venues. Please contact LitFest for arrangements for particular events
What's On:
Contemporary writers of international stature in a wide range of literary events, readings, performances, cabaret, writing workshops, in prose and poetry writing. LitFest promotes and celebrates writing through a variety of events and activities
Historical Background:
The festival is 21 years old, previous guests include Ted Hughes, Seamus Heaney, Fay Weldon, Roddy Doyle and Brian Keenan. The LitFest also runs events

throughout the year including readings and workshops as well as the Spotlight live literature event
Media/Public Comments:
LitFest runs an annual poetry competition which offers a special opportunity to winners, as their work is printed in book form, as an anthology of the 30 best entries selected by professional judges
General Information:
Lancaster is a beautiful Georgian town, the county town of Lancashire and a few miles from the world-famous Lake District. The city offers numerous museums, galleries, parks and a lively arts and entertainment scene

Worldbeat Weekend

Type of Festival: **Music**
Contact: **Keith Lamb**
Address:
Arts and Events Office
Palatine Hall
Dalton Square
Lancaster
Lancashire
LA1 1PW
Tel. No: **01524 582828**
Fax No: **01524 582323**
Date(s) of Festival:
28th - 30th August 1998
Times of Festival: **Various**
Cost for Adults: **Mostly free**
Tickets available from:
Not required
Routes by Car:
M6 Junction 34/35 signposted to Morecambe
Train/Other:
Mainline to Lancaster, branch line to Morecambe
Venue:
Various venues including "The Platform", a cabaret venue, Morecambe Promenade
Facilities (Parking): **Town parking**
What's On:
A festival of world music featuring musicians from all around the world

Heritage Festival

Type of Festival: **Mixed**
Contact: **Keith Lamb**
Address:
Arts and Events Office
Palatine Hall
Dalton Square
Lancaster
Lancashire
LA1 1PW
Tel. No: **01524 582828**
Fax No: **01524 582323**
Date(s) of Festival:
20th September 1998
Times of Festival: **All day**
Cost for Adults: **Free**
Cost for Children: **Free**
Tickets available from:
Not required
Routes by Car:
M6 Junction 34/35 signposted
Train/Other:
Mainline to Lancaster, branch line to Morecambe
Venue:
Promenade, Morecambe Seafront
Facilities (Parking):
Town Centre parking
What's On:
350 vintage vehicles on display, face painters, brass bands, street entertainers, street theatre, acrobatics, Punch and Judy, town market open with craft and market stalls. The major highlight of the day is the Red Arrows aeronautical display in the afternoon
Historical Background:

Festival started as a vintage vehicle display and has grown from there

Caribbean Calypso

Type of Festival: **Music**
Contact: **Keith Lamb**
Address:
Arts and Events Office
Palatine Hall
Dalton Square
Lancaster
Lancashire
LA1 1PW
Tel. No: **01524 582828**
Fax No: **01524 582323**
Date(s) of Festival:
16th -19th August 1998
Times of Festival: **Various**
Cost for Adults: **Mostly Free**
Tickets available from: **Not required**
Routes by Car:
M6 Junction 34/35 signposted to
Morecambe
Train/Other:
Mainline to Lancaster, branch line
to Morecambe
Venue:
Various venues throughout the district including The Promenade, Morecambe Seafront
Facilities (Parking): **Town parking**
What's On:
On the 16th August a Caribbean Extravaganza at the Open Air Arena, Morecambe followed by a spectacular firework display

Summer Breeze '98

Type of Festival: **Music**
Contact: **Keith Lamb**
Address:
Arts and Events Office
Palatine Hall
Dalton Square

Lancaster
Lancashire
LA1 1PW
Tel. No: **01524 582828**
Fax No: **01524 582323**
Date(s) of Festival:
18th -19th July 1998
Times of Festival: **Various**
Cost for Adults: **Mostly free**
Cost for Children: **Free**
Tickets available from: **At the event**
Routes by Car:
M6 Junction 34/35 signposted to
Morecambe
Train/Other:
Mainline to Lancaster and branch
line to Morecambe
Venue:
Morecambe Arena, The Promenade, Morecambe Seafront
Facilities (Parking):
Town Centre parking
What's On:
A weekend of coolgrooves on the Bay. Blues, jazz, rock, etc

Festival of Light and Water

Type of Festival: **Music/Fireworks**
Contact: **Keith Lamb**
Address:
Art and Events Office
Palatine Hall
Dalton Square
Lancaster
Lancashire
LA1 1PW
Tel. No: **01524 582828**
Fax No: **01524 582323**
Date(s) of Festival:
8th - 9th August 1998
Times of Festival:
Varying. The fireworks are at 9.45pm each evening

Cost for Adults: **Free**
Cost for Children: **Free**
Tickets available from:
Not required
Routes by Car:
M6 Junction 34/35 signposted to Morecambe
Train/Other:
Mainline to Lancaster branch line to Morecambe
Venue:
Morecambe Arena, The Promenade, Morecambe Seafront
Facilities (Parking): **Town Centre**
What's On:
Music all day in the Arena followed at 9.45pm each night by a spectacular display of fireworks

Streetbands Festival

Type of Festival: **Music**
Contact: **Keith Lamb**
Address:
Arts and Events Office
Palatine Hall
Dalton Square
Lancaster
Lancashire
LA1 1PW
Tel. No: **01524 582828**
Fax No: **01524 582323**
Date(s) of Festival:
1st - 2nd August 1998
Times of Festival: **Various**
Cost for Adults: **Free**
Cost for Children: **Free**
Tickets available from:
Not required
Routes by Car:
M6 Junction 34/35 signposted - Morecambe
Train/Other:
Mainline to Lancaster
Venue:
Morecambe and Lancaster and surrounding areas

Facilities (Parking): **Town Centre**
What's On:
2 days of swinging street music throughout the district

Saddleworth Rushcart

Type of Festival:
Traditional Rushbearing
Contact: **Richard Hawkinson**
Address:
3 Moorgate Drive
Carrbrook
Stalybridge
Lancashire
SK15 3LX
Tel. No: **01457 834871**
Date(s) of Festival:
22nd - 23rd August 1998
Cost for Adults: **Free**
Cost for Children: **Free**
Tickets available from: **Not required**
Routes by Car:
Uppermill lies on A670 off A62, Oldham-Huddersfield Road
Train/Other:
Greenfield Railway Station
Venue: **Uppermill, Saddleworth**
What's On:
Traditional Pennine Rushcart procession and displays of English traditional morris dancing
Historical Background:
Prior to the days of stone floored churches, rushcarts were a way of supplying the church with rushes to cover the earthen floor in winter. The practice was stopped in 1826 at Saddleworth following a visit to the church by Bishop Law
General Information:
The Rushcarts were still built but the rushes were sold for animal bedding. The railways were the death knell of the Rushcarts which continued sporadically until

around 1919. The current Rushcart was revived in 1975 and has continued annually since

Saddleworth Folk and Roots Festival

Type of Festival: **Roots, Traditional**
Contact: **Tony Green**
Address:
Fernthorpe Hall
Saddleworth
Lancashire
OL3 6DP
Tel. No: **01457 872035**
Date(s) of Festival:
18th -19th July 1998
Times of Festival: **All day**
Cost for Adults:
Weekend Ticket £17
Cost for Children:
Ages 13-16 Weekend £9. Under 13s £1. Under 5s Free
Special discounts:
Weekend Adult £15. 13-16s £8 (booked before 30 June)
Tickets available from:
Fernthorpe Hall (see above)
Routes by Car:
From the M62 Junction 20, A627M, turn off Oldham bypass A669 or Junction 21, A640, A6052 or Junction 22 , A672 left to A6052
Train/Other:
Via Leeds or Manchester
Venue:
Uppermill venues including the Civic Hall, the Museum and Commercial Hotel
Facilities (Parking):
Camping available for non-weekend ticket holders
Facilities (Disabled):
Disabled access to most venues
What's On:

Over 30 gigs including Jez Lowe, Marie Little, Peter Ryder, Rocky Mountain Ploughboys, Jack at a Pinch, Lancashire Wallhoppers and the Milltown Cloggies. Singarounds, sessions, ceilidh, dance displays, craft fair, workshops and Tumble Tots (play area)
Historical Background:
Saddleworth's first festival

LEICESTERSHIRE

Leicester Comedy Festival

Type of Festival:
Arts - Focus on Comedy
Contact:
Delphine Manley
Festival Manager
Address:
The City Room
Hotel Street
Leicester
Leicestershire
LE1 5AW
Tel. No: **0116 2915511**
Fax No: **0116 2915510**
Date(s) of Festival:
February 1999 (TBC)
Times of Festival: **Various**

Cost for Adults:
Varies according to venue
Cost for Children:
Concessions available at most venues
Tickets available from:
Each venue. Please phone Hotline: 0891 100702 for further information
Venue:
Various venues within Leicester
Facilities (Parking):
The festival is committed to improving access to events and provides sign interpreted shows and a subsidised transport scheme
Facilities (Disabled):
The £1 Transport and Escort Scheme has been set up for people with mobility difficulties. You can also book an escort at no cost. For more details phone Hotline for more information (see above)
What's On:
150 events over 10 days in 30 venues across Leicestershire. Includes stand-up comedy, theatre, film, special events, workshops, discussions and interviews and lots more
Historical Background:
In 1999 the Festival is in its 6th year and in 1998 attracted an audience of over 21,000 during the 10 days. The festival has a well-respected community and education programme which aims to increase local participation
Media/Public Comments:
"The fifth Leicester Comedy Festival boasts acts from here and abroad, there's a healthy percentage of female comics as well as films, plays, radio recordings and general comic pandemonium on an epic scale" The Independent

Leicester Caribbean Carnival

Type of Festival: **Carnival**
Contact:
Leicester Caribbean Carnival Ltd
Address:
Carnival Office
138 Charles Street
Leicester
Leicestershire
LEI ILB
Tel. No: **0116 253 0491**
Fax No: **0116 291 1719**
Date(s) of Festival: **1st August 1998**
Times of Festival: **10am - 8pm**
Cost for Adults: **Free**
Cost for Children: **Free**
Tickets available from:
Not required
Routes by Car: **M1/M69**
Train/Other:
Midland mainline. National Rail enquiries: 0345 48 49 50
Venue: **Leicester Town Centre**
Facilities (Parking):
Parking available on the park. Food and drink stalls
Facilities (Disabled):
Disabled access and disabled parking
What's On:
The Carnival procession headed by the Queen Mama, Prince and Princess, a host of troupes and floats, live music including steel bands, calypso, soca, soul and reggae. Party on the Park, live events on main stage, funfair, craft/art stalls, workshops and lots more
Historical Background:
The Carnival began life in 1984 with the first carnival staged in August 1985 to commemorate Emancipation Day, as a public cel-

ebration of the 150th anniversary of the abolition of slavery in the British Empire
Media/Public Comments:
"We are all enriched by this vibrant affirmation of music, dance and joy of living; the Carnival inspires us in all efforts to develop Leicester as a true community of communities" Bishop of Leicester
General Information:
The Carnival is now the largest event of its kind in the Midlands. It attracts participants from across the region and is celebrated by all age groups

Heart Link Leicester, Street Organ Festival

Type of Festival: **Music**
Contact: **Mr and Mrs M Dilks**
Address:
25 London Lane
Wymeswold
Loughborough
Leicestershire
LE12 6UB
Tel. No: **01509 880803**
Date(s) of Festival:
Saturday 8th May 1999
Times of Festival: **9.30am - 4.30pm**
Cost for Adults: **Free**
Cost for Children: **Free**
Tickets available from: **Not required**
Routes by Car:
All routes into Leicester
Train/Other:
Leicester Station, London Road. St Margarets Bus Station
Venue: **Leicester City Centre**
Facilities (Parking):
Parking is available in city centre car parks or via park and ride
What's On:

Around 40 street organs and several fair organs playing in and around Leicester city centre collecting for "Heart Link", the East Midlands Children's Heart Care Association, Glenfield Hospital, Leicester
Historical Background:
6th Street Organ Festival in Leicester with participants coming from all over the world
Media/Public Comments:
Widespread coverage in local press and radio. Very well received by general public
General Information:
Organised by Heart Link Children's Charity and Leicester Promotions. Event sponsored by various local businesses and shops

Heart Link Steam and Vintage Festival

Type of Festival:
Traditional Steam Rally
Contact: **Mr and Mrs M Dilks**
Address:
25 London Lane
Wymeswold
Loughborough
Leicestershire
LE12 6UB
Tel. No: **01509 880803**
Date(s) of Festival:
25th - 26th July 1998
Times of Festival: **11am -5pm**
Cost for Adults: **£2.50**
Cost for Children: **£1.50**
Special discounts: **OAPs £1.50**
Tickets available from: **On entry**
Routes by Car:
On A6006, signposted from A6, A60 and A46
Train/Other:

Nearest Station Loughborough.
Kinch Bus Service No 8 operates
from Loughborough Bus Station
Venue:
**Hillside Farm, Rempstone Road,
Wymeswold, Loughborough**
Facilities (Parking):
**Parking nearby (by donation). Bar
and refreshments. Overnight caravan parking (Friday and Saturday)
available on site. Enquiries to contact. Dogs welcome if kept on lead**
Facilities (Disabled):
Disabled parking on site
What's On:
**Over 300 working exhibits: steam
and mini steam engines, vintage
cars, commercials, motorbikes,
tractors, barn engines, fair organs,
hand crafted models marquee,
craft marquee, trade market,
arena events, marching bands etc**
Historical Background:
**8th Steam and Vintage Festival or-
ganised by Heart Link Children's
Charity Festival Committee. All
proceeds go to the Charity of
Glenfield Hospital, Leicester**
Media/Public Comments:
**Increasingly popular event known
as "the friendly rally"**

Tutbury Arts Festival

Type of Festival: **Arts**
Contact:
**Simon Nickerson
Marketing Manager**
Address:
**Whippletree House
Beresford Court
Newton Road
Heather
Leicestershire**
Tel. No: **01530 262272**
Fax No: **01530 261322**

Date(s) of Festival:
19th - 21st June 1998
Times of Festival:
**Various times according to pro-
gramme**
Cost for Adults: **Various**
Tickets available from:
**Box Offices:
Pots and Pine, 2 High Street:
01283 813123
Tutbury Sheepskin Tanners:
01283 814967
Tourist Information, Burton on
Trent: 01283 516609
Charles Foulds Ltd, Derby
01332 344842**
Routes by Car:
**Tutbury is situated on A511 (old
A50) between Burton on Trent and
Uttoxeter**
Train/Other:
**Tutbury and Hatton Railway Sta-
tion (5 mins walk from village
centre)**
Venue:
Various venues within Tutbury
Facilities (Parking):
**Public car parks at Monk Street
and Cornmill Lane, Tutbury. Exten-
sive car parking for visitors to
Tutbury Castle. Wide selection of
public houses, restaurants and tea
and coffee shops**
Facilities (Disabled):
Disabled access to all events
What's On:
**"Festival Art" exhibition of paint-
ings and sculpture, orchestral
music of Vivaldi's Italy, Macbeth in
the grounds of Tutbury Castle, An
anthology of the works and
speeches of Charles Dickens**
Historical Background:
**The Festival was established in
1997 with the aid of lottery grants.**

The creation of the Tutbury Arts group was the culmination of a long tradition of staging art events in the village centred at the priory church of St Mary

General Information:
Other visitor attractions include the ruined 11th century **Norman Priory church, two glass crystal works, numerous antique and gift shops and Ye Olde Dog and Partridge 15th century coaching Inn famous throughout the Midlands and beyond**

LINCOLNSHIRE

Cleethorpes Beer Festival

Type of Festival: **Beer**
Contact: **Janet Barber**
Address:
Winter Gardens
Kingsway
Cleethorpes
Lincolnshire
Tel. No: **01472 692925**
Fax No: **01472 692925**
Date(s) of Festival:
30th April - 2nd May 1999
Times of Festival: **Various**

Cost for Adults:
£1 lunch, £2.50 evenings
Special discounts:
CAMRA card carrying members free
Tickets available from: **Pay on door**
Routes by Car: **A180 or A16**
Train/Other: **Cleethorpes Station**
Venue:
Winter Gardens, Kingsway, Cleethorpes Seafront
Facilities (Parking):
Ground floor accommodation and parking. Snacks and meals available
What's On:
Over 40 real ales. Music from live bands (not yet confirmed)
Historical Background:
15th annual event
Media/Public Comments:
"Voted Number 1 attraction"

Folk Dance Festival

Type of Festival: **Music and Dance**
Contact: **Robert Elwes**
Address:
Elsham Hall Country and Wildlife Park
Elsham
Lincolnshire
DN20 0QZ
Tel. No: **01652 688698 (day)**
Fax No: **01652 688240**
Date(s) of Festival:
30th - 31st August 1998
Times of Festival: **11am - 5pm**
Cost for Adults: **£3.95**
Cost for Children:
£2.50. Under 5s free
Special discounts:
OAPs £3.75
Tickets available from:
Robert Elwes (see above)
Routes by Car:

Signposted from Barnelby Top, Junction 5, M40
Venue:
Elsham Hall Country and Wildlife Park
Facilities (Parking): **Ample parking**
Facilities (Disabled):
Access for disabled. Disabled facilities

Grimsthorpe International Dance and Music Festival

Type of Festival:
Folk Music and Dance
Contact: **Iona Sadler**
Address:
**South Kestover District Council
St Peters Hill
Grantham
Lincolnshire
NG31 6PZ**
Tel. No: **01476 406155**
Fax No: **01476 591810**
Date(s) of Festival:
17th - 19th July 1998
Cost for Adults: **Weekend £25**
Cost for Children: **£15**
Special discounts:
Concessions available on request
Tickets available from:
Stanford Arts: 01780 763203
Routes by Car:
A1 then A151 (between Stanford and Grantham) Colsterworth roundabout then head towards Bourne
Venue:
Various venues within Grimsthorpe
Facilities (Parking):
Free on site parking
What's On:
Performances and concerts by some of the best folk bands and
dance companies, circus for the younger visitors. Also workshops in dance including Flamenco, African, Appalatian Clog and African drumming, Palmas, singing
Historical Background:
Now in its 6th year, the dance and music festival is the climax of the week of events following the theme "Folk and Food, Drink and Dance"

Street Festival

Type of Festival:
Music Entertainers
Contact: **Liz Wilson - Arts Officer**
Address:
**Lincoln City Council
City Hall
Lincoln
Lincolnshire
LN1 1DJ**
Tel. No: **01522 564514**
Fax No: **01522 560049**
Date(s) of Festival:
24th - 25th July 1998
Times of Festival:
12 noon - 4pm both days
Cost for Adults: **Free**
Cost for Children: **Free**
Tickets available from:
Not required
Routes by Car: **A15, A46, A57**
Train/Other:
Lincoln Central Station
Venue: **Lincoln City Centre**
Facilities (Parking): **Available**
Facilities (Disabled):
Access for disabled
What's On:
Street entertainment, theatre

Early Music Festival

Type of Festival:
15th Century Music
Contact:
Lincoln Tourist Information Centre
Address:
Castle Square
Lincoln
Lincolnshire
Tel. No: **01522 529828**
Date(s) of Festival:
12th -16th August 1998
Times of Festival:
7.30pm. All day on Sunday
Cost for Adults: **£6 - £7**
Cost for Children: **£4 - £5**
Special discounts:
UB40's, OAPs, students: £4 - £5
Tickets available from:
Tourist Information Centre:
01522 529828
Routes by Car: **A15, A46, A57**
Train/Other:
Lincoln Central Railway Station
Venue:
Various venues within Lincoln
Facilities (Parking):
Parking available
What's On:
Tingagel, Frotolla, Bergamasca, Sinfonye and the Oxford Girls Choir concerts
General Information:
Festival brochure available from any Lincolnshire Tourist Information Office

Water Carnival

Type of Festival: **Traditional**
Contact:
Liz Wilson - Arts Officer
Address:
Lincoln City Council
City Hall
Lincoln
Lincolnshire
LN1 1DJ
Tel. No: **01522 564514**
Fax No: **01522 560049**
Date(s) of Festival:
11th - 12th July 1998
Times of Festival:
Saturday: 12 noon - 10pm
Sunday: 12 noon - 6pm
Cost for Adults: **Free**
Cost for Children: **Free**
Tickets available from:
Not required
Routes by Car: **A15, A46, A57**
Train/Other:
Lincoln Central Station
Venue: **Brayford Pool Area**
Facilities (Parking): **Available**
Facilities (Disabled):
Access for disabled
What's On:
Boat races, model boats, water ballet, entertainment, displays, mayor street parade, craft fairs, stalls, funfair, wine festival . . .

International Clowns Festival

Type of Festival: **Clowns**
Contact:
Liz Wilson - Arts Officer
Address:
Lincoln City Council
City Hall
Lincoln
Lincolnshire
LN1 1DJ
Tel. No: **01522 564514**
Fax No: **01522 560049**
Date(s) of Festival:
24th - 27th September 1998
Cost for Adults: **Free (excluding Gala performance)**

Tickets available from:
01522 523303 (for Gala perform-ance)
Routes by Car: **A15, A46, A57**
Train/Other:
Lincoln Central Station
Venue: **Lincoln City**
Facilities (Parking): **Available**
What's On:
Featuring Charlie Cairoli Junior, Pierre Picton, Ron Moody, Chitty Chitty Bang Bang, al fresco shows, street entertainment, workshops and Gala performance at the Thea-tre Royal "An Evening with Ron Moody"
Historical Background:
Clowns International was founded in 1947 as the International Circus Clowns Club. In 1978 its name changed to Clowns International

July Festival of Western Music and Dance

Type of Festival: **Music**
Contact:
Roger and Brenda Bessent
Address:
119 New Road
Whittlesey
Peterborough
Cambridgeshire
PE7 1SX
Tel. No: **01733 206930**
Fax No: **01733 768110**
Date(s) of Festival:
10th - 12th July 1998
Cost for Adults:
Weekend pass £30. Evening dance ticket £7. Single day pass £15
Cost for Children: **Under 14s half price. Under 10s free**
Tickets available from:
Roger/Brenda 01733 206930 or by

post **(see above)**
Venue:
Springfields Exhibition Centre, Camelgate, Spalding, Lincolnshire
Facilities (Parking):
Free parking for cars, caravans and tents. Also toilets, showers, wash-ing facilities, disposal facilities, food and bar
What's On:
Dance workshops with: Pam and Dave Chilvers, John and Eileen Starmer, Roger and Brenda and guest instructors. Dance to Rebel Yell, Miles West Duo, The Dean Bros, Tex Therapy, TJ McCall and Country Disco
General Information:
Also featuring the UK Country and Western Dance Championships 1999 - Eastern qualifying heats

Tallington Beer Festival

Type of Festival: **Beer and Music**
Contact: **Paul Appleton**
Address:
Rock House
Scotgate
Stamford
Lincolnshire
PE9 2YQ
Tel. No: **01780 763063/480560**
Fax No: **01780 765788**
Date(s) of Festival:
13th - 17th May 1998
Times of Festival:
13th-14th: 6.30pm -11pm
15th: 5.30pm - 11.30pm
16th: 11am - 11.30pm
17th: 11am - 5.30pm
Cost for Adults:
Daytime £4, evenings free. Satur-day/Sunday free admission to Tallington Steam and Country Fes-tival

Cost for Children:
Daytime £1, evenings free.
Special discounts:
OAPs daytime £3, evenings free
Routes by Car:
3 miles east of Stamford and A1. 7 miles north of Peterborough
Train/Other:
Peterborough Station. Free courtesy bus Saturday and Sunday lunchtime. Local CAMRA group run minibuses in the evening
Venue:
Barham Road Showfield, Tallington
Facilities (Parking):
Free parking. Full catering. Beer tent opens early on Wednesday and is established as an event in its own right
Facilities (Disabled):
Disabled parking and toilets
What's On:
50 plus real ales from Britain's micro breweries, live bands every night
13th: Platform 4 (Glam Rock) 14th: Hurl the Jack (Irish/Folk) 15th: Kick 'n' Rush (Skiffle/Rock) DI Appleschnapps (German Umpah band) each night "Doctor Busker"
Historical Background:
Beer Festival is an extension to the successful Tallington Steam and Country Festival established in 1992
General Information:
Steam and Country Festival sponsored by Old Glory Magazine. Beer Festival sponsored by The Taste Magazine

GREATER LONDON

City of London Festival

Type of Festival: **Arts**
Contact: **Joe Paton**
Address:
Bishopsgate Hall
230 Bishopsgate
London
EC2M 4QD
Tel. No: **0171 377 0540**
Fax No: **0171 377 1972**
Date(s) of Festival:
23rd June - 16th July 1998
Times of Festival: **Various**
Cost for Adults: **Various**
Tickets available from:
Barbican Box Office: 0171 638 8891
Train/Other:
Liverpool Street, Fenchurch Street, Canon Street Stations
Venue: **Bishopsgate Hall**
Facilities (Parking): **Limited parking (NCP and street) in City**
What's On:
107 events. Shakespearean drama, orchestral concerts, recitals, operas, chamber music, jazz, masterclasses, dance, free open air events, theatre, Mozart string quartet/quintet cycle, perform-

ances from all around the world

Historical Background:

Now in its 36th year the festival has gained an international reputation for presenting world-class performances within the famous square mile of the City. The festival has a strong history of promoting the arts through a wide range of events

Media/Public Comments:

"Broader in scope and more international than ever"

Wall Street Journal

"For 3 weeks in June and July, London's cultural emphasis shifts eastwards from the West End and South bank, to the City of London Festival" Daily Telegraph

General Information:

The Festival prides itself on consistently being able to attract some of the world's most distinguished and celebrated artists. In 1964 the Festival hosted the first London performance of Benjamin Britten's Symphony for Cello and Orchestra with Rostropovich

Festival for Life

Type of Festival:

Complimentary Health

Contact: **K Darley**

Destiny Fairs

Address:

8 Hoecourt Court

Hoe Lane

Enfield

Middlesex

Tel. No: **01992 850357**

Fax No: **0973 343688**

Date(s) of Festival:

29th - 31st August 1998

Times of Festival: **11am - 7pm**

Cost for Adults:

£3 per day, £5 per weekend

Cost for Children: **Free**

Special discounts:

UB40's, OAPs, students £2.50

Routes by Car:

From Blackwall Tunnel take A2 to Central London, follow signs to concert halls. From south take A2 and signs to Blackheath

Train/Other:

British Rail: Blackheath from Charing Cross or London Bridge

Venue: **Blackheath**

Facilities:

Bars, cafés and lots of restaurants close by. Nearest hotel is Clarendon Hotel

Facilities (Disabled):

Disabled access to main exhibition. No access to psychics or to attend lectures

What's On:

Over 90 exhibitors offering a wide range of complimentary therapies, including shiatsu, aromatherapy, reiki and osteopathy, along with stalls selling books, pottery, jewellery and tarot cards. Demonstrations of T'ai Chi, belly dancing and Yoga, live music etc

Historical Background:

Natural development from New Age Fair. Now grown to one of best value events of its type in the UK

Media/Public Comments:

"Good atmosphere, fair prices"

"I always come, 'cos its great"

Sample of opinion from general public via questionnaire

General Information:

Lots of people attend both days. It can get very busy. Credit cards are accepted in all stands (a small service charge may be applicable)

Chinese New Year Festival

Type of Festival: **Traditional**
Contact:
Chinatown Chinese Association
Address:
Chinatown
Gerrard Street
London
W1
Tel. No: **0171 734 5161**
Date(s) of Festival:
First Sunday after Chinese New Year
Cost for Adults: **Free**
Cost for Children: **Free**
Train/Other:
Leicester Square, Piccadilly Circus, Tottenham Court Road
Venue:
Chinatown; around Soho, Gerrard Street, Newport Place, Leicester Square in the West End
What's On:
Stalls selling crafts and delicacies overflow from the main Gerrard Street/Newport Place area. Lions and dragons snake their way through the streets, gathering gifts of money and food. Stage for performers in Leicester Square
Media/Public Comments:
"The New Year Festival is the high spot of the Chinese calendar. The atmosphere is exotic" Time Out
General Information:
Early Chinese history is told to anyone who will listen. Afterwards dine in the Chinese restaurants and eat from special Dim Sum menus

Costermongers Pearly Harvest Festival

Type of Festival: **Religious**
Tel. No: **0171 930 0089**
Date(s) of Festival:
4th October 1998
Times of Festival: **2pm**
Cost for Adults: **Free**
Cost for Children: **Free**
Venue:
St Martin in the Fields, Trafalgar Square, London WC2
What's On:
Dressed in their traditional costumes, a barrow load of cockneys - Pearly Kings, Queens and Princesses from all the London boroughs, gather for a harvest thanksgiving every year
Historical Background:
"Costermongers were originally apple sellers but became popular local figures due to their flamboyant dress encrusted with thousands of buttons. This popularity encouraged them to raise money for charity" Time Out

Covent Garden Flower Festival

Type of Festival: **Horticultural**
Contact: **Eileen Woods**
Address:
Vantage Productions and Events Ltd
19a Floral Street
Covent Garden
London
WC2E 9DS
Tel. No: **0171 379 7020**
Date(s) of Festival:
21st - 28th June 1998
Times of Festival: **11am - 7pm daily**

Cost for Adults:
Free. Programme costs £2
Cost for Children: **Free**
Tickets available from:
Festival Office: 0171 379 7020
Train/Other: **Charing Cross Station, Covent Garden tube**
Venue: **Covent Garden**
Facilities (Parking):
NCP car parks in the area. Restaurants and rest areas available within the festival
Facilities (Disabled):
Unrestricted access for disabled
What's On:
Floral displays, performances, new products, nursery exhibitors, demonstrations, retail, guided walks
Media/Public Comments:
Ambassadors for London Awards 1997: Special Judges certificate

Dance Umbrella

Type of Festival: **Dance**
Contact: **Betsy Gregory**
Address:
Dance Umbrella
20 Chancellors Street
London
W6 9RN
Tel. No: **0181 741 4040**
Fax No: **0181 741 7902**
Date(s) of Festival:
2nd October - 28th November 1998
Times of Festival: **Various**
Cost for Adults: **Various**
Tickets available from:
Box Office: 0181 7414040
Venue:
Queen Elizabeth Hall, Riverside Studio, Barbican Theatre, Sadlers Wells
What's On:
The programme will be announced mid-August

Historical Background:
Dance Umbrella was founded in 1978 and since then has presented a festival in London each autumn, showcasing the best contemporary dance from around the world
Media/Public Comments:
"London's annual celebration of all that's fresh and funky in contemporary dance"
The Independent

Guinness London Fleadh

Type of Festival: **Irish Folk Festival**
Contact: **Dora Masullo**
Address:
Mean Fiddler
London
Tel. No:
Info Line: 0181 963 0940
Dora Masullo: 0181 961 5490
Fax No: **0181 961 5743**
Date(s) of Festival: **6th June 1998**
Times of Festival: **Various**
Cost for Adults: **£28 in advance**
Tickets available from:
TicketMaster: 0541 500044. Also available from 0171 344 0044 and 0541 504444
Venue: **Finsbury Park, London**
Facilities (Parking):
Limited parking available
What's On:
A feast of music including Simple Minds, Sinead O'Connor and many more big names waiting to be confirmed

Greenwich and Docklands International Festival

Type of Festival: **Multi Arts**
Contact: **Susan Edwards**
Address:
6 College Approach
London
SE10 9HY
Tel. No: **0181 305 1818**
Fax No: **0181 305 1188**
Date(s) of Festival:
10th - 19th July 1998
Times of Festival: **Various**
Cost for Adults: **£6 - £15**
Cost for Children: **£3 - £7**
Special discounts:
Full time students, income support/housing benefit from £3 - £7
Venue:
Various venues in the Greenwich and Docklands area
Facilities (Parking):
Parking and disabled access details for each festival venue are in the brochure
What's On:
Open air concerts, spectacular firework displays, sky ballet and celestial aerial carillon, fire shows, dance, promenade performances, theatre, picnic concerts which include Lesley Garrett with the Bournemouth Symphony and the ever popular Jools Holland
Historical Background:
The Greenwich Festival was established by the London borough of Greenwich in 1970. 24 years later the Greenwich Festival was established as an independent arts organisation. In 1996 it became the Greenwich and Docklands International Festival
Media/Public Comments:
"Paving the way to the Millennium experience"
Guardian Guide
"A dazzling fortnight of festivities"
Evening Standard
"An exciting programme of free family entertainment" Time Out
"A veritable plethora of colourful events" The Times
General Information:
Maintaining a strong classical programme on both sides of the river, the festival will include more of the free public spectacle events for which it is noted

Hampton Court Palace Festival

Type of Festival: **Music**
Contact: **Jamie Jeeves**
Address:
IM9
3 Burlington Lane
Hampton Court
London W4 2TH
Tel. No: **0181 233 5847**
Fax No: **0181 233 5801**
Date(s) of Festival:
11th - 20th June 1998
Times of Festival:
7.30pm but times do vary
Cost for Adults: **£29.50 - £85**
Tickets available from:
TicketMaster: 0171 3444444
Routes by Car:
A3 from Central London then follow the AA signs
Train/Other:
Hampton Court Palace Station
Venue: **Hampton Court**
Facilities (Parking): **Free**
Historical Background:
6th year of this internationally celebrated classical music festival

Islington International Festival

Type of Festival:
Multi Disciplinary Arts
Contact: **Catherine Reiser**
Address:
**9 Islington Green,
Islington
London N1 ZXH**
Tel. No: **0171 354 2535**
Fax No: **0171 354 4282**
Date(s) of Festival:
15th - 27th June 1998
Cost for Adults:
£12.50. Final day is free
Special discounts:
OAPs, UB40s, students: £8.50
Tickets available from:
Festival Office: 0171 354 2535
Routes by Car:
A1 to Islington
Train/Other:
Highbury & Islington, North London line
Venue:
Upper Street, Islington and surrounding area
Facilities (Parking): **Limited parking**
Facilities (Disabled):
Access for disabled
What's On:
Two week celebration of contemporary art culminating with a grand finale firework display showcasing the best of local and international street performance, dance, music and contemporary art
Historical Background:
Started in 1995 and now in its 4th year. Started as a way to animate the urban landscape
Media/Public Comments:
**"An orgy of entertainment"
The Big Issue**

General Information:
1998's festival highlights the UK premiere of Que Cir Que - (French avant garde circus), comedy, cabaret, poetry events in world famous 1920's Spiegel tent. Also Martin Parr's photographic exhibition of West Bay in Dorset, sited in Islington Museum

Festival of Artist Bears

Type of Festival: **Teddy Bear**
Contact: **Frances Duncan**
Address:
**Hugglets Publishing
P O Box 290
Brighton
East Sussex
BN2 1DR**
Tel. No: **01273 697974**
Fax No: **01273 626255**
Date(s) of Festival:
23rd May 1999
Times of Festival:
12noon - 4.30pm
Cost for Adults: **£4**
Cost for Children: **Under 16s £2**
Special discounts:
Family (2 adults and 2 children) £10
Tickets available from:
Hugglets Publishing: see above cheques, Visa, MasterCard accepted
Train/Other:
Kensington High Street Tube
Venue:
Kensington Town Hall, Hornton Street, Kensington, London
Facilities (Parking):
Easy parking under the venue
Facilities (Disabled):
Facilities for disabled people to reach all parts of the venue
What's On:

Over 100 stands showing hand made artist bears, many one-offs, limited editions and show specials. Suppliers of bear making components and fabrics. Opportunity to meet leading bear makers from the UK and around the world

Historical Background:
Previously this festival was held in Stratford-upon-Avon but outgrew the venue. The only festival devoted to bear artists

General Information:
Join the Teddy Bear Association. Privileges include free early entry to all the fairs plus a copy of the new Teddy Bear Guide and an exclusive enamel badge. Details from Hugglets Publishing

Teddies Festival

Type of Festival: **Teddy Bear**
Contact: **Frances Duncan**
Address:
**Hugglets Publishing
P O Box 290
Brighton
East Sussex
BN2 IDR**
Tel. No: **01273 697974**
Fax No: **01273 626255**
Date(s) of Festival:
30th August 1998
Times of Festival: **12noon - 4.30pm**
Cost for Adults: **£4**
Cost for Children: **Under 16s £2**
Special discounts:
Family ticket (2 adults and 2 children) £10
Tickets available from:
Hugglets Publishing (see above)
Routes by Car:
Train/Other:
Kensington High Street
Venue:

Kensington Town Hall, Hornton Street, Kensington, London
Facilities (Parking):
Easy parking under the Town Hall
Facilities (Disabled):
Easy access for disabled plus good facilities
What's On:
150 exhibitors with thousands of bears for sale. Antique, modern, one-offs, limited editions and show specials. Repairs, books, accessories
Historical Background:
The biggest and the original Teddy Bear Fair now in its 10th year. All the leading shops and makers from the UK plus many guests from overseas
General Information:
 Join the Teddy Bear Association. Privileges include free entry to all the fairs at earlier time of 10.30am plus a copy of 1998 UK Teddy Bear Guide and lots more

Winter Bearfest

Type of Festival: **Teddy Bear**
Contact: **Frances Duncan**
Address:
**Hugglets Publishing
P O Box 290
Brighton
East Sussex
BN2 IDR**
Tel. No: **01273 697974**
Fax No: **01273 626255**
Date(s) of Festival:
28th February 1999
Times of Festival: **12 noon - 4.30pm**
Cost for Adults: **£4**
Cost for Children: **Under 16s £2**
Special discounts:
Family ticket (2 adults and 2 children) £10
Tickets available from:

Hugglets Publishing (see above)
Train/Other:
Kensington High Street
Venue:
Kensington Town Hall, Hornton Street, Kensington, London
Facilities (Parking):
Easy parking under the Town Hall
Facilities (Disabled):
Easy access for disabled people plus good facilities
What's On:
Enjoy a fun packed day amidst more than 10,000 Teddy Bear and items of Bearaphenalia! 150 exhibitors spread across 5 Halls offering bears both old and modern
Historical Background:
This will be the 10th Winter Bearfest. One of the originals and still one of the best featuring the best UK shops, old bear dealers, makers and guests from overseas
General Information:
Join the Teddy Bear Association. Privileges include free entry to all the fairs at earlier time of 10.30am plus a copy of 1998 UK Teddy Bear Guide and lots more

London Beat Sessions

Type of Festival: **Music, Jazz**
Contact: **Paul Vials/Anne Marie**
Address:
The Blue Note Club
1 Hoxton Street
London
N1 6NU
Tel. No: **0171 729 8440**
Fax No: **0171 729 4857**
Date(s) of Festival:
10th - 20th September 1998
Times of Festival: **All day**
Cost for Adults: **Free - £30**
Tickets available from: **TBC**

Train/Other:
Tube to Oxford Circus, Tottenham Court Road, Leicester Square
Venues:
Soho, Shoreditch, Royal Albert Hall, Ronnie Scotts, Blue Note, London Astoria, The Atlantic Bar, Club 333, The Lux Cinema, The Canteloupe, Moving Image Gallery
Facilities (Parking):
Check each venue
What's On:
Live jazz, art exhibitions, jamming on streets, Finley Quaye, Nuyorican Soul, Roni Size, Courtney Pine, Georgie Fame, Jamiroquai (TBC) and lots more
Historical Background:
1st year of festival. LBS is currently in negotiations with Jazz FM to ensure that the festival is well promoted
General Information:
Exclusive performances will be staged every lunchtime in Soho Square while live music will also be heard at over 12 different venues around Soho all day on street corners or outside bars, all free of charge

London International Mime Festival

Type of Festival: **Visual Theatre**
Contact:
Helen Lannaghan/Joseph Seelig
Address:
Directors
35 Little Russell Street
London
WC1A 2HH
Tel. No: **0171 637 5661**
Fax No: **0171 323 1151**
Date(s) of Festival:

9th - 24th January 1999
Times of Festival:
Evenings usually 7.45pm or 8pm
Cost for Adults: **From £8.50 - £14**
Cost for Children:
Discounts on some events only
Special discounts:
OAPs, UB40s, students approximately £2 off
Tickets available from: **0171 637 5661**
Venue:
Various throughout London including Royal Festival Hall, ICA, BAC, Circus Space and others
What's On:
16-20 Companies at performances workshops, lectures. Programme of theatre, cabaret and children's events
Historical Background:
Started in 1977
Media/Public Comments:
"A breathtaking range of work which reminds us, just once a year, that theatre should engage all the senses" The Guardian

Notting Hill Carnival

Type of Festival: **Arts and Carnival**
Contact:
Notting Hill Carnival Trust
Address:
Notting Hill
London
Tel. No: **0181 964 0544**
Fax No: **0181 964 0545**
Date(s) of Festival:
30th - 31st August 1998
Times of Festival:
Steelbands Panorama, Saturday 29th August at Hornimans Pleasance in Notting Hill from 7pm - 11.30pm
Cost for Adults: **Free**
Cost for Children: **Free**

Tickets available from:
Not required. Press Office of Notting Hill Carnival Trust open from June 1998
Routes by Car:
London Travel Information: 0171 2221234
Train/Other:
Underground: Notting Hill Gate, Westbourne Park, Bayswater, Queensway, Holland Park. Bus: 7, 12, 18, 23, 31, 36, 52, 94 and 302. Special Express route 12X from Notting Hill Gate - Victoria
Venue:
Streets of Notting Hill, London
Facilities:
Food stalls selling exotic food from all over the world
What's On:
As well as the procession of costume soca and steel bands, which winds its way over a route of 3 miles, the area plays host to 45 licensed static sound systems, each playing their own soca, reggae, jazz, soul, hiphop, funk music, hundreds of street stalls
Historical Background:
1998 is the Carnivals 33rd year. It began from the energies of black immigrants from the Caribbean, particularly Trinidad where the carnival tradition is very strong and from people living locally who dreamt of creating a festival to bring people together
Media/Public Comments:
The Carnival is the largest arts festival in Europe and in carnival terms is second only to Rio. Three live stages featuring local bands, top international artistes and music from all over the world This year franchised to Radio One, Kiss

FM and SA Square

General Information:

In recent years the carnival has grown reflecting our multi culture with groups participating from Afghanistan, Khurdistan, Bangladesh, the Philippines and many other places as well as from the Caribbean, Africa, South and Central America

Great British Beer Festival

Type of Festival: **Beer**

Contact: **Campaign for Real Ale**

Address:

230 Hatfield Road,
St Albans
Hertfordshire

Tel. No: **01727 867201**

Fax No: **01727 867670**

Date(s) of Festival:

4th - 8th August 1998

Times of Festival:

Tuesday: 5pm - 10.30pm
Wednesday: 11.30am - 3pm
Thursday: 11.30am - 3pm
Friday: 11.30am -10.30pm
Saturday: 11am - 7pm

Cost for Adults:

Varies from £1 - £5 for members; £1.50 - £6 for non-members

Cost for Children:

Under 18s not allowed

Special discounts:

Season tickets covering all sessions: £12.50 for members, £15 for non-members. Advance special prices available, members only day tickets for both sessions, Wednesday or Thursday; £4

Tickets available from:

The door or call: 01727 867670

Train/Other:

Olympia is a very well known exhibition centre in West London, easily reached by tube, train or bus

Venue: **Olympia**

Facilities (Parking):

Family room where accompanied children can stay. Entertainment laid on in the family room, which last year closed at 9pm (this is not a supervised creche). Hot and cold food served at all times. Seating for over 1000 people

What's On:

Largest selection of real ales, ciders, perries, and imported beers found under one roof. Live music every session in the National Hall. Hank Wangford will be performing on the Thursday 6th August

Historical Background:

21st Anniversary of the festival. The festival is entirely run by volunteers from CAMRA, the Campaign for Real Ale

Media/Public Comments:

For full information about UK breweries and pubs in London purchase the 1998 Good Beer Guide (£10.99 from CAMRA + postage outside the UK). This lists all UK Breweries and 5000 pubs recommended for the quality of their beer

General Information:

Champion Beer of Britain, the most important beer competition in Britain is judged and announced just before the festival opens to the public on Tuesday. 1997 Overall Champion: Mordue Workie Ticket

Pride Arts Festival

Type of Festival: **The Arts**
Contact: **Tom Brooks**
Address: **Pride Arts Festival Ltd**
BM PAF
London
WCIN 3XX
Tel. No: **0171 737 5763**
Fax No: **0171 737 5763**
Date(s) of Festival:
20th June - 12th July 1998
Tickets available from:
Pride Art Festival
Venue:
50 venues throughout Greater London
What's On:
Covering 50 events of interest to lesbian and gay people in London. Cabaret, theatre, film, visual arts, The club scene and spoken word
Historical Background:
Founded in 1995 as a volunteer, non profit making organisation, it has established itself as one of the biggest Gay Arts Festivals in Europe
General Information:
1998 highlights include: Concert by London Gay Symphony Orchestra, Gay Art Installation in Whitechapel, Queenies Lesbian beauty contest and the Warhol retrospective at the Barbican Art Gallery

Leap into Dance

Type of Festival: **Dance**
Contact: **Nigel Cutting**
Address:
London Borough of Richmond
Langholme Lodge
146 Petersham Road
Richmond
London
TW10 6UX
Tel. No: **0181 831 6138**
Fax No: **0181 940 7568**
Date(s) of Festival:
Early Spring 1999 (dates TBC)
Times of Festival: **Various**
Cost for Adults: **Various**
Tickets available from:
Richmond Theatre, Old Town Hall Richmond
Venue:
Various venues within Richmond
Facilities (Disabled):
Disabled access to most events
What's On:
A wide range of dance performances and workshops plus social dance events eg. ceilidhs, tea dances. Featuring everything from ballet to ballroom, contemporary to cossack; all sorts of dance for all sorts of people
Historical Background:
Founded in 1992. Now one of the Country's largest broad based dance festivals

Upstream Jazz

Type of Festival: **Music**
Contact: **Nigel Cutting**
Address:
London Borough of Richmond
Langholme Lodge
146 Petersham Road
Richmond
London
TW10 6UX
Tel. No: **0181 831 6138**
Fax No: **0181 940 7568**
Date(s) of Festival:
6th - 7th June 1998
Times of Festival: **1pm - 8pm**
Cost for Adults: **Free**
Cost for Children: **Free**
Tickets available from: **Not required**
Routes by Car: **Close to M3 and M4**

Train/Other:
Richmond Station (frequent trains from Waterloo). Plus District Line Underground
Venue: **Richmond Riverside**
Facilities (Parking): **Town parking**
What's On:
Top British contemporary jazz bands including Indo Jazz Fusions, Zubop, Clare Hurst, The Soothsayers . . .
Historical Background:
Founded in 1994

On the Edge

Type of Festival: **Music**
Contact: **Nigel Cutting**
Address:
**London Borough of Richmond
Langholme Lodge
146 Petersham Road
Richmond
London
TW10 6UX**
Tel. No: **0181 831 6138**
Fax No: **0181 940 7568**
Date(s) of Festival:
1st - 2nd August 1998
Times of Festival: **1pm - 6pm**
Cost for Adults: **Free**
Cost for Children: **Free**
Tickets available from:
Not required
Routes by Car: **Close to M3 and M4**
Train/Other:
Richmond Station and District Line Underground
Venue: **Richmond Riverside**
Facilities (Parking): **Town parking**
What's On:
Top folk and acoustic roots bands from Britain and around the world
Historical Background:
Founded in 1995

Book Now

Type of Festival: **Literature**
Contact: **Nigel Cutting**
Address:
**London Borough of Richmond
Langholm Lodge
146 Petersham Road
Richmond
London
TW10 6UX**
Tel. No: **0181 831 6138**
Fax No: **0181 940 7568**
Date(s) of Festival:
1st - 30th November 1998
Times of Festival: **Various**
Cost for Adults: **Various**
Tickets available from:
**Old Town Hall
Whittaker Avenue
Richmond**
Venue:
Various venues in Richmond and Twickenham
Facilities (Disabled):
Disabled access to most venues
What's On:
A range of talks and discussions featuring major writers of serious fiction. Poetry and biography plus workshops, exhibitions and much more
Historical Background:
Founded in 1997
General Information:
The largest annual literature festival in London

London Bach Festival

Type of Festival: **Music**
Contact:
**Mrs Margaret Steinitz
Festival Director**
Address:
London Bach Society

73 High Street
Old Oxted
Surrey
RH8 9LN
Tel. No: **01883 717372**
Fax No: **01883 715851**
Date(s) of Festival:
**31st October -14th November
1998**
Times of Festival: **Daily**
Cost for Adults:
**£5 - £25. Become a friend of LBS
and be eligible for discounts, pri-
ority bookings. Annual
subscription: £25(single) £30 (fam-
ily) £20 (over 60s), students free**
Special discounts:
Yes on application
Tickets available from:
**London Bach Society or from the
venues**
Venue:
**Royal College of Music
Royal Academy of Music
St Bartholomew the Great
St John's Smith Square**
Facilities (Parking):
Limited parking: see programme
Facilities (Disabled): **See programme**
What's On:
**Programme available from 1st
September. Festival sponsors in-
clude Belmont International Ltd,
Pairing Scheme Award Winners**
Historical Background:
**The London Bach Festival was
founded in 1990 to develop, extend
and foster the purpose of the Lon-
don Bach Society**
General Information:
**Concerts are 100% professional. Also
included is an education programme
and community programme**

Southwark Festival

Type of Festival:
Music, Arts, Community
Contact: **Michele McLusky**
Address:
**Southwark Festival Association
6 Southwark Street
London
SE1 1TQ**
Tel. No: **0171 4037474**
Date(s) of Festival:
**10th October - 9th November
1998**
Times of Festival:
Lunchtimes, evenings, weekends
Cost for Adults:
**Concerts: free lunchtimes, charge-
able evenings. Exhibitions: free.
Prices available via Box Office**
Special discounts:
**Discounts available for UB40s,
OAPs, students**
Tickets available from:
**Southwark Tourist Office: 0171
4037400**
Routes by Car:
RAC signs to London Bridge
Train/Other:
**London Bridge Station Tube/Bus
London Bridge and Borough**
Venue: **Southwark**
Facilities (Parking): **City parking.**
Facilities (Disabled):
**Most venues have disabled access.
For certain venues it is advisable
to phone in advance. Attendants
can assist.**
What's On:
**Exhibitions, concerts, community
events, food fair, workshops,
masterclasses, cookery food
classes etc**
Historical Background:
**Formerly a series of concerts in
Southwark now grown to a series**

of events covering a month. Festival also celebrates the 25th year of Britain's membership of the European Community

General Information:

Concerts: Southwark Cathedral, Guys Hospital, St George the Martyr, Borough Hayes Gallery

Spitalfields Festival

Type of Festival:

Early and Contemporary Music

Contact:

Luke O' Shaughnessy
Assistant Manager

Address:

Christchurch
Commercial Street
London
E1 6LY

Tel. No: **0171 377 0287**

Fax No: **0171 247 0494**

Date(s) of Festival:

3rd - 24th June 1998

Times of Festival:

Events throughout the day and evening concerts

Cost for Adults:

Ranges from £3 - £25. Also free events

Special discounts:

20% discounts for groups; £2 off top bands for UB40s and OAPs

Tickets available from:

Festival Box Office Hotline:
0171 377 1362

Train/Other:

Liverpool Street and Underground/Mainline 5 mins walk

Venue:

Christchurch, Commercial St, Spitalfields, London E1 6LY

Facilities (Parking):

Parking in Whites Row car park opposite the church

Facilities (Disabled):

Full access for disabled and lift for wheelchairs. Helpers for partially sighted

What's On:

Recitals, ensembles, choirs of St Johns College, Cambridge and Winchester Cathedral, vocal, festival bands, readings, lectures, education and community work

Historical Background:

Festival was founded in 1975

St Ceciliatide International Festival of Music

Type of Festival: **Music**

Contact:

Bernard Rapson
Society of Gentlemen

Address:

Bank Cottage
Old Forge Lane
Preston Capes
Northamptonshire
London
NN11 3TD

Tel. No: **01327 361380**

Fax No: **01327 361415**

E-mail: **Fmusical@aol.com**

Date(s) of Festival:

15th - 22nd November 1998

Times of Festival: **6.30pm for 7pm**

Cost for Adults:

£20 concert. £70 dinner

Cost for Children: **£14 concert**

Special discounts:

Groups (4+) £14 concert only

Tickets available from:

Bernard Rapson (see above)

Train/Other:

St Paul's Underground Station

Venue:

Stationer's Hall, Ave Maria Lane,

London

Facilities (Parking):
NCP car park in Ave Maria Lane, off Ludgate Hill
Facilities (Disabled):
Disabled access
What's On:
Fiori Musicali, Monica Huggett, Natalie Clein, Julius Drake, Scottish Early Music Consort, Lindsay String Quartet, first class music, food and wine at one of the capital's most beautiful and historic livery halls
Historical Background:
A week long celebration of the feast of St Cecilia, patron saint of music - revival of the 17th century tradition
Media/Public Comments:
"A civilised little festival" The Independent
"A splendid and appropriate venue." The Times
"Classical music without the boring bits"
"Superbly played" The Express
General Information:
An opportunity to hear leading artists from around the world in elegant surroundings with optional dinner by candlelight afterwards. First class food and fine wines. Presented in association with the Financial Times

Stoke Newington Midsummer Festival

Type of Festival: **Multi Arts**
Contact:
Fiona Fieber
Festival Programmer
Address:
59 Lynaston Road
Stoke Newington

London
N16 0EB
Tel. No: **0171 923 1599**
Fax No: **0171 923 1599**
Date(s) of Festival:
15th - 20th June 1998
Times of Festival: **Various**
Cost for Adults: **Various**
Tickets available from:
Enquiries: 0171 9231599
Train/Other:
Stoke Newington main line station. Also buses No. 73,106,149
Venue:
Various venues across Stoke Newington
Facilities (Disabled):
Contact Arts Line: 0171 388 2227 for disability information
What's On:
Music, theatre, comedy, dance, live art and poetry
Historical Background:
6 years old and offers a platform to Hackney-based performers and artists in alternative spaces. In 1997 there were 1200 performers/ artists and 130+ events
Media/Public Comments:
"The Edinburgh Festival of North London" Big Issue
General Information:
Organised by local artists and performers this festival has a huge voluntary input

Streets of London Festival 1998

Type of Festival: **Street Arts**
Contact: **Karen Poley**
Address:
Zap Productions
7a Middle Street
Brighton
East Sussex

BS2 2SR
Tel. No: **01273 821588**
Fax No: **01273 206960**
Date(s) of Festival:
Mid June - mid September 1998
Times of Festival: **All day**
Cost for Adults: **Free**
Cost for Children: **Free**
Tickets available from:
Not required. Call: 01273 821588
for brochure (from mid June)
Venues:
Covent Garden, Islington, Lewi-
sham, Kingston, Canary Wharf,
and others
Facilities (Parking):
Limited London parking
What's On:
Music, dance, circus, comedy, thea-
tre, visual arts, stilted walkabouts,
educational workshops including.
Circus skills and carnival props
Historical Background:
Part of the national Street Arts
Festival inspired by the French tra-
dition of free street entertainment

Thames Festival

Type of Festival: **River**
Contact: **Adrian Evans**
Address:
Thames Festival
99 Upper Ground, South Bank
London
SE1 9PP
Date(s) of Festival:
13th September 1998
Times of Festival: **From 7pm**
Cost for Adults: **Free**
Cost for Children: **Free**
Tickets available from: **Not required**
Venue:
Starts Victoria Embankment
Hungerford Bridge
Facilities (Parking):

City parking. Advisable to park and
ride in via the Underground or
take the bus
What's On:
Procession involving thousands of
people carrying lit objects
Historical Background:
The procession imagines a parade
of glorious images sent as poetic en-
voys from rivers around the world -
both real and mystical
General Information:
The procession starts on Victoria
Embankment by Hungerford
Bridge, proceeds east crosses
Blackfriars Bridge, runs the length
of Upper Grounds and finishes on
Waterloo Bridge

Haydn Festival

Type of Festival: **Music**
Contact:
Alison Godlee
Royal Northern College of Music
Address:
The Grange
Clay Lane
Handworth
Cheshire
Tel. No: **01625 530140**
Date(s) of Festival:
8th -10th January 1999
Times of Festival:
First concert at 2pm. Last concert
10th January at 7.30pm
Cost for Adults: **TBC**
Tickets available from:
Box Office: 0161 907 5278/5279
Routes by Car:
Close to Manchester City Centre
via motorway network
Train/Other:
Manchester Piccadilly
Venue:
Royal Northern College of Music,

124 Oxford Road, Manchester
Facilities (Disabled):
Access for disabled
What's On:
All 71 String Quartets by Haydn to be performed in one weekend - by professionals, amateurs, young and old. Recitals, Master Classes, seminars 'Haydn Seek' for children
Historical Background:
First of its kind intended to be an annual event. Haydn in 1999. Another composer, possibly Shostakovich, in 2000

GREATER MANCHESTER

"Streets Ahead"

Type of Festival: **Street Arts**
Contact: **Anne Tucker**
Address:
**3 Birch Polygon
Rusholme
Manchester
Greater Manchester
M14 5HX**
Tel. No: **0161 224 0020**
Fax No: **0161 248 9331**
Date(s) of Festival:
1st - 31st May 1999

Times of Festival:
Every weekend and Bank Holiday
Cost for Adults: **Free**
Cost for Children: **Free**
Tickets available from: **Not required**
Routes by Car:
Motorways to Manchester
Venue:
Street festivals in the boroughs of Greater Manchester: Salford, Stockport, Rochdale, Bolton etc
Facilities (Parking):
All sites fully accessible. All festival areas pedestrianized.
Facilities (Disabled):
Toilets for the disabled provided, disabled parking available
What's On:
International events such as street theatre, music, puppets, circus, dance, visual arts, large scale spectacle, fireworks, parades, outdoor dance, parades, etc
Historical Background:
Greater Manchester's millennial festival for everyone. Theme: keeping town centres alive (against threat of Trafford Centre). Families to work the streets at night in safety
General Information:
Festival has a reputation for its wonderful warm atmosphere, its continental feel. A month long Festival that takes place every year in May heralding the onset of summer and outdoor life

Manchester International Caribbean Carnival

Type of Festival:
Music and Carnival
Contact:
Dan Aris/Anthony Brown

Address:
Moss Side and Hulme Business Federation
Greenheys Bus Centre
10 Pencroft Way
Hulme
Manchester
M15 6JJ
Tel. No: **0161 226 0486**
Fax No: **0161 226 0587**
E-mail:
101533.234@compuserve.com
Date(s) of Festival: **12th July 1998**
Times of Festival: **12pm - 9pm**
Cost for Adults: **Free**
Cost for Children: **Free**
Tickets available from: **Not required**
Routes by Car: **A5103**
Venue:
Carnival procession through the streets of Moss Side and Hulme
Facilities (Parking):
Temporary Car park available
What's On:
Calypso, global cuisine, music, carnival floats, showcase of live bands, trading stalls, children's and cultural marquee, spectacular costumes, funfair and much more
Historical Background:
Dynamic development plan to launch the 1998 Caribbean Carnival on a year on year expansion to the Commonwealth Games in 2002. Tony Lloyd MP officially launched the activities to prepare for the "One Love" carnival at Manchester Zion Arts Centre, Hulme
Media/Public Comments:
"Notting Hill of the North"
General Information:
The annual carnival is set to grow dramatically as a 5 year plan unfolds to attract fun and business to the city. By 2002 the carnival at- mosphere will take over in Manchester during the Commonwealth Games

New World Music '98

Type of Festival:
Contemporary Music
Contact:
MalcolmDuffin/Richard Oyarzabal
Address:
World Music Days
48 Princes Street
Manchester
Tel. No: **0161 237 3368**
Fax No: **0161 237 3423**
Date(s) of Festival:
17th - 25th April 1998
Times of Festival: **Various**
Cost for Adults: **Various**
Routes by Car:
All major motorway links
Train/Other:
All train links to Manchester
Venue:
Various venues throughout Manchester
What's On:
Over 50 performances by the world's leading artists and ensembles at venues across the city. Outdoor events, orchestral events, dance and performance, family events, world and UK premieres

Manchester Umbro International

Type of Festival: **Football**
Contact: **David Shepherd**
Address:
Euroworld Wide Events Ltd
The Grange
Holly Road
South Wilmslow
Cheshire
Tel. No: **01625 536609**

Fax No: **01625 536610**
Date(s) of Festival:
26th July 1998 - 1st August 1998
Tickets available from:
EuroWorld Wide Events Ltd
Routes by Car:
Exit end of M56 Motorway
Venue:
**University   sports   field,
Northernden, off M63, Junction 9**
Facilities (Parking):
**Parking available, medical ameni-
ties, refreshments etc**
What's On:
**Manchester United New Museum
and Stadium Tour. Participate in
Football Festival, coaching pro-
gramme with Manchester United
and Manchester City Football
Clubs**
Historical Background:
**First formed by Manchester
United Football Club 6 years ago,
now organised independently as
sponsored by Umbro**
Media/Public Comments:
**"Britain's largest International
Football Festival - 300 teams from
20 nations"**

MERSEYSIDE

Hope Street Festival

Type of Festival: **Arts**
Contact:
The Hope Street Association
Address:
**Liverpool Business School
98 Mount Pleasant
Liverpool
Merseyside
L3 5UZ**
Tel. No: **0151 231 3359**
Date(s) of Festival:
19th - 28th June 1998
Times of Festival: **Various**
Cost for Adults:
**Free except for concerts and
picket event**
Tickets available from:
Liverpool Tourist Information Centre
Venue:
**Various venues in Hope Street, Liv-
erpool including the Philharmonic
Hall, Everyman Bistro, Josephine
Butler car park, The Picket, Ye
Cracke and The Pilgrim, Public
Houses**
Facilities (Parking): **Town Parking**
Facilities (Disabled):
All events "wheelchair friendly"
What's On:
Puddingfest competition, craft

stalls, schools concert, picket event, stalls, poetry, **BBQ, quiz, World Cup screening, lots of ale! Banners competition, art exhibition, stand up comedy . . .**

Historical Background:
The festival is entering into its 3rd year and wishing to widen the spectrum so that there are events for children; gigs and DJ nights for students and young people; films, classical music and drama and poetry as an alternative night out

Brouhaha International

Type of Festival: **Street Theatre**
Contact:
Karen Miller - Administrator
Address:
Brouhaha International
Graphic House
107 Duke Street
Liverpool
Merseyside
L1 4JR
Tel. No: **0151 709 3334**
Fax No: **0151 709 4994**
Date(s) of Festival:
1st - 10th August 1998
Times of Festival:
Throughout the day
Cost for Adults: **Free**
Cost for Children: **Free**
Tickets available from:
Festival Hotline: 0151 709 3334
Routes by Car:
M62 into City Centre
Train/Other: **Liverpool Lime Street**
Venue: **Liverpool City Centre**
Facilities (Parking): **Parking available**
Facilities (Disabled):
Mostly pedestrianised. Disabled access to all venues
What's On:
Drumming, drama, dance and

comedy from all around the world descend onto the streets of Liverpool. **Presents the best in performance art from across Europe, South Africa and Cuba. Death defying pavement mountaineers, Cuban Conga and more**
Historical Background:
In 1995 it was decided to take this festival from the theatres of Liverpool onto the streets of Liverpool. Performers from all over the world attend this Brouhaha (Victorian "a great big to do")

Liverpool Cathedral Festival

Type of Festival: **Music**
Contact:
The Festival Administrator
Address:
6 Cathedral Close
Liverpool
Merseyside
L1 7BR
Tel. No: **0151 708 8471**
Fax No: **0151 708 8471**
Date(s) of Festival:
2nd - 19th July 1998
Times of Festival:
7.30pm for all concerts
Cost for Adults: **£6 - £20.**
Special discounts:
Discounts for groups
Tickets available from:
The Festival Administrator (see above)
Routes by Car:
M62, M53 to Liverpool
Train/Other:
Mainline and Suburban stations within 10 mins
Venue: **Liverpool Cathedral**
Facilities (Parking): **Good parking**
What's On:

Choral Baroque concert, Bach organ recital, guitar/organ concert, close harmony, cathedral lectures
Historical Background:
12th year of festival to celebrate the anniversary of the foundation of the Cathedral

Listen to Africa (Africa Oye)

Type of Festival:
African, Caribbean Latin Music
Contact:
Kenny Murray
Project Director
Address:
2A Franceys Street
Liverpool
Merseyside
Tel. No:
0151 7086200
0151 709 7102 (24 hrs)
Date(s) of Festival:
18th - 21st June 1998
Times of Festival:
1pm - 9pm; 9pm - 2am
Cost for Adults:
Free (except late night events)
Special discounts:
Concessions available for OAPs, UB40s, students
Tickets available from:
Cream Liverpool: 0151 708 9979
Routes by Car:
M62 into Liverpool from M6
Train/Other: **Liverpool Lime Street**
Venue:
Various venues on Merseyside
Facilities (Parking): **City Parking**
Facilities (Disabled):
Access for disabled
What's On:
Soukous dance party, food and Latin dance party, music and Fuji

dance party, 3 bands downtown in Concert Square, 6 Bands in Birkenhead Park
Historical Background:
Founded in 1990 it remains the only black music festival in the UK. Oye is a unique blend of free events and late night club African ambience performances, at the world famous Cream, among others. Oye is known throughout Europe for quality and sheer class
Media/Public Comments:
"African music is Oye" Radio One
General Information:
Best kept secret Africa Oye is meshed into Liverpool's unique cultural heritage. Oye brings world class black artists from Africa and the black diaspora

NORFOLK

Lakeside Jazz Festival

Type of Festival: **Music**
Contact: **The National Trust**
Address:
Events Office
Blickling Hall
Blickling
Norfolk
NR11 6NF

Tel. No: **01263 731660**
Fax No: **01263 731660**
Date(s) of Festival:
17th - 19th July 1998
Times of Festival:
17 and 18th: 6pm start
19th: 11am - 2pm
Cost for Adults:
Advance tickets: 17th £14, 18th £12.50, 19th £5
Tickets available from:
Events Office: 01263 731660
Routes by Car:
1 mile west of Aylsham on B1354, signposted off A140 Norwich to Cromer Road
Train/Other:
Norwich to Wroxham, Narrow Gauge from Wroxham to Aylsham (1 mile from Blickling)
Venue: **Blickling Hall**
Facilities (Parking): **Free Parking**
Facilities (Disabled):
Full access for the disabled
What's On: **Jazz and blues bands**
Historical Background:
Third annual event

Festival of Norfolk Food and Drink

Type of Festival: **Food and Drink**
Contact: **David Manning**
Address:
Aylesham Agricultural Show Assistant
Ebridge Farm
Witton
North Walsham
Norfolk
Tel. No: **01692 403069**
Date(s) of Festival:
8th - 9th May 1999
Times of Festival: **10.30 - 4pm**
Cost for Adults: **£2.50**

Cost for Children:
Free for accompanied children
Special discounts: **None**
Tickets available from: **The door**
Train/Other: **Norwich Station**
Venue:
Blickling Hall, Aylsham, Norwich
Facilities (Parking): **Free parking**
Facilities (Disabled):
Easy access for disabled
What's On:
Cooking demonstrations, local food exhibitions, army field kitchen, scouts campfire cooking
Historical Background:
Third annual event

Downham Market Festival

Type of Festival: **Magic and Mystery**
Contact: **Margaret Fox - Secretary**
Address:
Downham Market Festival Committee
19 Beech Road
Downham Market
Norfolk
PE38 9PH
Tel. No: **01366 382963**
Date(s) of Festival:
24th - 31st May 1998
Times of Festival: **Free**
Cost for Adults: **Free**
Tickets available from: **Not required**
Routes by Car:
Due south from Kings Lynn A10 then A1122
Venue:
Downham Market Town Centre
Facilities (Parking):
Town parking. Food stalls etc
What's On:
Concerts, coffee mornings, dances, French café day, band concerts,

arts exhibition. **Main event is Carnival Day which includes arena events, parade of decorated floats, bands, walking groups, decorated cycles, charity stalls, children's entertainment etc**

General Information:

There is another event on Saturday 30th May on the Howdale with a host of participating events plus an exemption dog show and stalls

Poetry Festival

Type of Festival: **Literature**
Contact: **Tony Ellis**
Address:
19 Tuesday Market Place
Kings Lynn
Norfolk
PE20 1JW
Tel. No: **01553 691661**
Fax No: **01553 691779**
Date(s) of Festival:
26th - 28th September 1998
Times of Festival:
26th 7.30pm - 9.30pm
27th 11am - 10pm
28th 11.30am - 5pm
Cost for Adults: **£6.50 per event**
Cost for Children: **Half price**
Special discounts:
£1 off for UB40s, OAPs and students
Tickets available from:
Mr Tony Ellis (see above)
Routes by Car:
From London M11 and A10
Train/Other:
From London Kings Cross
Venue:
Thoresby College, South Quay, Kings Lynn
Facilities (Parking):
Plenty of parking available
What's On:

8 top class writers will stay in Kings Lynn for the weekend and take part in readings and discussion sessions. Also enjoy the sights of this ancient market and seafaring town

Historical Background:

1998 will be the 14th annual festival originally founded with the help of the late George MacBeth. Annual sponsorship from Janneau Armagnac

Media/Public Comments:

"The Poetry Festival is established as one of the finest in the country where the audience has the opportunity of seeing various aspects of the poet in action at close quarters"

Fiction Festival

Type of Festival: **Literature**
Contact: **Tony Ellis**
Address:
19 Tuesday Market Place
Kings Lynn
Norfolk
PE30 1JW
Tel. No: **01553 691661**
Fax No: **01553 691779**
Date(s) of Festival:
12th - 14th March 1999
Times of Festival: **Various**
Cost for Adults:
£6.50 per event. £28 for season ticket
Cost for Children:
Half price for single events
Special discounts:
OAPs, UB40s and students £1 off
Tickets available from:
Tony Ellis (see above)
Routes by Car:
From London M11 and A10
Train/Other:
London Kings Cross direct line
Venue: **Town Hall, Kings Lynn**

Facilities (Parking):
Plenty of parking available
Facilities (Disabled):
The Town Hall has lift access for disabled people and the loop for hearing aids
What's On:
Readings and discussions, new writing events. Top class writers will stay in Kings Lynn for the whole weekend and take part in various events
Historical Background:
1999 will be the 11th annual festival
Media/Public Comments:
The festival is sponsored by Macallan and highly regarded by writers and audiences alike

Leap

Type of Festival: **Dance**
Contact: **Fiona Carter**
Address:
Norfolk and Norwich Festival Productions
42 - 58 St Georges Street
Norwich
Norfolk
NR3 1AB
Tel. No: **01603 614921**
Fax No: **01603 632303**
Date(s) of Festival:
2nd - 5th July 1998
Times of Festival: **All day**
Cost for Adults:
£6.50 (£6 workshops). Events, free
Cost for Children: **Under 16s £3**
Special discounts:
UB40s, students, OAPs £3.50
Tickets available from:
The Ticket Shop: 01603 764764
Routes by Car:
M11, A11 from London
Train/Other:
Liverpool Street Station to Norwich, Anglian Railways

Venue: **Venues across Norwich**
Facilities (Parking):**Parking stations**
Facilities (Disabled):
Good disabled access to most venues
What's On:
Adzido Pan African Dance Ensemble, RJC Dance Theatre, Jiving Lindy Hoppers, Random Dance Company, Bootleg and Mayhem Youth Dance Companies, dance workshops, Club night and dance project
Historical Background:
Norfolk's first ever professional dance festival

Norfolk and Norwich Festival

Type of Festival:
Music, Comedy, Theatre, Film
Contact: **Fiona Carter**
Address:
Norfolk and Norwich Festival Productions
42-58 St Georges Street
Norwich
Norfolk
NR3 1AB
Tel. No: **01603 614921**
Fax No: **01603 632303**
Date(s) of Festival:
7th -18th October 1998
Times of Festival:
Lunchtimes, evening and late night events
Cost for Adults:
£2 - £28. Some free events
Special discounts:
Concessions available for UB40s, students and Registered Disabled.
Tickets available from:
The Ticket Shop: 01603 764764
Routes by Car:
M11, A11 from London
Train/Other:

Liverpool Street Station to Norwich, Anglia Railways
Venue:
Various across Norfolk and Norwich
Facilities (Parking): **Available**
Facilities (Disabled):
Most venues have good disabled access
What's On:
St Petersburg Symphony Orchestra, Schidlof Quartet, Purcell's "Indian Queen", Courtney Pine, Tubby the Tuba, Peter and the Wolf, De Palfi the Clown, jazz cruises, guided walks, Barry Douglas pianist, Philharmonia Orchestra with Steven Isserlis
Historical Background:
Oldest City festival in Britain. It is 226 years old
Media/Public Comments:
"the Norfolk and Norwich Festival is fast becoming one of the most exciting arts festivals in the UK." Chief Executive of Eastern Arts Board

Walpole St Peters Church Flower Festival

Type of Festival: **Flower**
Contact: **Reverend A R Treen**
Address:
The Rectory
Walpole St Peter
Norfolk
Tel. No: **01945 780252**
Date(s) of Festival:
30th May - 5th June 1998
Times of Festival: **10am - 6pm**
Cost for Adults: **Free**
Cost for Children: **Free**
Tickets available from:
Not required
Routes by Car:

Clearly signposted look out for signs to Walpole off the A17 and A47 between Kings Lynn and Wisbech
Venue:
St Peters Church, Walpole St Peters
Facilities (Parking): **Free**
Facilities (Disabled):
Disabled facilities available
What's On:
Magnificent blooms beautifully displayed. Stalls and popular catering outside the building
Historical Background:
37th annual festival - oldest and grandest festival of its kind
Media/Public Comments:
Featured on Anglia and Yorkshire TV in 1997
General Information:
Church is recognised as a masterpiece of 14th century architecture

NORTHAMPTONSHIRE

Northampton Balloon Festival

Type of Festival: **Hot Air Balloons**
Contact: **The Events Office**
Address:
Northampton Borough Council
Cliftonville House

Bedford Road
Northampton
Northamptonshire
NN4 7NR
Tel. No: **01604 238791**
Fax No: **01604 238796**
E-mail:
events@northampton.gov.uk
Date(s) of Festival:
14th - 16th August 1998
Times of Festival:
Balloon flights 6am - 6pm daily.
Main entertainment; Friday and
Saturday: 11am - 10.30pm
Sunday: 11am - 7pm
Cost for Adults: **Free**
Cost for Children: **Free**
Tickets available from:
Not required
Routes by Car:
AA signs guide visitors from all major routes into the town
Train/Other:
Site 15 mins walk from Northampton Station
Venue:
Northampton Racecourse Park, Kettering Road, Northampton
Facilities (Parking):
Main on site car park £7.50; Early Bird parking £2; coaches £15
Facilities (Disabled):
Designated disabled parking £1. Wheelchair loan scheme
What's On:
Mass Balloon launches up to 90 Balloons. Daily arena entertainment including White Helmets motorcycle display team, Anchor men Drum Corps, Devils Horsemen, Chariots of Fire. Also village green entertainment for all the family, trade fair, children's entertainment
Historical Background:
Festival is now in its 9th year and

has become the premier event of
its kind in the country
General Information:
The festival's international reputation attracts over 200,000 visitors to watch mass ascents by balloons of all shapes and sizes. The magic of the evening balloons glows and grand firework displays should not be missed

GTI Festival

Type of Festival: **Motor Sports**
Contact: **Brian Burrows**
Address:
Enterprise House
133 Blyth Road
Hayes
Middlesex UB3 1AD
Tel. No: **0181 573 8761**
Fax No: **0181 561 9114**
Date(s) of Festival:
8th - 9th August 1998
Times of Festival:
10am Saturday - 6pm Sunday
Cost for Adults: **£10 per day**
Cost for Children: **Free**
Tickets available from:
Brian Burrows (see above)
Routes by Car:
M1 Junction 14, signposted
Train/Other:
Bedford or Northampton
Venue:
Santa Pod Raceway, Podington, nr Wellingborough
Facilities (Parking):
Loads of parking including camping if required
What's On:
GTI drag racing, GTI concours, trade stands and side shows
Historical Background:
The festival is 6 years old

Bug Jam

Type of Festival:
VW Beetle Festival
Contact: **Now Promotions**
Address:
Santa Pod Raceway
Unit 5
Airfield Road
Podington
Wellingborough
Northamptonshire
NN29 7XA
Tel. No: **01234 782828**
Fax No: **01234 782818**
Date(s) of Festival:
24th - 26th July 1998
Times of Festival:
9am start. All day.
Cost for Adults:
£28 on the gate. £24 in advance
Cost for Children:
12-16s half price. Under 11s free
Tickets available from:
Further details from Ian Whitehorn (see above)
Routes by Car:
Junctions 14/15/16 off M1 (RAC sign posted)
Train/Other:
St Pancras to Wellingborough
Venue:
Santa Pod Raceway, Airfield Road, Podington
Facilities (Parking):
On site parking, hot showers, caterers, camping
Facilities (Disabled):
Disabled viewing,
What's On:
VW drag racing, jet cars, traders, 5 arenas of music, comedy tent, BMX/skate ramps, autojumble, side shows, funfair, "Miss VW" contest, live entertainment. Focus of the event is the quarter-mile dragstrip.
Historical Background:
When the first VW event was staged in 1987 it triggered the whole Cal-look Beetle boom in Britain and some 12 years later, it's still going strong
Media/Public Comments:
"The best festival I have ever been to" Michael Eavis
"The Bug Jam at Santa Pod remains the focal point of the calendar for enthusiasts of the "new-wave" VW scene - enter the gates of the Pod and prepare to be amazed"

NORTHUMBERLAND

Alnwick International

Type of Festival: **Music and Dance**
Contact: **Mr John Moodie**
Address:
11 Daky Balks
Alnwick
Northumberland
NE66 2QE
Tel. No: 01665 602682
Fax No: 01665 602682
Date(s) of Festival:
1st - 8th August 1998

Times of Festival: **10.30am-4.30pm**
Cost for Adults:
Outdoor events are free
Tickets available from:
The Playhouse: 01665 510785
Routes by Car:
30 miles north of Newcastle off main A1 Road
Train/Other:
Alnmouth - Newcastle/Edinburgh. Newcastle airport, Newcastle ferry terminal
Venue: **Alnwick**
Facilities (Parking):
Parking available. Good restaurants
Facilities (Disabled):
Alnwick Tourist Information Office The Shambles Alnwick Northumberland Tel: 01665 510665
What's On:
Traditional music and dancing in the Market Place. Costumes are worn by all dance groups. Over 300 artists, groups from around the world. Enjoy the surrounding countryside, coastline and castles, craft shops, art galleries etc
Historical Background:
This festival has been running since 1976. It started as a 2 day event and evolved into an 8 day event and believed to be the largest independent festival in the UK. Entertainers visit the event from all over the world and perform daily in the market place
Media/Public Comments:
Excellent reports. The media takes an interest in the festival
General Information:
Alnwick is the home of His Grace The Duke of Northumberland and the Castle with its medieval and Italian Renaissance style. The surrounding areas of the Castle were landscaped by Capability Brown

Amble 1998 Sea Fayre Festival

Type of Festival: **Marine and Food**
Contact:
J Aston
Amble Development Trust
Address:
The Fourways
Bridge Street
Amble
Morpeth
Northumberland
Tel. No: **01665 712929**
Fax No: **01665 712707**
Date(s) of Festival:
4th -5th July 1998
Times of Festival:
11am - 4pm both days
Cost for Adults:
Free except Celebrity MasterChef
Routes by Car:
Follow signs to "Amble Braid"
Train/Other:
Nearest Station is Alnmouth approximately 5 miles. There is a bus connection Newcastle/Alnwick
Venue: **Amble**
Facilities (Parking): **Available**
Facilities (Disabled):
Disabled parking available
What's On:
Raft race, beach storm by Royal Engineers, American trucks/ military vehicles, water sports, Puffin cruises, angling, beach casting competition, music, line dancing, Celebrity MasterChef, Junior MasterChef ,"Can't Cook" (audience participation)

Historical Background:
1998 is the festival's 2nd year. Set up as part of secret kingdom Festival of Food(1997) to promote Seafood and Fishing Industry
Media/Public Comments:
"All favourable - looking forward to next one"

Berwick upon Tweed May Day

Type of Festival: **Traditional**
Contact: **Mr Derek Sharman**
Address:
**Berwick May Fair Committee
50 Dean Drive
Tweedmouth
Berwick upon Tweed
Northumberland
TD15 2DQ**
Tel. No: **01289 330218**
Date(s) of Festival:
22nd - 24th May 1999
Times of Festival:
10.30am - 4pm daily
Cost for Adults: **Free**
Cost for Children: **Free**
Tickets available from: **Not required**
Routes by Car:
A1 to Berwick upon Tweed
Train/Other:
East Coast Main line station at Berwick
Venue:
Main Street, Berwick upon Tweed
Facilities (Parking):
Town Centre car parks within 200 metres
What's On:
Traditional street market and Street entertainment. Funfair, crafts, music, children's entertainment, hands-on Victorian science. Motorcycle display on Saturday.

Sunday is a Victorian theme day
Historical Background:
Held by Royal Charter since the Middle Ages
Media/Public Comments:
"Colourful fun day out for all the family in a historic setting"

Hexham Abbey Festival

Type of Festival: **Music and Arts**
Contact: **Kevin Stephens**
Address:
**17 Tynedale Gardens
Stocksfield
Northumberland
NE43 7EZ**
Tel. No: **01661 843347**
Fax No: **01661 844399**
Date(s) of Festival:
19th - 26th September 1998
Times of Festival:
Concerts every evening
Cost for Adults:
Mostly £10 and £12
Cost for Children: **Half price**
Special discounts:
Students and UB40s half price
Tickets available from:
**Queens Hall Box Office:
01434 607272**
Routes by Car:
A69 from Newcastle or Carlisle. A68 from Darlington or Scotland
Train/Other:
Regional Railways NE from Newcastle or Carlisle
Venue:
Hexham Abbey, Beaumont Street, Hexham. Also events at Queens Hall Arts Centre, Beaumont Street, Hexham
Facilities (Parking):
Some car parking in nearby streets, large car park (Wentworth) 5 mins walk

Facilities (Disabled):
Limited disabled facilities at Hexham Abbey. Telephone: 01434 606787 to discuss requirements
What's On:
Classical music, opera, evensong, classic jazz, piano recitals, organ recitals, candlelight concert, festival chorus, Abbey tours and walks, art exhibition, poetry reading
Historical Background:
Leading arts festival of the North region since 1952. Events are focused on the historic Abbey and it is currently developing educational work

The Fourth Hexham Jazz Festival

Type of Festival: **Jazz**
Contact: **Mylee Hall**
Address:
**Queens Hall Arts Centre
Beaumont Street
Hexham
Northumberland
NE46 3LS**
Tel. No: **01434 606 787**
Fax No: **01434 606043**
Date(s) of Festival:
12th - 14th June 1998
Times of Festival: **Various**
Cost for Adults: **Various**
Tickets available from:
Queens Hall Arts Centre Box Office: 01434 607272
Routes by Car:
Via A69 Trunk Road connection M6 at Carlisle and the A1(M) at Newcastle
Train/Other:
Regional railways NE from Newcastle or Carlisle
Venue: **Various venues in Hexham**

Facilities (Parking):
Good town parking. Local hotels and restaurants
What's On:
Chris Blount's New Orleans Jazz Band, Vo-De-O-Do Orchestra, Harlem Hot Stompers, Tyne Valley Stompers, Merseysippi Jazz Band, Chicago Teddy Bears Society Jazz Band, Ben Cohen Hot Seven, Frank Brooker Quartet, Bruce Adams, Alan Barnes and much more
Historical Background:
Encouraged by the fact that audience numbers have been rising by 30 - 40% each year, it has been decided to increase the number of concerts/events from 27 last year to 34 for 1998, all taking place in handy venues within Hexham
General Information:
Hexham is an attractive historic market town 20 miles from Newcastle, 37 miles from Carlisle and only a few miles from the historic Hadrian's Wall, an internationally known World Heritage Site

Kielder Festival and Forest Open Day

Type of Festival: **Forest and Music**
Contact: **Miss Pippa Kirkham**
Address:
**Forest Enterprise
Eals Burn
Bellingham
Northumberland
NE48 2AJ**
Tel. No: **01434 220242**
Fax No: **01434 220756**
Date(s) of Festival:
1st - 2nd August 1998
Times of Festival:
1st: ceilidh 8pm - midnight

2nd: open day 10am - 5pm
Cost for Adults:
£2 open day, £3 ceilidh
Cost for Children: **Half price**
Tickets available from: **On the gate**
Routes by Car:
Signposted from A69 Corbridge - Hexham, A68 Otterburn and B6357 Newcastleton
Train/Other:
Nearest Station is Hexham. Coach service available from Newcastle City Centre on Festival Sunday
Venue: **Kielder Forest**
Facilities (Parking):
Coach and car parking, toilet facilities. Refreshments including a real ale bar and barbecue
Facilities (Disabled):
Facilities for disabled including parking, toilets and chair lift
What's On:
Falconry displays, visit the working forest and see all aspects of forest work including kielders, super machines, chainsaws, wood carving, craft stalls, country crafts, folk music. Chidren's activities, circus theatre, pony trekking, border games
Historical Background:
1998 will be the festival's 13th year. It was designed as an opportunity for people to enjoy what their forests can offer and to learn how they are managed
General Information:
1998 will see an introduction to the festival of a Husky Dog Sled to the list of attractions

Rothbury Traditional Music Festival

Type of Festival: **Music**
Contact: **Mary Bathgate**
Address:
Garleigh House
Rothbury
Morpeth
Northumberland
NE65 7RB
Tel. No: **01669 620718**
Date(s) of Festival:
17th - 19th July 1998
Times of Festival:
Friday evening. Saturday all day. Sunday until 4pm
Cost for Adults: **£1 to £3.50**
Special discounts: **None**
Routes by Car:
Travel from Newcastle on A1, then A697 Coldstream Road, then B6334 to Rothbury
Train/Other:
Train or bus to Newcastle/Morpeth then as above
Venues: **Various within Rothbury**
Facilities (Parking):
Parking available in majority of halls
What's On:
Ceilidhs, concerts. singarounds and pub sessions, outdoor dance displays, Northumberland pipe workshop, competitions, fiddle, accordion, highland pipes, singing dialect poetry, flute/recorder, original composition tune, song and more
Historical Background:
The festival has been running for 21 years
General Information:
Small festival, purely traditional music with the majority of performers being local and regional

NOTTINGHAMSHIRE

Riverside Festival

Type of Festival: **River**
Contact:
Paul Morgan - Events Officer
Address:
**Dept of Leisure and Community Services
51-57 Castle Gate
Nottingham
Nottinghamshire
NG1 6AF**
Tel. No: **0115 9153595**
Date(s) of Festival:
1st - 2nd August 1998
Times of Festival:
**1st: 12 noon - 11pm
2nd: 12noon -10pm**
Cost for Adults: **Free**
Cost for Children: **Free**
Tickets available from: **Not required**
Routes by Car:
M1 Junction 25, A52
Venue:
Victoria Embankment, Nottingham
What's On:
Unique atmosphere with a street fair, organ festival, street performers, music and river activities. As a finale there will be a spectacular firework display

General Information:
It's is estimated that 90,000+ people will attend this event

Wollaton '98
(What a Weekend)
Type of Festival: **Mixed**
Contact:
Paul Morgan - Events Officer
Address:
**Dept of Leisure and Community Services
51-57 Castle Gate
Nottingham
Nottinghamshire
NG1 6AF**
Tel. No: **0115 9153595**
Date(s) of Festival:
21st - 30th May 1999
Times of Festival:
23rd: 1pm - 10.30pm, 24th: 11am - 10pm, 25th: 11am - 6pm
Cost for Adults: **Free**
Cost for Children: **Free**
Tickets available from: **Not required**
Routes by Car:
M1 Junction 25, A52
Venue:
Wollaton Park, Nottingham
What's On:
Music stage featuring classical, jazz, rock/pop. 70s and 80s disco, Radio Trent Roadshow featuring the latest chart artists and bands, craft fair, floral art show models and hobbies tent, children's entertainment, fair, trade stands, street theatre, sports . . .
General Information:
There's also the ever popular AEC vintage bus and lorry rally on Sunday 24th and the City of Nottingham Shire Horse Show on Monday 25th

Bramley Festival

Type of Festival:
Music, Arts, Sports
Contact:
Mark Stephens
Arts and Marketing Manager
Address:
Newark and Sherwood District
Council
Leisure Services
Kelham Hill
Newark
Southwell
Nottinghamshire
NG23 5QX
Tel. No: **01636 605111**
Fax No: **01636 708267**
Date(s) of Festival:
24th - 27th September 1998
Times of Festival: **Various**
Cost for Adults: **Various**
Tickets available from:
Newark Tourist Office:
01636 678962
Routes by Car:
Southwell is located on the A612,
8 miles from Newark and 12 miles
from Nottingham
Train/Other:
Newark Northgate Station/
Newark Castle Station then taxi
Venue:
Various venues within Southwell
and surrounding area i.e. Saracens
Head Hotel, Cross Keys Upton,
Lowes Wong School, etc
Facilities (Parking):
Ample parking at the various venues
What's On:
"Cooking Apples" demos, food and
drink quizzes, live music, Bramley
Apple King and Queen judging,
jazz and blues evenings, Bramley
apple food fayre, guided walks,
apple painting competitions, bak-
ing competitions, morris dancers,
concerts, parades, apple bike ride
Historical Background:
The original Bramley apple grew
from a seed first planted in 1810
in a garden in Southwell which was
later occupied by Matthew
Bramley. Henry Merryweather
took cuttings and they were called
"Bramley Seedling". The original
apple tree still bears fruit today
Media/Public Comments:
"A celebration of Nottingham-
shire's world famous apple"
General Information:
There is a beer, cider and folk festi-
val running alongside the Bramley
Festival in Cross Keys, Upton. The
festival is featured every day at 8pm
except Sunday 27th September.
The programme for 1998 festival is
available from July 1998

OXFORDSHIRE

Abingdon Traditional Morris Dancers

Type of Festival:
Traditional Morris Dancers
Contact: **Mr Lee Argyll**
Address:

Abingdon Morris Men
105 Ock Street
Abingdon
Oxfordshire
Tel. No: **01235 526732**
Date(s) of Festival:
20th - 21st June 1998
Times of Festival: **9.45am -9pm**
Cost for Adults: **Free**
Cost for Children: **Free**
Tickets available from:
Not required
Routes by Car:
A34/A415 to Abingdon Town Centre
Venue: **Abingdon Town Centre**
Facilities (Parking):
Town centre car parks
Facilities (Disabled):
What's On:
ancient ceremony of electing the mayor, street dancing and procession, Mayor making ceremony and the dancing in of the Mayor, traditional dancing and chairing. Visiting sides: Abbots Bromley Horn Dance, Iknield Morris Men, Minehead Hobby Horse
Historical Background:
By the 15th century it was usual for young people to elect a leader for their May games or festivities and this person would be called Robin Hood, Queen of the May, Lord of Misrule or Mock Mayor. Abingdon maintains this tradition of Mayor Making
General Information:
The festival ends with the Morris men and invited guests going to Mayor making supper at the Guildhall, Abbey Close

Henley Festival of Music and the Arts

Type of Festival:
Music and Visual Arts
Contact: **Sam Gordon Clark**
Address:
Henley Festival Limited
42 Bell Street
Henley-on-Thames
Oxfordshire
RG9 2BG
Tel. No: **01491 410414**
Fax No: **01491 410482**
Date(s) of Festival:
8th -12th July 1998
Times of Festival:
8th -9th: 6pm - midnight
10th: 6pm -1am; 11th 6pm - 2am
12th: 12.30pm - 5pm
Cost for Adults: **Various**
Cost for Children: **Various**
Tickets available from:
Box Office: 01491 411353
Routes by Car:
From London take the M4 Junction 8/9 or M40 Junction 4 via Marlow bypass
Train/Other:
Please phone Paddington 0345 484950. Local taxis include Cars: 01491 579696 and Talbot Taxis: 01491 574222
Venue: **Henley-on-Thames**
Facilities (Parking):
Car Parking available. Picnics are welcome in the car park. Excellent catering etc
Facilities (Disabled):
The festival welcomes disabled patrons. There is ample wheelchair access to all events and every effort is made by management to ensure a trouble free visit to the festival

What's On:
Orchestral concerts on the floating stage, cabaret, jazz, Humphrey Lyttelton and Helen Shapiro, Reduced Shakespeare Company, Jiving Lindy Hoppers, Dazzling Riverside Display, The Entrantress (an astonishing hypnotic experience), Celtic rock, and much more
Historical Background:
The festival is now in its 16th year. Originally founded to make fuller use of Regatta tentage, it is now an annual event in its own right
General Information:
Gentlemen are requested to wear Black Tie, although suits or blazers with a tie are acceptable. Ladies are invited to wear long or short evening dress or evening trousers. Festival is primarily an outdoor event and a shawl or wrap may be needed

Chinese New Year Celebration

Type of Festival: **Traditional**
Contact: **Estella Packwood**
Address:
Oxfordshire Chinese Community and Advice Centre
44b Princes Street
Oxford
Oxfordshire
OX4 1DD
Tel. No: **01865 204188**
Fax No: **01865 242188**
Date(s) of Festival:
21st February 1999 (6th day of the Chinese New Year)
Times of Festival: **1pm - 4pm**
Cost for Adults: **£4**
Cost for Children: **£2 (ages 4 -12)**
Tickets available from:
Oxfordshire Chinese Community

Advice Centre (see above)
Routes by Car:
Oxford City Centre Westgate Car park (5 minutes walk from Town Hall)
Train/Other:
Oxford station is a 20 minute walk from Town Hall
Venue: **Oxford Town Hall**
Facilities (Parking):
Westgate car park, 5 minute walk
Facilities (Disabled):
Elevator available for disabled. Disabled parking
What's On:
Chinese song and dance. Charity raffle (drawn by the Lord Mayor and Chairman of the Council), bouncy castles, games and craft stalls, buffet lunch. Over 900 participants each year
General Information:
The first day of the Chinese New Year is 16th February 1999

Apple Day

Type of Festival: **Traditional**
Contact: **Maureen Jeffrey**
Address:
Sulgrave Manor
Manor Road
Sulgrave
Oxfordshire
OX17 2SD
Tel. No: **01295 760205**
Fax No: **01295 760205**.
Web site:
http: //www.stratford.co.uk/sulgrave
Date(s) of Festival:
17th - 18th October 1998
Times of Festival: **10am -5pm**
Cost for Adults: **£4.50**
Cost for Children: **Half price**
Special discounts: **Family £12**
Tickets available from: **On the day**

Routes by Car:
7 miles from Junction 11 M40. Banbury (7 miles), Brackley (6 miles) Oxford and Stratford (30 miles) and London via M1 or M40 (70 miles)
Train/Other:
Nearest station is Banbury
Venue:
Sulgrave Manor, Sulgrave village
Facilities (Parking): **On site parking**
What's On:
Apple identification, over 200 varieties, apple cookery, including Sophie Grigson, ciders, juices, fruit wines, apple market, specialist nurseries, arts and crafts, stalls galore. Good food and drink, plants and gardens
Historical Background:
The Manor is the home of George Washington's ancestors. It is a superb example of a modest manor house and garden of the time of Shakespeare. In 1914 the Manor was presented to the peoples of GB and the USA in celebration of 100 yrs of peace between them
Media/Public Comments:
"A celebration of apples and orchards"
General Information:
One of the many attractive features of the Manor is the garden. Lavender grows in profusion and many thousands of bags of Sulgrave Lavender have crossed the Atlantic since the house was opened

Towersey Village Festival

Type of Festival: **Music and Dance**
Contact:
Towersey Village Festival

Address:
P O Box 296
Aylesbury
Buckinghamshire
Tel. No: **01296 433669**
Fax No: **01296 392300**
Date(s) of Festival:
28th - 31st August 1998
Times of Festival:
Friday 7.30pm - Monday late
Cost for Adults: **£3**
Cost for Children: **Free**
Special discounts:
Concessions available
Routes by Car:
M40 or A40 then A428 15 miles east of Oxford
Train/Other:
Haddenham/Thame Parkway or Princes Risborough. Bus to Thame
Venue:
Towersey Village and various village venues
Facilities (Parking):
Parking facilities within a short walk of the main site
Facilities (Disabled):
Disabled parking. Access to all areas
What's On:
Concerts, dances, open air arena, International shows, processions, full children's, craft and music fair, market stalls, fairground, fete
Historical Background:
One of the most famous villages in recent history. Festival is in its 34th year
Media/Public Comments:
"A musical treat for all"
Oxford Mail
General Information:
1998's Festival presents the cream of the crop of young musicians and singers who have emerged onto the folk scene in recent years

Wantage Festival of Arts

Type of Festival: **Arts**
Contact:
Mrs J Hannaby
Festival of Arts Committee
Address:
"Lesters"
High Street
Childrey
Oxfordshire
OX12 9VA
Tel. No: **01235 751464**
Date(s) of Festival:
13th June - 11th July 1998
Times of Festival: **Various**
Cost for Adults: **Various**
Tickets available from:
Wantage Tourist Information Centre
Routes by Car:
From Abingdon, Didcot A417, From Newbury B4494, from Faringdon A417, from Oxford A338
Venue:
Various venues within Wantage and surrounding areas
Facilities (Parking):
Ample Parking in town
What's On:
Wide range of music, drama, talks, workshops, dance, exhibitions. The majority of participants are local people and demonstrate the excellent high standard of talents, both professional and semi-professional
Historical Background:
1998 is the festival's 3rd year. This amalgam of local culture and talent has created a programme in which all age groups will find some interest and enjoyment. 1996 and 1997 were very successful festivals

General Information:
1998 Programme brochure can be obtained by contacting the Wantage Tourist Information Office

Blenheim Horse Trials

Type of Festival: **Sports**
Contact: **Horse Trials Department**
Address:
Blenheim Palace
Woodstock
Oxfordshire
Tel. No: **01993 811091**
Date(s) of Festival:
10th - 13th September 1998
Times of Festival: **9am - 6pm**
Cost for Adults: **TBC**
Cost for Children: **TBC**
Tickets available from:
Tourist Information Centre:
01993 811038
Routes by Car: **A44 to Woodstock**
Train/Other:
Oxford, Charlbury or Long Hanborough. Bus to Woodstock
Venue:
Blenheim Palace, Woodstock
Facilities (Parking): **Available**
Facilities (Disabled):
Parking and access available for disabled
What's On:
Show jumping, cross country, exhibitions, stands, Blenheim Park. Enjoy the beauty of the Cotswolds and visit the quaint teashops and public houses
General Information:
A selection of Cotswold publications are available by phoning or writing to: The Tourist Information Centre, Hensington Road, Woodstock, Oxon, OX20 1JQ

SHROPSHIRE

Bridgenorth Folk Festival

Type of Festival: **Music and Dance**
Contact: **Alan Surtees**
Address:
1 Kidderminster Road
Bridgenorth
Shropshire
WV15 6BW
Tel. No: **01746 768813**
Fax No: **01384 410306**
E-mail:
alan.surtees@btinternet.com
Date(s) of Festival:
28th - 30th August 1998
Times of Festival:
7.30pm Friday 28th - 1am Saturday,
then non-stop until Sunday at mid-
night
Cost for Adults: **£27.50**
Cost for Children:
Under 10s free, 10-16 half price
Special discounts:
£18 weekend ticket
Tickets available from:
Alan Surtees (see above)
Routes by Car:
30 min down the M6 the M5 or M54
Venue:
Oldbury Wells School, Bridgenorth

Facilities (Parking):
Plenty of on site parking, camping
available
Facilities (Disabled):
Access and toilets for disabled
What's On:
Concerts, ceilidhs, singarounds,
children's events, story telling,
dance displays, craft fair, pub ses-
sions, Festival steam train, acoustic
stage, workshops, meet the artists.
Also Albion Band, The Poozies, Rory
McLeod, The New Bushbury and
lots more
Historical Background:
The festival started in 1997
Media/Public Comments:
"Yes the 1998 Folk Rattle and Roll
trip will be aboard a five carriage
steam train"
". . . whole weekend of events which
will be purely ACOUSTIC!!!"
"It just keeps getting better"
General Information:
Folk Rattle and Roll is free to Week-
end Ticket Holders. A new venue
has been added this year. "The
Theatre on the Steps", near the
Town Centre, half way up a cliff face.
Purely acoustic sounds. Bridgenorth
is one of the most spectacular towns
in Shropshire

English Haydn Festival

Type of Festival: **Classical Music**
Contact: **John Reid/Sandra Day**
Address:
24a St Marys Street
Newport
Shropshire
TF10 7AB
Tel. No: **01952 811829**
Fax No: **01952 812011**
Date(s) of Festival:
29th May - 7th June 1998

Times of Festival:
Main concerts start at 7pm. Also coffee/lunch/afternoon concerts at various times.
Cost for Adults: **From £5 - £25**
Tickets available from:
Festival Box Office (see above)
Routes by Car:
Junction 10 off M5 (north) follow A454
Train/Other:
Wolverhampton/Telford are nearest stations
Venue:
St Leonards Church, Bridgenorth
Facilities (Parking):
Festival car parks will be clearly signposted from all roads approaching Bridgenorth accommodating coaches and cars
Facilities (Disabled):
Disabled access (prior notification required)
What's On:
7 orchestral concerts including 2 choral. 8 chamber concerts, 2 recitals. Artists include Willard White, Nancy Argenta, Crispian Steele-Perkins, Catherine Bott, Anthony Halstead, John Moore, Ronald Brautigam and Ivan Monighetti
Historical Background:
Formed in 1993 as part of a town initiative by its founder, John Reid, who strives continually to bring fine music to the provinces
Media/Public Comments:
"An eccentric idea which deserves to succeed" The Times
General Information:
During each evening concert there is a supper interval of 70 minutes. Summer supper dishes with wine and champagne will be served in the marquee. There is a full bar. Alternatively there are restaurants and pubs within easy reach that are primed for this event

Ironbridge Bluegrass and Roots Festival

Type of Festival:
Music, Dance and Craft
Contact: **Mal Salisbury**
Address:
8 St Lukes Road
Doseley Telford
Shropshire
TF4 3BE
Tel. No: **01952 505565**
Fax No: **0410 409 004.**
E-mail:
information@ironbridgefest.enta.net
Date(s) of Festival:
12th - 14th June 1998
Times of Festival:
Friday 12th: 7.30pm -1am
Saturday 13th: 10.30am -12 midnight
Sunday 14th: 10.30am - 8.30pm
Cost for Adults:
£40 season ticket, Friday: £10, Saturday: £16, Sunday £12
Cost for Children:
Under 12s free. 12-16 years £18 season ticket
Special discounts:
10% reductions for UB40s, OAPs and students. Reductions for advanced booking on season and daily events
Tickets available from:
Festival Office (see above). If payment by Credit Card contact Oakengate Theatre: 01952 619020
Routes by Car:
Junction 4 or 6 from M54
Train/Other:

Telford Central. Taxi to Ironbridge (3 miles)

Venue: **Dale End Park, Ironbridge**

Facilities (Parking):

Day parking in Ironbridge. Weekend camping and parking on site. Real Ale, food etc

Facilities (Disabled):

On site access for disabled

What's On:

Bluegrass and Cajun music with Arcadian Ramblers, Austin Lounge Lizards, Kate Mackenzie and Out of the Blue, The Daily Planet, Feet First, Loosehound Drifters, John Otway, workshops, craft demonstrations, Stalls, dance displays, children's entertainment etc

Historical Background:

1998 is the 2nd year of the Festival.

Media/Public comments:

"Britain's premier Bluegrass and Roots Festival. Great family atmosphere"

General Information:

Music takes place on two all weather stages. Also on site is The Bluegrass Club tent launched in 1997 which offers a more intimate atmosphere for artists and performers as well as providing a workshop and performance area for the American visitors

Festival at the Edge

Type of Festival:

Music, Song and Storytelling

Contact: **Jackie Douglas**

Address:

3 High Point
Little Wenlock
Shropshire
TF6 5BT

Tel. No: **01952 504929**

Date(s) of Festival:

17th - 19th July 1998

Times of Festival:

7pm Friday - 6pm Sunday

Cost for Adults:

Weekend: £30, family weekend: £77.50. Day and session tickets available

Cost for Children:

Under 5s free; juniors (6-18) £15

Special discounts:

Adult weekend: £25, Junior Weekend: £12.50, family weekend: £65 (before 31st May 1998)

Tickets available from:

Jackie Douglas (see above)

Routes by Car:

Stokes Barn is near to Much Wenlock off the A458, Shrewsbury to Bridgenorth Road.

Venue:

Stokes Barn, Much Wenlock

Facilities (Parking):

Free parking. Also free camping on site for weekend ticket holders. Accommodation can be booked via Much Wenlock Tourist Information: 01952 727679

Facilities (Disabled):

Wheelchair access. Helpers available

What's On:

Stories, songs and music. All weekend craft fair, campfire tales, workshops, story walks, pub sessions, concerts, story rounds, special festival for children, games and sessions. On site catering and a real ale bar

Historical Background:

The festival is now in its 7th year.

Media/Public Comments:

"Trespassing in paradise"
"A weekend of delights: tall tales, terrific tellers, magical music together in a mystical setting"

Wem Festival

Type of Festival: **Carnival**
Contact:
Mrs Marie McKean - Press Officer
Address:
Wem Carnival Committee
67 Pyms Road
Wem
Shropshire
Tel. No: **01939 233000**
Date(s) of Festival:
5th September 1998
Times of Festival:
1.30pm and 7.45pm processions
Cost for Adults: **£1.50**
Cost for Children: **50p**
Special discounts: **OAPs 50p**
Tickets available from: **See above**
Routes by Car:
Signposted off A49
Train/Other:
On main line Shrewsbury-Crewe.
Local Bus Service
Venue: **Wem Town**
Facilities (Parking):
Parking available in Town Centre
What's On:
Field events between two processions eg: stalls, band concerts, dancing troupes, funfair and sideshows. This years main attraction is Paul Hendy - Children's TV Presenter
Historical Background:
Carnival revived in 1979 after 14 year break
Media/Public Comments:
"Best in Shropshire"
"Only carnival to have two processions"
General Information:
Can also contact: Miss Gaynor's Secretary, Wem Carnival Committee, 54 Station Road, Wem, Shropshire

Eckford Sweet Pea Society of Wem

Type of Festival:
Flower Show and Town Festival
Contact: **Mrs V Good - Hon Sec**
Address:
Eckford Sweet Pea Society of Wem
Lyndale Nook Farm
Nook Lane
Weston under Redcastle
Shropshire
SY4 5LP
Tel. No: **01948 840779**
Date(s) of Festival:
25th - 26th July 1998
Times of Festival:
Saturday: 10am - 5pm
Sunday: 10am - 4pm
Cost for Adults: **50p**
Cost for Children: **Free**
Special discounts: **None**
Tickets available from:
Mrs V Good (see above)
Routes by Car:
20 mins off M54, sign posted off A49 between Shrewsbury and Whitchurch
Train/Other:
Wem Station (Crewe - Shewsbury line)
Venue:
Held in the Talbot Market and Community Centre, High Street, Wem
Facilities (Parking):
Free Parking adjacent to show, coach parking details available upon request
Facilities (Disabled):
Show venue all on ground level
What's On:
Flower show, flower festivals in churches and chapels, decorated shops and businesses.

Sunday only: vintage cars. Charity stalls.

Historical Background:
To celebrate centenary of Henry Eckford V.M.H. opening seed business in Wem 1888. Carried on by local committee at Town's request and popular demand. Closeby is the Bridgemere Garden Centre, Ironbridge Gorge Museum and Hawkestone Historical Park.

Media/Public Comments:
Appeared on ITV with Ann Swithenbank "Heart of England". Liverpool Daily Post, Birmingham Mail, Evening News all give good reviews at seed sowing time.

General Information:
The Society sells over 35 varieties of the old fashioned Sweet Peas. List on request to above address.

Midland Festival of Transport

Type of Festival:
Historic Vehicle Show

Contact:
John Chatwin, Country Fairs

Address:
9 Beechfield Rise
Lichfield
Staffordshire

Tel. No: **01543 417878**

Date(s) of Festival:
4th - 5th April 1999

Times of Festival: **10am - 5pm**

Cost for Adults: **£5**

Cost for Children: **£2**

Tickets available from:
Weston Park Enterprises
Box Office: 01952 850207

Routes by Car:
6 miles from M6 on A5, 3 miles from Junction 3 M54

Train/Other: **Shifnal Station.**

Venue:
Weston Park, Weston under Lizard

Facilities (Parking):
Parking next to Showground, first aid teams available, toilets etc

Facilities (Disabled):
Full disabled access and parking, disabled toilets

What's On:
Thousands of vintage and classic vehicles. All day arena attractions, various displays, light aircraft, hovercraft, Wall of Death, hot air balloons, flight simulators, helicopter flights, autojumble, trade stands, miniature railway, club displays

Historical Background:
Now in its 13th year and accepted by Motoring Press as the premier motoring event of the year

Media/Public Comments:
"Good value for money"
Express and Star
"Refreshing to find so much for all members of the family"
Birmingham Post and Mail

Weston Park Music Festival

Type of Festival: **Music**

Contact: **Catherine Lloyd**

Address:
Weston Park
Weston under Lizard
Telford
Shropshire
TF11 8LE

Tel. No: **01952 850207**

Fax No: **01952 850430**

Date(s) of Festival:
13th - 16th August 1998

Times of Festival:

13-14th: 6pm, 15th: 7.30pm, 16th: 7pm
Cost for Adults:
13th-14th: **£45 includes dinner.**
15th: **£18 on the night**
16th: **£16 on the night**
Special discounts:
Saturday: £16 in advance
Sunday: £14 in advance
Tickets available from:
Weston Park Box Office (see above)
Routes by Car:
On the A5, 3 miles from the M54 Junction 3 or 8 miles from M6 Junction 12
Train/Other: **Shifnal Station**
Venue:
Weston Park, Weston under Lizard
Facilities (Parking):
Parking next to Showground, First Aid teams available, toilets etc
Facilities (Disabled):
Full disabled access and parking, disabled toilets
What's On:
Popular Opera, a masked opera evening, Last night at the Proms, The Full Weston Monty (Hot Chocolate, Steve Harley, Cockney Rebel, Them People and the Fraud Monty)

Shakespeare in the Park

Type of Festival: **Shakespeare**
Contact: **Catherine Lloyd**
Address:
Weston Park
Weston under Lizard
Telford
Shropshire
TF11 8LE
Tel. No: **01952 850207**
Fax No: **01952 850430**
Date(s) of Festival:

6th - 7th June 1998
Times of Festival:
6th: **7.30pm, 7th: 2.30pm**
Cost for Adults:
£8 in advance. £10 on the night
Tickets available from:
Weston Park Box Office (see above)
Routes by Car:
On A5, 3 mile from M54 Junction 3 or 8 miles from M6 Junction 12
Train/Other: **Shifnal Station**
Venue:
Weston Park, Weston under Lizard
Facilities (Parking):
Parking next to Showground, First Aid teams available, toilets etc
Facilities (Disabled):
Full disabled access and parking, disabled toilets
What's On:
Performance of Shakespeare's Macbeth, directed by Donald Sompter

Balloon Nightglow Spectacular

Type of Festival: **Family**
Contact: **Catherine Lloyd**
Address:
Weston Park
Weston under Lizard
Telford
Shropshire
TF11 8LE
Tel. No: **01952 850207**
Fax No: **01952 850430**
Date(s) of Festival: **18th July 1998**
Times of Festival: **5pm**
Cost for Adults:
£12 per car on the night
Special discounts:
£10 per car in advance
Tickets available from:
Weston Park Box Office

(see above)
Routes by Car:
On the A5, 3 miles from M54 Junction 3 or 8 miles from M6 Junction 12
Train/Other: **Shifnal Station**
Venue:
Weston Park, Weston under Lizard
Facilities (Parking):
Parking next to showground, First Aid teams available, toilets etc
Facilities (Disabled):
Full disabled access and parking, disabled toilets
What's On:
Mass balloon ascent, arena activities, nightglow, fireworks, funfair, craft fair, trade stands

SOMERSET

Bath International Music Festival 1998

Type of Festival: **Music**
Contact: **Bath Festivals Box Office**
Address:
Church Street
Abbey Green
Bath
Somerset
BA1 1NL
Tel. No: **01225 463362**

Fax No: **01225 310377**
Date(s) of Festival:
21st May - 6th June 1999
Cost for Adults: **From £6**
Cost for Children:
Concessions to under 20s
Special discounts:
Concessions to disabled, students, Jazz Card, Stagepass, Sonic Arts, SPNM card holders
Tickets available from:
Box Office: 01225 463362
Routes by Car:
From north M5 to Junction 15, M4 to Junction 18, A46 to Bath. From London M4 to Junction 18, A46 to Bath
Train/Other: **Bath Spa Station**
Venue:
Various venues within Bath Town Centre
Facilities (Disabled):
Patrons in wheelchairs welcomed at all venues. Please inform the Box Office in advance
What's On:
This years artists include: Willard White, Yuri Bashmet, Moscow Soloists, Kronar Quartet, Arditti Quartet, Gabrieli Consort. Kings Consort, Bournemouth Symphony Orchestra, Jools Holland, John Surman, Lynn Sissay, Steve Martland Band
Historical Background:
1998 is the festival's 50th anniversary. It was founded in 1948 to present an annual celebration of the world's best music. Today, Bath Festivals Trust, led by Tim Joss, is working to establish Bath as a Festivals City with a growing portfolio of events
Media/Public Comments:
The Daily Telegraph, The Inde-

pendent on Sunday, Financial Times, The Guardian, The Times and The Independent gave the 1997 Bath Music Festival glowing reviews

Bath Fringe

Type of Festival: **Arts**
Contact: **Wendy Matthews**
Address:
The Fringe Office
103 Walcot Street
Bath
Somerset
BA1 5BW
Tel. No: **01225 480079**
Fax No: **01225 480079**
Date(s) of Festival:
22nd May - 7th June 1998
Times of Festival: **Various**
Cost for Adults:
Ticketed and free events. Programme available in April
Tickets available from:
Programme send SAE (A5) to Fringe Office (see above)
Venue: **Bath**
What's On:
Full programme of theatre, music and comedy. Street performance weekend, 2 days of children's festival, outdoor concerts, visual art exhibitions and studio tours
Historical Background:
Started in 1981 to complement the International Music Festival. The dates now overlap

Chard Festival of Women in Music

Type of Festival: **Music**
Contact: **Angela Willes**
Address:
3 Howards Row

Chard
Somerset
Tel. No: **01460 66115**
Fax No: **01460 66048**
Date(s) of Festival:
19th - 4th May 1999
Times of Festival:
10am - midnight
Cost for Adults:
Events £3-£7, season tickets: £70 (admits to all concerts and workshops)
Day Tickets: Saturday: £30, Sunday: £32, Monday: £24.
Workshops from £2-£5
Cost for Children: **£2 up to 12 years**
Special discounts:
UB40s, OAPs, students £2 - £5 Day tickets: Saturday: £20, Sunday: £22, Monday: £16
Tickets available from:
01460 66115 (see above) or
Box Office: 01460 66115
Routes by Car: **On the A30**
Train/Other:
Paddington - Taunton (12 miles) or Waterloo - Crewkerne (7 miles)
Venue: **In an around Chard**
Facilities (Parking):
Parking, camping facilities available. Creche available Saturday 23rd
Facilities (Disabled):
Wheelchair access to 95% of the venues. Exception: Town Hall
What's On:
Classical, world, jazz, roots, folk, voice, contemporary. Chard presents music composed by women, performed by men and women and enjoyed by everyone. Festival has an open air stage in town centre, a new May tent for late night gigs
Historical Background:
Began in 1990 dedicated to

showcasing music by women hidden from standard repertoire and other concert programmes.

Media/Public Comments:

"Excellent varied programme. Very high standard. A surfeit of wonders!"

"A bold event with an intriguing mix of classical, jazz, folk and world music" Classic Music Magazine

"In its quiet way, Chard will make waves" The Independent

General Information:

Chard is a pioneering town in Somerset, close to Blackdown Hills and the Devon and Dorset Coast

6th Long Weekend Clevedon's Annual Jazz Festival

Type of Festival: Jazz

Contact:

Trevor Tomasin
Clevedon Jazz Club

Address:

c/o Ground Floor Flat
1 Woodlands Road
Clevedon
Somerset
BS21 7QD

Tel. No: 01275 343210

E-mail:

jazzclub@tomasin.u-net.com

Date(s) of Festival:

4th - 6th September 1998

Times of Festival:

4th: 7pm - midnight,
5th and 6th: 2pm - 11.30pm

Cost for Adults:

Full weekend:£24, Friday: £7
Saturday and Sunday: £10

Cost for Children:

Under 13s free (if accompanied)

Special discounts:

Advance tickets available until 15th August 1998. Cheques made payable to: Clevedon Jazz Club.

Tickets available from:

Clevedon Jazz Club (see above)

Routes by Car:

From M5 Junction 20.

Venue:

Princes Hall, Princes Road, Clevedon

Facilities (Parking):

Town Parking, B&B available, caravan and camping, bar and food available

What's On:

Numerous jazz bands from Britain and the USA, exhibitions of paintings and prints, dancing, parades

Historical Background:

This is the festival's sixth consecutive year.

General Information:

Clevedon is between Bristol and Weston Super Mare is a small Victorian seaside town on the Bristol Channel and is host to the oldest established jazz festival in Somerset

Great Elm Music Festival

Type of Festival: Classical Music

Contact:

Maureen Lehane Wishart

Address:

Bridge House
Great Elm
Frome
Somerset
BA11 3NY

Tel. No: 01373 812383

Fax No: 01373 812083

Date(s) of Festival:

19th June - 5th July 1998

Times of Festival:

Varying times
Cost for Adults:
£8 - £20. A buffet supper is included in the price of all evening events, a cream tea for afternoons and coffee to precede Mendelssohn
Cost for Children:
Under 14s half price
Special discounts:
Friends of the Festival 10% discount. Apply to: Mrs Jean Grierson, The Secretary, Friends of the Great Elm Music Festival, 35 Critchill Road, Frome, Somerset BA11 3HE
Tickets available from:
Box Office: 01373 812772
Routes by Car:
Due south from Bath on A362
Venue:
Bridge House, Great Elm and various venues in Frome and surrounding area
Facilities (Parking): Available
What's On:
Opera, concerts and lecture recital performances, piano, violin, song Viola da Gammba and harpsichord recitals, a children's experimental magic adventure (devised as a children's workshop), Jackdaws art exhibition
Historical Background:
Festival was created in 1987 by Maureen Lehane Wishart, as a tribute to her late husband, Peter Wishart, composer and Professor of music. They had for many years invited the Music Dept to an annual summer picnic in the garden of their home, Bridge House
Media/Public Comments:
"The players showed astonishing powers of synchronisation and co-ordination, managing also to convey a marvellous sense of style and sheer enjoyment of the music" Classical Guitar magazine
General Information:
Dame Joan Sutherland is the festival's President and the patrons are the Earl and Countess of Oxford and Asquith

Glastonbury Abbey Classical Extravaganza

Type of Festival: Classical Music
Contact:
Glastonbury Festivals Ltd
Address:
28 Northload Street
Glastonbury
Somerset
BA6 9JJ
Tel. No: 01458 834596
Fax No: 01458 833235
Date(s) of Festival:
14th - 15th August 1998
Cost for Adults: Day ticket £20
Tickets available from:
Tourist Information Centre and Glastonbury Abbey Shop : 01458 832020. For information tel: 01749 890470
Routes by Car:
M5 Junction 23 then A39. On the A361. From Bristol A37 then A361
Venue: Glastonbury Abbey
Facilities (Parking): Available
What's On:
Classical Extravaganza with the Royal Philharmonic Orchestra. Friday 14th: Virtuoso Night, an evening with Kennedy. Saturday 15th: Symphonic Idylls Orchestral and Choral Favourites and spectacular Fireworks and Water Display

Glastonbury Festival of Contemporary Performing Arts

Type of Festival:
Music and Contemporary Performing Arts
Contact:
Glastonbury Festivals Ltd
Address:
28 Northload Street
Glastonbury
Somerset
BA6 9JJ
Tel. No: **01458 834596**
Fax No: **01458 833235**
Date(s) of Festival:
26th - 28th June 1998
Times of Festival:
Admittance from 9am on 24th June. Admission is by advance ticket only
Cost for Adults:
£80 and £3 handling charge each. VAT and all site events included. Demand will be heavy so early application advisable. Allow 21 days. No postal applications after 30th May. Caravan/campervans need separate advance ticket £20
Cost for Children:
Under 14s free accompanied by an adult
Tickets available from:
Ticket Hotline: 0870 6077380
Postal: Glastonbury Festivals Ltd, Bristol BS38 7EN
Routes by Car:
M5 Junction 23 then A39. On the A361. From Bristol, A37 then A361
Venue:
Worthy Farm, Pilton, Shepton Mallet
Facilities (Parking):
Ample parking available. Camping,

first aid, welfare, The Samaritans etc
Facilities (Disabled):
Disabled access
What's On:
This year sees the introduction of an extra venue, the New Bands Tent to give some scope for the legions of talented musicians. This year Greenpeace will taking a large area. Lots of bands of the very highest standards
Historical Background:
In aid of Greenpeace and world environmental issues
General Information:
The INFO LINE is now open providing information: 0839 668899. (Calls charged at 49p per min) TICKETLINE: 01179 767 868

Priddy Irish Set Dance

Type of Festival:
Traditional Irish Dance
Contact: **Val Knight**
Address:
3 The Court
Dinder
Nr Wells
Somerset
PA5 3PT
Tel. No: **01749 675805**
Date(s) of Festival:
30th October - 1st November 1998
Times of Festival:
Full weekends of events
Cost for Adults:
£30 for full weekend. Separate event tickets also available
Tickets available from:
01749 675805 (see above)
Routes by Car:
A39/A37 to Wells via Bath or Bristol or M5 Junction 21 via Cheddar Gorge to Priddy

Train/Other:
Templemeads, Bristol. Then 367 bus Bristol - Yeovil - Wells then taxi to Priddy
Venue: **Priddy Village Hall**
Facilities (Parking):
Parking available. Good facilities, accessible to campsite nearby
Facilities (Disabled):
Access for disabled
What's On:
Friday: Welcome Party in local pub with musicians and dancing. Saturday: Daytime workshops in dance. Evening, ceilidh, full band and caller, bar etc. Sunday: repeat of Saturday with different ceilidh bands etc
General Information:
Irish Set Dance is square dancing to traditional Irish music, as enjoyed by the people of Ireland. It is not solely step dancing although it does contain some basic steps

Somerton Summer Arts Festival

Type of Festival: **Arts**
Contact: **Liz Laker - Ticket Office**
Address:
London Cigarette Card Company Shop
West Street
Somerton
Somerset
TA11 6NB
Tel. No: **01458 274148**
Fax No: **01458 273515**
Date(s) of Festival:
10th - 18th July 1998
Times of Festival:
Mostly evenings and weekends
Cost for Adults: **From free -£6**
Tickets available from:

Ticket Office: 01458 274148
Train/Other:
Taunton or Castle Cary
Venue:
Various venues within Somerton
Facilities (Disabled):
Disabled facilities available
What's On:
Over 35 events including art exhibitions, craft and market fairs.
Historical Background:
Festival now in its 11th year
Media/Public Comments:
"Well organised, value for money. Entertainment for all the family"
General Information:
A 52 page souvenir programme covering the 9 days of the festival which contain free competitions, full details of artists, date times and price of tickets. Available from Liz Laker (£1.40 including p&p) from 1st June 1998

Watchet Viking Festival

Type of Festival:
Historical Re-enactment
Contact: **Veronica Murray**
Address:
Watchet Town Council
Swain Street
Watchet
Somerset
TA23 0AB
Tel. No: **01643 862011**
Fax No: **01984 633344**
Date(s) of Festival:
5th - 6th September 1998
Times of Festival: **9.30am - 10pm**
Cost for Adults: **Free**
Cost for Children: **Free**
Tickets available from:
Not required. Information from Taunton and Minehead Railway and Tourist Offices

Routes by Car:
A39 from Bridgewater, A358 from Taunton
Train/Other: **Taunton and Minehead**
Venue: **Watchet Town**
Facilities (Parking):
Car and coach parking.
Facilities (Disabled):
Disabled parking. Marshals and stewards on hand to help
What's On:
Living history Viking village, authentic costumes, crafts, skills, re-enactment of combat, village life, marquees and stalls, Viking longships, hog roast, fireworks, archery, falconry, torchlit procession (Saturday evening at 8pm)
Historical Background:
Watchet celebrates its Viking history 1000 years after last invasion when Vikings came to raid local Royal Mint
Media/Public Comments:
"Very authentic and very thrilling" Quay West Radio
General Information:
Supported by funds from Town and District Council, matched by European Leader project

Yeovil Festival of Transport

Type of Festival: **Transport**
Contact: **Mr J Legge**
Address:
Festival of Transport
P O Box 40
Yeovil
Somerset
BA20 1PR
Tel. No: **01935 422319**
Date(s) of Festival:
8th - 9th August 1998
Times of Festival:

From 10am each day
Cost for Adults: **£5**
Cost for Children: **£3**
Special discounts: **OAPs £3**
Tickets available from: **The gate**
Routes by Car:
Just off A37 Dorchester Road, Yeovil - well sign posted
Train/Other:
Yeovil Junction or Yeovil Pen Mill
Venue: **Yeovil**
Facilities (Parking): **Free Car Parking**
What's On:
Attractions include: Monster Trucks, thousands of cars, bikes, commercials, steam and military vehicles, mini tractor pulling, models, autojumble, Company and Trade stands, side shows, crafts, and much more
Historical Background:
1998 is the festival's 27th year

STAFFORDSHIRE

Leek Arts Festival

Type of Festival: **Music and Drama**
Contact: **P H Davis**
Address:
The Old Vicarage
Meerbrook
Leek

Staffordshire
ST13 8SJ
Tel. No: **01538 300492**
Date(s) of Festival:
28th April - 31st May 1998
Times of Festival: **Various**
Cost for Adults: **Various**
Special discounts:
Discounts available for students and OAPs
Tickets available from:
Tourist Information, Market Place, Leek
Venue:
Various venues within Leek Town
Facilities (Parking):
Good parking close to all venues
What's On:
Choral music, drama, brass band, barbershop choir, folk, jazz, workshops, art, floral art etc

Lichfield Jazz Festival

Type of Festival: **Music**
Contact: **Mr Dan Reynolds**
Address:
94 Main Street
Rosliston
Derbyshire
Lichfield
Staffordshire
Tel. No: **01283 762120**
Date(s) of Festival:
5th - 6th June 1998 and
12th - 14th June 1998
Times of Festival: **Midday to late**
Cost for Adults:
Varies from free to £8.50
Special discounts:
Discounts available for students
Tickets available from:
Tourist Information:
01543 252109
Train/Other: **Lichfield Station**
Venue:

Various venues within Lichfield City Centre
Facilities (Parking):
Plenty of parking in City Centre
Facilities (Disabled):
Venues are suitable for disabled
What's On:
Jazz of a range of styles. Formal concerts, Elaine Dolman and Tommy Burton, Liz Disney and CIE Laurie. . .
Historical Background:
11th year. Rated in the top 6 Jazz Festivals in the UK

Lichfield Fringe Festival

Type of Festival:
Music, Theatre, Community Arts
Contact: **Sue Patios**
Address:
Lichfield District Arts Association
Donegal House
Bore Street
Lichfield
Staffordshire
WS13 6NE
Tel. No: **01543 262223**
Fax No: **01543 417308**
Date(s) of Festival:
5th - 11th July 1998
Times of Festival: **Various**
Cost for Adults:
Many events are free, others £4-£6
Cost for Children: **Half price**
Special discounts: **None**
Tickets available from:
Box Office: 01543 262223
Routes by Car:
A5127 to Lichfield
Venue:
Lichfield City Centre and Grove Fields (marquee)
Facilities (Parking):
City parking available. Catering and bar facilities

Facilities (Disabled):
Disabled access
What's On:
Choirs, theatre, bands, flea market, craft market, fringe, service, street theatre, dance. Workshops, art workshops, circus skills, story telling, community sing along
Historical Background:
Festival is now in its 15th year and is regarded as the biggest community festival in the area
Media/Public Comments:
"Smashing"

Lichfield Real Ale, Jazz and Blues Festival

Type of Festival: **Music**
Contact: **Brian Pretty**
Address:
Lichfield District Arts Association
Donegal House
Bore Street
Lichfield
Staffordshire
WS13 6NE
Tel. No: **01543 262223**
Fax No: **01543 417308**
Date(s) of Festival:
25th - 28th June 1998
Times of Festival: **Various**
Cost for Adults: **From £2 - £15**
Special discounts:
Discounts on family tickets and to CAMRA members
Tickets available from:
Box Office: 01543 262223
Routes by Car:
Close to M6/M42 - A51 passes venue
Train/Other:
Free Jazz Bus Saturday/Sunday service from City Bus Station.
Venue: **Lichfield Rugby Club**

Facilities (Parking):
Free parking, campsite, showers etc, catering
Facilities (Disabled):
Reasonable access for disabled.
What's On:
40+real ales to drink and 30 hours of jazz, blues, Latin jive.
Historical Background:
Started as a one off 9 years ago and since built a reputation for a small but distinctive festival
Media/Public Comments:
"Good location aimed at distinctive music. Good atmosphere and good company"
General Information:
Take a break in the lovely Cathedral City of Lichfield and enjoy the City and its surrounding countryside

Lichfield International Arts Festival

Type of Festival: **Music and Arts**
Contact: **Paul Spicer**
Address:
Festival Office
7 The Close
Lichfield
Staffordshire
WS13 7LD
Tel. No: **01543 257298**
Fax No: **01543 415137**
Date(s) of Festival:
3rd - 12th July 1998
Times of Festival: **All day**
Cost for Adults:
Prices range from £2 - £23
Special discounts:
Concessions available
Tickets available from:
Box Office: Tourist Information Centre, Bore Street, Lichfield: 01543 257557

Routes by Car:
From south M40/M6 -M42/A446/ A38. From north M1/A38; or M6 and cross country via Rugeley
Train/Other:
Birmingham, New Street and Lichfield City
Venue:
Various venues within Lichfield and surrounding area
Facilities (Parking):
Ample car parking.
Facilities (Disabled):
Disabled parking in Cathedral Close only
What's On:
60 events over 9 days. Concerts, drama, films, talks, exhibitions, jazz, light music, comedy, walks, outdoor events and fringe. Venues include: Lichfield Cathedral, Samuel Johnson's birthplace, country churches, spectacular firework displays
Historical Background:
The festival was founded in 1982. Originally based in the 13th century cathedral. Now major event with various venues
Media/Public Comments:
"on a summers day, there is no more lovely setting for a festival than Lichfield" The Guardian
General Information:
Lichfield is a medieval city surrounded by beautiful Staffordshire countryside. Visit the fascinating potteries, Shugborough (Lord Lichfield's Home), Drayton Manor Park, Ironbridge etc

Lichfield Winter Beer Festival

Type of Festival: **Beer**
Contact: **Brian Pretty**
Address:
Lichfield District Arts Association Dojeam House Bore Street Lichfield Staffordshire WS13 6NE
Tel. No: **01543 262223**
Fax No: **01543 417308**
Date(s) of Festival:
15th - 16th January 1999
Times of Festival: **Noon - 11pm**
Cost for Adults:
Free before 6pm. £2.50 after 6pm
Cost for Children: **Free**
Special discounts: **None**
Tickets available from:
Not required before 6pm. At the door thereafter.
Routes by Car: **A5127 to Lichfield**
Venue:
Guildhall, Lichfield Town Centre
Facilities (Parking):
City Centre parking
Facilities (Disabled):
Good access for disabled
What's On:
30+ real ales and acoustic music each evening
Historical Background:
Regular festival specialises in small brewer's ales
Media/Public Comments:
Excellent response from visitors

Lichfield Cajun Festival

Type of Festival: **Music**
Contact: **Brian Pretty**
Address:
Lichfield District Arts Association

Donegal House
Bore Street
Lichfield
Staffordshire
WS13 6NE
Tel. No: **01543 262223**
Fax No: **01543 417308**
Date(s) of Festival: **4th July 1998**
Times of Festival: **Noon - midnight**
Cost for Adults:
£10 for full day, £6 for half day
Special discounts:
Discounts available on family tickets
Tickets available from:
Box Office: 01543 262223
Routes by Car:
A5127 Lichfield
Venue:
Guildhall, Lichfield City Centre
Facilities (Parking):
Parking in City Centre. Campsites available
Facilities (Disabled):
Good access for disabled
What's On:
Full day of Cajun music, workshops, jam sessions, Cajun food
Historical Background:
The Arts Association has run regular Cajun evenings for three years. This will be the 3rd festival
Media/Public Comments:
"The best venue in the west Midlands"

Newborough Well Dressing

Type of Festival:
Traditional May Day Celebration
Contact: **Brian Draper**
Address:
Eason Farm
Duffield Lane
Newborough
Staffordshire
DE13 8SH
Tel. No: **01283 575430**
Date(s) of Festival:
1st Monday in May 1999
Times of Festival: **11am**
Cost for Adults: **Free**
Cost for Children: **Free**
Tickets available from: **Not required**
Routes by Car: **A515/A5234**
Train/Other:
Burton Station then taxi
Venue: **Newborough Village**
Facilities (Parking):
Ample parking in cricket ground
What's On:
Morris dancers, clog dancers, maypole, May Queen, fancy dress, village band, children's entertainment, marquee and stalls, fair, sideshows, floral displays and more
Historical Background:
This festival originated in the 14th century during plague times. The wells were blessed and so the festival is a celebration of the village freed from infection

Tamworth Folk Moot

Type of Festival:
Traditionally Derived Music and Dance
Contact:
Tamworth Tourist Information Centre
Address:
Town Hall
Market Street
Tamworth
Staffordshire
B79 7LY
Tel. No: **01827 59134**
Fax No: **01827 59134**
Date(s) of Festival:
23rd - 25th April 1999

Times of Festival:
7.30pm Friday to 5pm Sunday
Cost for Adults:
£12 season Ticket. Many events are free
Cost for Children: **Under 16s free**
Special discounts: **None**
Tickets available from:
Tamworth Folk Moot, P O Box 6219, Sutton Coldfield, West Midlands B75 6HE (Cheques to "Tamworth Folk Moot")
Routes by Car:
Junction 10 M42/A5 to Tamworth
Train/Other:
Tamworth Station (location maps sent out with tickets by mail order)
Venue:
Tamworth Town Centre
Facilities (Parking):
Good Town parking. Campsite (free to season ticket holders), real ale bar, home-made food
What's On:
Most forms of folk dance in the town. Concerts featuring some of the finest acts from Britain's folk scene, street music, music sessions, and singarounds, ceilidhs, barn dances etc
Historical Background:
1999 is the 13th year of Moot, which has gradually grown from very small beginnings as a dance only event in the streets of Tamworth. Now attracts visitors from all over Britain.
Media/Public Comments:
**"Singers and dancers from all over Britain descended on Tamworth at the weekend cheering shoppers and proving once again that the town's annual Folk Moot is a winner"
Tamworth Herald**

SUFFOLK

Aldeburgh Poetry Festival

Type of Festival:
Contemporary Poetry
Contact: **Michael Laskey**
Address:
**Aldeburgh Poetry Trust
Goldines
Goldines Lane
Leiston
Aldeburgh
Suffolk
IP16 4EB**
Tel. No: **01728 830631**
Fax No: **01728 832029**
Date(s) of Festival:
6th - 8th November 1998
Times of Festival:
A dozen events throughout the weekend
Cost for Adults:
From £3 - £6 per event
Cost for Children: **Half price**
Special discounts:
Season Tickets, day tickets, half prices concessions
Routes by Car:
5 miles off A12 between Ipswich and Lowestoft

Train/Other:
To Saxmundham (6 miles) via Ipswich
Venue: **Aldeburgh**
Facilities (Parking):
Parking available
Facilities (Disabled):
Access for disabled
What's On:
Poetry reading by leading National and International Poets, workshops, and masterclass, lectures, cabaret spot, free fringe events, children's events
Historical Background:
Founded in 1989, best attended annual Poetry Festival in England with average audiences in excess of 200
Media/Public Comments:
"Thank you for giving me the best weekend for years. I've been boring everyone with my enthusiasm ever since. Unprofessional maybe, but I'd pay to read at Aldeburgh again" **(Charles Boyle - Poet). One of many glowing reviews of the festival**
General Information:
Delightful small seaside town with good restaurants, pubs etc. Lifeboat station, martello tower and the picturesque River Alde

Aldeburgh Festival of Music and the Arts

Type of Festival: **Music and Arts**
Contact:
Sue Coffer
Director of Press and Marketing
Address:
Aldeburgh Productions
High Street
Aldeburgh
Suffolk
IP15 5AX

Tel. No: **01728 452935**
Fax No: **01728 452715**
Date(s) of Festival:
19th - 28th June 1998
Times of Festival: **Daily**
Cost for Adults: **Various**
Special discounts:
Discounts for advanced bookings, standby, OAPs, under 24s, UB40s, groups of 12+ and Stage Pass holders
Tickets available from:
Sue Coffer (see above)
Routes by Car:
From A12 take A1094 turn right at Snape Church
Train/Other:
Nearest Station Ipswich (mainline); nearest branchline Sadmundham.
Venue:
Various venues within Aldeburgh
Facilities (Parking):
Free parking. Coaches by prior arrangement
Facilities (Disabled):
Disabled parking, access for disabled, ramp access, space for wheelchairs in Hall
What's On:
Opera, concerts, Shakespeare, drama, Boston Youth Symphony Orchestra, film premieres, string quartets, exhibitions, lectures, fringe festival, festival walks and much more
Historical Background:
Founded in 1948 by Benjamin Britten, Peter Pears and Eric Crozier

Felixstowe Fuchsia Festival

Type of Festival: **Floral**
Contact: **Heather Carpenter**
Address:
Felixstowe and District Fuchsia Society
14 Dellwood Avenue
Felixstowe
Suffolk
IP11 9HP
Tel. No: **01394 278239 (evenings)**
Date(s) of Festival:
22nd - 23rd August 1998
Times of Festival:
22nd: 11am - 5.30pm
23rd: 10.30am - 4.30pm
Cost for Adults: **£1**
Cost for Children: **Free**
Tickets available from:
The door. For advice call Felixstowe Tourist Information: 01394 276770
Routes by Car:
RAC signposted route from A14 Eastbound A12
Train/Other: **Ipswich to Felixstowe**
Venue:
Orwell High School, Maidstone Road, Felixstowe
Facilities (Parking): **Free parking**
Facilities (Disabled):
Wheelchairs available
What's On:
An abundance of fuchsias on display. Plants to buy, tombola, experts on hand to ask, British Fuchsia Society display, keybox game, bowling competition, excellent general viewing
Historical Background:
10th year anniversary of the Felixstowe Society. 20 years of fuchsia displays at the school
Media/Public Comments:

"A Fuchsia grower's dream day out"
"A warm and welcoming atmosphere"
"This is an event not to be missed by experienced growers or those just starting out"

Hacheston Rose Festival

Type of Festival: **Floral**
Contact: **Mrs Helen Brookes**
Address:
Hamblestead
Woodbridge
Hasteston
Suffolk
IP13 0DP
Tel. No: **01725 746408**
Bus. **01725 685277**
Date(s) of Festival:
17th - 19th July 1998
Times of Festival:
17th: from 6pm
18th and 19th: from 11am
Cost for Adults:
Flower demonstrations, lectures £5. Line dancing at Pettistree £2.50. Hacheston Church free (donations are requested)
Tickets available from:
Flower demo/lectures: 01728 747547. Line dancing, Pettistree: 01473 622807
Routes by Car:
A12 and B1116 to Hacheston or B1345 to Pettistree
Train/Other:
Liverpool Street to Wickham Market. Bus routes 82 from Ipswich
Venue:
Hacheston Church, Notcutts Rose Fields at Pettistree, Pettistreet Town Centre
Facilities (Parking):

Parking free at both locations. Refreshments in church yard

Facilities (Disabled):
Ramp for access into Hacheston Church. Disabled parking near church

What's On:
Roses arranged by Stowmarket Flower Club in Hacheston Church, transforming the church into a blaze of colour and smell. Also craft fair, flower demonstration, family entertainment. Tour of Notcutts Nurseries, Pettistree and line dancing

Historical Background:
Started in 1985. Notcutts, the major landowner in the village, donates all the roses and profits are shared between the Church (Norman), Village Hall and Retinoblastoma Society (eye cancer in young children)

General Information:
Rose bushes are cultivated in different fields every year; some years they grow near to the church. For 1998 they are in Pettistree

Martime Ipswich

Type of Festival: **Mixed**
Contact: **Jan Davies**
Address:
Ipswich Borough Council
Civic Centre
Civic Drive
Ipswich
Suffolk
IPI 2EE
Tel. No: **01473 262052**
Fax No: **01473 262033**
Date(s) of Festival:
20th - 21st June 1998
Times of Festival:
Saturday: 10am - 11pm

Sunday: 10am - 6pm
Cost for Adults: **£3**
Cost for Children:
Free when accompanied by an adult
Special discounts: **None**
Routes by Car:
A12 from London, A24 from midlands and the north
Train/Other:
Ipswich Station
Venue: **Ipswich Town Centre**
Facilities (Parking):
Park and Ride facility
What's On:
Big band, clowns, circus workshop, Treasure Island, Pirates of Penzance, morris dancers, craft stalls, trade stands, Dragon Boat regatta, Children's Dragon Boat regatta, fancy dress competition and much more

Newmarket Guineas Festival

Type of Festival:
Racing, Music, Art and Heritage
Contact: **Sue Scott**
Address:
Forest Heath District Council
College Heath Road
Mildenhall
Suffolk
Tel. No: **01638 719305**
Fax No: **01638 716493**
Date(s) of Festival:
28th April - 16th May 1999
Times of Festival: **Various**
Cost for Adults:
Various. Some events free
Tickets available from:
Newmarket Tourist Centre:
01638 667200
Routes by Car: **South of A14 bypass**

Train/Other: **Newmarket Station**
Venue:
Kings Theatre, Leisure Centre, Tattersalls, National Horseracing Museum, Newmarket Town Centre
Facilities (Parking):
Free Town parking available
Facilities (Disabled):
Access for disabled
What's On:
Comedy and line dance, piano recital, art exhibition, auctions, morris dancers, street entertainment, living history, children's entertainment (artists to be confirmed)
Historical Background:
1999 will be the 5th Newmarket Guineas Festival to take place in the town. It is now beginning to make a name for itself

Snape Proms

Type of Festival: **Music**
Contact:
Sue Coffer
Director of Press and Marketing
Address:
Aldeburgh Productions
High Street Aldeburgh
Suffolk
IP15 5AX
Tel. No: **01728 452935**
(01728 453074)
Fax No: **01728 452715**
Date(s) of Festival:
1st - 31st August 1998
Times of Festival: **Daily events**
Cost for Adults: **Various**
Special discounts: **TBC**
Tickets available from:
Aldeburgh Productions (see above)
Routes by Car:
From A12 take the A1094 then right at Snape Church

Train/Other:
Train enquiries: 0345 484950
Venue:
Snape Maltings Concert Hall
Facilities (Parking):
Free parking, coach by prior arrangement
Facilities (Disabled):
Access for disabled. Infra red hearing system, disabled parking, ramp access
What's On:
Jazz, folk, blues, world music, theatre, opera and orchestras and much more
Historical Background:
The festival started as a 5 day series in the 1980s and has grown into a one month festival (longest music festival outside London)

The Anglo-Saxon Festival

Type of Festival: **Historical**
Contact: **Liz Proctor**
Address:
The Visitor Centre
West Stowe Country Park
Icklingham Road
West Stowe
Suffolk
IP28 6HG
Tel. No: **01284 728718**
Fax No: **01284 728277**
Date(s) of Festival:
1st - 31st August 1998
Times of Festival:
10.30am - 5pm (last admission 4.15pm)
Cost for Adults: **£4.50**
Cost for Children: **£3**
Special discounts:
Family Ticket £12.50
Tickets available from:
Visitor Centre on the day

Routes by Car:
Village is signposted off A14 and A1101 6 miles Bury
Train/Other:
Bury St Edmunds Station then taxi/cycle/bus for 6miles. Bus No 156 on Sunday and Bank Holidays
Phone **01473 583358 for details**
Venue: **West Stowe**
Facilities (Parking):
Ample free parking
Facilities (Disabled):
Access for disabled, ramps to Visitor Centre. Village sandy but accessible
What's On:
Pole lathe turning, costumed Anglo-Saxons, reconstruction of buildings, crafts/skills, authentic stalls, story telling, guided tours. Market on the last two days of festival

SURREY

The Old Fair of Abinger

Type of Festival: **Traditional**
Contact: **A S G Sparrow**
Address:
Abinger Fair Committee
Griffins
Sutton Lane
Abinger Hammer
Surrey
RH5 6PS
Tel. No: **01306 731083**
Date(s) of Festival:
13th June 1998
(2nd Saturday in June every year)
Times of Festival: **2pm - 5pm**
Cost for Adults:
Free (Parking £2 per car)
Cost for Children: **Free**
Tickets available from:
Car parks and event
Routes by Car:
A25 to Abinger Hammer follow yellow signs to the "Fair"
Train/Other:
Dorking Station (4 miles) Guildford Station (6 miles)
Venue: **Abinger Town**
Facilities (Parking):
Ample parking at a charge of £2 per car within 100yds of site. Ice cream, refreshments etc
What's On:
Procession onto Green, crowning of May Queen, maypole dancing, juggling, tug of war, falconry, flowers and music in church, Punch and Judy, raffle, produce stalls, roast lamb on spit, arts and crafts, books, tossing the sheaf and much more
Historical Background:
Post war revival of the medieval churchyard fair which provided food and entertainment for pilgrims en route to Canterbury
Media/Public Comments:
It has always been very well received. The profits have always been split between local charities, local amenities and Abinger Church

International Playwriting Festival

Type of Festival: **Playwriting**
Contact: **Rose Marie Vernon**
Address:
Warehouse Theatre
Dingwall Road
Croydon
Surrey
CRO 2NF
Tel. No: **0181 681 1257**
Fax No: **0181 688 6699**
E-mail: **warehouse@dircon.co.uk**
Date(s) of Festival:
27-29 November 1998
How to Enter:
Entries welcome from all parts of the world. Scripts and 2 SAEs (one script size) should reach Warehouse by end of first week in July, accompanied by entry form (available from Theatre)
Routes by Car:
The Warehouse Theatre is adjacent to East Croydon Station on the corner of George Street and Dingwall Road. Follow the signs to Fairfields Halls then East Croydon Station
Train/Other:
Turn right out of the station and right again. Less than a minutes walk. Or travel to West Croydon Station and it's a 10 minutes walk through the town. Buses to East Croydon include 54, 64, 130, 166, 197, 353, 367 and 726
Venue: **Warehouse Theatre**
Facilities (Parking):
Multi storey car parks are located on Dingwall Road and Hazeldean Road. Please note there is no parking on Dingwall Road until further notice (due to Tramlink)
What's On:

Annual competition for full- length, unperformed plays, judged by a panel of theatre professionals. Finalists given rehearsed readings. Previous winners include Kevin Hood "Beached", Anne Aylor "Children of the Dust" and Mark Bunyan "Dinner"
Historical Background:
The festival was founded in 1985. Now shares plays with partner festival in Italy, the Premio Candoni Arta Terme
General information:
Please contact the Box Office on 0181 680 4060 for more details

Autocaravan VW Swapfest

Type of Festival:
VW Swap Festival
Contact: **Joan Whitehair**
Address:
Autocavan Ltd
103 Lower Weybourne Lane
Badshot Lea
Farnham
Surrey
GU9 9LG
Tel. No: **01252 346825**
Fax No: **01252 346811**
Date(s) of Festival:
27th September 1998
Times of Festival: **Opens 9am**
Cost for Adults:
£2 and £1.50 per van
Cost for Children: **Under 16s free**
Tickets available from: **On the gate**
Routes by Car:
A331 off M3 Junction 4, A287 Junction 5, M3, A31 from Alton and Winchester
Venue:
T. S. Swiftsure, Lower Weybourne

Lane, Badshot Lea
Facilities (Parking):
Extensive parking. Five acre Swapmeet site. On site refreshments and catering
What's On:
Thousands of new and used parts, trade stands, Show 'n' Shine race and custom car display, competitions and prize draw
Historical Background:
Festival in its 2nd year
Media/Public Comments:
Many congratulations from the general public on lasts years festival

Guildford Festival Markets

Type of Festival:
Craft Market and Entertainment
Contact: **Jonathan Tatlow**
Address:
14a The Mount
Guildford
Surrey
GU2 5HN
Tel. No: **01483 536981**
Date(s) of Festival:
4th - 11th July (except Sunday 5th July) 1998
Times of Festival:
10.30am (9.30 Sats) - 4.30pm (5.30pm Sats)
Cost for Adults: **Free**
Cost for Children: **Free**
Tickets available from: **Not required**
Routes by Car:
Off A3 to Town Centre
Train/Other:
Intercity from London Waterloo (30 mins). River Wey Navigation passes through Town Centre
Venue: **Guildford Town Centre**
Facilities (Parking):

Town Centre car parks and Park and Ride
What's On:
Local and national craft stalls, free street entertainers (Saturdays)
Historical Background:
Daily centrepiece of Guildford's Summer Festival - held annually since 1983
Media/Public Comments:
"Consistently popular and successful hence - long life"
General Information:
Potential stall holders: (British Crafts only) apply to: Organiser, Guildford Borough Council (promotes the whole Summer Festival)

Guildford Summer Festival

Type of Festival: **The Arts**
Contact:
Julie Maskery - Administrator
Address:
Guildford Borough Council
Millmead House
Millmead
Guildford
Surrey
Tel. No: **01483 444719**
Fax No: **01483 444717**
Date(s) of Festival:
28th June - 13th July 1998
Times of Festival: **Various**
Cost for Adults:
£2 up to £15 depending on event
Cost for Children:
Concessions available
Special discounts:
Concessions available
Tickets available from:
Festival Box Office outlets:
Electric Theatre: 01483 444789
Civic Hall: 01483 444555

Tourist Information Centre:
01483 444334
Routes by Car:
A3 from London and the South Coast. Park and Ride, many of which are just outside the City Centre
Train/Other:
Intercity from London Waterloo (30 mins)
Venue:
Guildford and surrounding area
Facilities (Parking):
4 main car parks - all accessible to town. There is also Park and Ride
What's On:
Theatre, concert in Shalford Park, jazz with Acker Bilk, Last Night at the Proms with fireworks, songs and dance, exhibitions, drama, river events, craft market, workshops, guided walks and tours, boating rally. Children's entertainment, street theatre etc
Historical Background:
The festival has been running for 13 years
Media/Public Comments:
"The Summer Festival is the most colourful of the Guildford Festivals with many open air events, a High Street craft market, plays in the Castle grounds, music in Shalford Park, the decorated boats and alfresco art exhibitions" The Mayor

Guildford Book Festival

Type of Festival: **Literature**
Contact: **Joan Koenig**
Address:
Old Coach House
Cuifaill
Lewes
East Sussex
BN7 2BE

Tel. No: **01273 478943**
Fax No: **01273 478943**
Date(s) of Festival:
24th October - 1st November 1998
Times of Festival:
Day and evening events
Cost for Adults: **£2 - £5**
Cost for Children: **Free**
Tickets available from:
Box Office: 01483 444334
Routes by Car:
A3 from London and the South Coast. Park and Rides, many of which are just outside the city centre
Train/Other:
Intercity from London Waterloo (30 mins)
Venue: **Guildford**
What's On:
Exhibitions, literary day schools, literary lunch at the Guildhall, poetry, interviews with many famous writers such as Roy Hattersley, Kathy Staff, Tom Baker to name a few. Literary launches, theatre etc
Historical Background:
Held for the first time in 1990, the festival aims to attract as broad a cross section of people. Aims to seek a balance between lesser known writers and media personalities and best selling authors and poets
General Information:
Adult writing competition. For details please telephone: 01483 440253
Box Office Outlets:
Electric Theatre: 01483 444789
Festival Box Office: 01483 444334
Guildford Civic Centre: 01483 444555, Yvonne Arnaud Theatre: 01483 440000

Guildford Fusion Festival '98

Type of Festival: **Music**
Contact: **Tony Scott**
Address:
54 Haydon Place
Guildford
Surrey
GU1 4NE
Tel. No: **01483 454159**
Fax No: **01483 306551**
Date(s) of Festival:
7th - 9th August 1998
Times of Festival:
7th: 6pm - 11pm
8th: midday - 11pm
9th: midday - 9pm
Cost for Adults: **TBC**
Tickets available from:
Tony Scott (see above)
Routes by Car:
A3 takes the visitor within sight of the festival
Train/Other:
Guildford station (5 mins walk)
Venue:
Stoke Park, Guildford
Facilities (Parking):
Town Parking. Camping facilities
Facilities (Disabled):
High standard of facilities for the disabled
What's On:
60 top live acts on 3 separate stages, children's area, carnival parade, bazaar, beer tents
Historical Background:
7th year of festival
Media/Public Comments:
"The best line up all year" 1997 festival goer
General Information:
The festival is next to the Guildford Spectrum - a multicomplex
sports arena comprising of ice rink, swimming, ten pin bowling. This is a very popular venue for visitors to Guildford

Ambient Green Picnic

Type of Festival:
Music, DIY Culture, Environmental
Contact:
Liam Rich and Craig Mills (The Coalition)
Address:
P O Box 217
Guildford
Surrey
GU1 1WS
Tel. No: **01483 203245 or 01483 826224**
Fax No: **01483 203212**
Date(s) of Festival: **11th July 1998**
Times of Festival: **12 noon - 9pm**
Cost for Adults:
Free (donation entry)
Cost for Children: **Free**
Tickets available from: **Not required**
Routes by Car:
A3 to Guildford. Park in Guildford and then walk to site. Park and Ride available
Train/Other:
Park and Ride. Guildford Station. Regular Buses. The organisers emphasise to leave the car at home as it is a "Green Fair"
Venue:
Millmead Island, Guildford
Facilities (Parking):
Town Centre parking. Park and Ride. Site is within walking distance of most parking areas within Guildford Town Centre
Facilities (Disabled):
Access for disabled
What's On:
Dance stage, acoustic stage, caba-

ret tent, ambient lounge, healing area, children's area, stalls, food

Historical Background:

First festival was in 1994 as a protest against restrictive measures of the Criminal Justice Act 1994. Now 5000 strong, it now has full council support

Media/Public Comments:

"Please don't come by car - it's a Green Fair. Spectate and participate. Bring what you expect to find - instruments, food, drink and good vibes!" The Coalition

The Great Gardening Show

Type of Festival: **Horticultural**

Contact:

Linda Calvete

Good Timing Events

Address:

242 Connaught Road

Brookwood

Woking

Surrey

GU24 0AE

Tel. No: **01483 797332**

Fax No: **01483 476350**

Date(s) of Festival:

24th - 26th July 1998

Times of Festival: **10am - 6pm**

Cost for Adults: **£5**

Cost for Children: **Free**

Special discounts:

OAPs, UB40s and students: £4

Groups of 10+ £3.50 in advance

Tickets available from:

At the gate (can book in advance at above number)

Routes by Car:

Just off the B3000 - signposted Compton from A3 or A3100

Train/Other:

Nearest station is Guildford, then taxi to Loseley (10/15 mins). Bus from Guildford, but this involves a very long walk

Venue: **Loseley Park, Guildford**

Facilities (Parking):

Easy and free car park, excellent refreshments including Loseley ice cream

Facilities (Disabled):

Disabled parking and toilets

What's On:

Several show gardens, large floral marquee, sundries marquee, trade stands with plants, furniture, garden equipment, garden crafts, speciality foods from Surrey and Sussex, "Gardeners Question Time", demonstrations, children's entertainment

Historical Background:

A local horticultural festival was needed to give people the chance to see some of the best Growers/Exhibitors in the country at sensible prices

Media/Public Comments:

"The perfect setting and wide variety offer a fine balance of interest for expert and beginner alike" Surrey Advertiser

"One of best shows we have been to" Grass Roots TV production team

Swan Upping Festival

Type of Festival:

Swan Conservation

Contact: **The Vintners' Company**

Address:

Vintners Hall

Upper Thames Street

London

Tel. No: **0171 236 1863**

Fax No: **0171 236 8177**

Date(s) of Festival:

20th - 24th July 1998

Times of Festival:

Start off at 9am and 10am each day. Loyal Toast is drunk between 4pm and 6pm on Monday. Closing ceremony between 4.30pm and 6pm on Friday

Cost for Adults: **Free**

Cost for Children: **Free**

Venue:

River Thames. Start Sunbury Lock, finish Abingdon Bridge

What's On:

It is possible to view the Swan Uppers at work from various points on the towpath alongside the River Thames and, although the Vintners' Company organises a Swan Voyage one of the days, this is a private function

Historical Background:

Several years ago the swans were considered to belong to the Crown, but other people could own swans with permission. The Vintners and Dyers Companies were granted privileges to own some swans. Said to go back to 1483 and exercised since 1510

Media/Public Comments:

"Every July, the Swan Uppers take to the boats to perform a centuries old ceremony. Last year we accompanied them on part of their journey as they skimmed the surface of the Thames"

General Information:

The purpose of the ceremony has been to mark the swans of the Queen and the two companies so that their ownership can be easily recognised. 6 rowing boats are used each with a Swan Keeper, Swan Master and Swan Marker

Harvest Home

Type of Festival: **Traditional**

Contact: **Henry Jackson**

Address:

Rural Life Centre,
Old Kiln Museum Trust
Reeds Road
Tilford
Surrey
GU10 2DL

Tel. No: **01252 795571 or 01252 792300**

Fax No: **01252 795571**

Date(s) of Festival:

4th October 1998

Times of Festival: **11am - 6pm**

Cost for Adults: **£3**

Cost for Children: **£1.50**

Special discounts:

UB40s, students, OAPS £2.50. Groups of 30+ by prior booking to Rural Life Centre

Tickets available from: **At the gate**

Routes by Car:

3 miles south of Farnham. Brown sign off the A287 (Hindhead A32 Farnham A31)

Train/Other:

Farnham Station 3 miles

Venue:

Eashing Chapel and at the Rural Life Centre

Facilities (Parking):

Parking on site, café, playground, shop etc

Facilities (Disabled):

Full facilities for disabled

What's On:

This traditional ceremony with corn dollies, the produce of the countryside and a Harvest Festival in the Eashing Chapel

Media/Public Comments:

"To those who preserve our past - our thanks"

Tilford Bach Festival

Type of Festival: **Music**
Contact:
Pete Wisbey - General Enquiries
Address:
Tilford Bach Society
12 White Cottage Close
Farnham
Surrey
Tel. No: **01252 782167**
Date(s) of Festival:
28th - 30th May 1998
Times of Festival: **8pm onwards**
Cost for Adults: **£5, £8, £10**
Cost for Children: **75% off**
Special discounts:
Concessions for students
Tickets available from:
Helen Malyon (at above address)
Routes by Car:
Via A3 on M3 through Farnham to Tilford
Train/Other:
Farnham Station then taxi (5 miles)
Venue:
All Saints Parish Church, Tilford, Great Hall of Farnham Castle
Facilities (Parking):
Free parking close to church
Facilities (Disabled):
Access for disabled
What's On:
The Bach Festival has been privileged to be involved in the early careers of singers such as Dame Janet Baker, Emma Kirkby, Ian Partridge, John Shirley Quirk, Rogers Covey-Crump, Robert Tear and many others
Historical Background:
The Festival began in 1952 and has continued to this day under the musical direction of Denys Darlow. The well-known harpsichordist,
Paul Nicholson joined Denys as co-ordinator of music. Denys Darlow has taught at the Royal College of Music for many years
General Information:
Tilford is a very small charming village with a green, pub and sloping cricket pitch. The village is featured in a number of TV commercials. The Festival is a fully professional production but younger performers are encouraged

Woking Beer Festival

Type of Festival: **Beer**
Contact: **Andrew Calfe**
Address:
Woking Park
Kingfield Road
Woking
Surrey
GU22 9BA
Tel. No: **01483 771122**
Fax No: **01483 776005**
Date(s) of Festival:
6th - 7th November 1998
Times of Festival:
3 sessions:Friday 6th: 6pm -11pm, Saturday 7th: 11am - 3.30pm and 6pm - 11pm
Cost for Adults: **£4**
Cost for Children:
£1 (only Saturday lunch time)
Tickets available from:
Woking Leisure Centre
Routes by Car:
Off Junction 10,11 M25. Follow signs to Woking
Train/Other:
10 minute walk from Woking Station
Venue:
Woking Park, Kingfield Road
Facilities (Parking): **Free car parking**
Facilities (Disabled):

Ramps etc for disabled
What's On:
Real ale, live bands, Wurlitzer organ
Historical Background:
Started in 1994 to help celebrate Woking's centenary year. So successful it was decided to keep it as an annual event
Media/Public Comments:
"Building up to become one of the most popular festivals in the South East"

EAST SUSSEX

Battle Festival
Type of Festival: **Mixed Arts**
Contact: **Judith Warrington**
Address:
Chairman Battle Festival Society
2 Archers Court
Shirlea View
Battle
East Sussex
TN33 0UV
Tel. No: **01424 775275**
Fax No: **01424 774928**
Date(s) of Festival:
22nd May - 7th June 1998
Times of Festival:
Varies. Evening events start at 7.30pm

Cost for Adults:
£4 - £10 depending on event
Cost for Children:
£1.50 - £5 depending on event
Special discounts:
Concessions for students
Tickets available from:
Tourist Information Office:
01424 773721
Routes by Car: **A21- A2100**
Train/Other:
Frequent services to and from Charing Cross, London (1hr 40 mins). Buses from Hastings and outlying areas
Venue:
Various venues within Battle town
Facilities (Parking): **Ample Parking**
Facilities (Disabled):
Disabled parking to Abbey and to Memorial Hall. No disabled toilets
What's On:
"Matters Matrimonial" with Wendy Craig and Francis Matthews Sunday 31st May. "Taste of Sussex" wine tasting 27th May, historical town walk including the cellars 26th May. street theatre, Medieval fair, open air art exhibitions, Flower Festival, art and craft exhibitions, organ recital, dance event, live folk/country and western band, children's entertainment
Historical Background:
38 years old, the Arts Festival began as an "Art" festival only (paintings) became "Mixed Arts". Later Sir Neville Marriner became Music Director and is now Hon. President
Media/Public Comments:
"Capacity crowd was wowed" (Honor Blackman 1997 Festival performer)
"Traditional mixture of entertainment"

Battle Medieval Fair

Type of Festival:
Street Market with Entertainment
Contact: **C H Smith**
Address:
39 High Street
Battle
East Sussex
TN33 0EE
Tel. No: **01424 774447**
Fax No: **01424 7763664**
E-mail: **chpsmith@lineone.net**
Date(s) of Festival:
23rd - 24th May 1999
Times of Festival: **10am - 4.30pm**
Cost for Adults: **Free**
Cost for Children: **Free**
Tickets available from: **Not required**
Routes by Car:
A2100 to Abbey Green in centre of Battle outside Abbey
Train/Other: **Battle Station**
Venue:
Abbey Green in centre of Battle outside Abbey
Facilities (Parking):
Car parking in Battle Abbey and public car parks in town
What's On:
Maypole dancing, street theatre, wandering minstrels, jesters etc. Stallholders all in costume, food fair, circus workshop, games and lots more
Historical Background:
Established by the Chamber of commerce as part of the promotion of Battle

"Bexhill 100" Festival of Motoring

Type of Festival: **Motoring**
Contact: **Brian Storkey**
Address:
The Bexhill 100 Ltd

49 Marina
Bexhill on Sea
East Sussex
TN40 1BQ
Tel. No: **01424 730564**
Date(s) of Festival:
2nd - 3rd May 1999
Times of Festival: **10am - 6pm**
Cost for Adults: **Free**
Cost for Children: **Free**
Tickets available from: **Not required**
Routes by Car:
From London via A21; A22; or M23 (was A23) Coast Road A269
Train/Other:
Regular trains from London Victoria via Eastbourne. Bexhill Station about ¼ mile from festival. Only 1¼ hours from Gatwick. 1¼ hrs from le Shuttle, 1 hr from Newhaven
Venue: **Bexhill on Sea**
Facilities (Parking):
Arranged car parks and Park and Ride. Toilet facilities and numerous food outlets
Facilities (Disabled):
Toilet facilities for the disabled
What's On:
Hundreds of vintage, veteran, classic, American, racing and military vehicles. Stands, stalls, shops, aerobatic displays, parachute drops, yachts at sea, parades, bands, clowns, entertainment arena, car clubs, simulators, funfair, trolley bus rides, etc
Historical Background:
In May 1902 the Earl De La Warr, in conjunction with the Automobile Club of GB and Ireland now known as the RAC, organised the first automobile racing on British soil in Bexhill. In 1990 four motoring enthusiasts started the "Bexhill 100" in commemoration.

Media/Public Comments:
"It's an event for all the family"
"One of the biggest and best shows in the South of England"
"A very friendly Festival"
General Information:
Bexhill on Sea is known as "the birthplace of British Motor Racing". Festival attracts a family audience in excess of 100,000 over the 2 days. Some of the rarest cars, valued at millions of pounds, take part

Brighton Festival

Type of Festival: **Mixed Arts**
Contact:
Lisa Wolfe - Marketing Manager
Address:
Brighton Festival Society Ltd
21-22 Old Steine
Brighton
East Sussex
BN1 1EL
Tel. No: **01273 292950**
Fax No: **01273 622453**
Web site:
www.brighton-Festival.org.uk
Date(s) of Festival:
1st May - 23rd May 1999
Times of Festival: **Various**
Tickets available from:
01273 292950 for brochure
Routes by Car:
A23 or A27 main routes into Brighton
Train/Other:
London Victoria (50 mins) or Thameslink via Kings Cross
Venue: **Various Brighton venues**
Facilities (Parking):
Varies according to venue
Facilities (Disabled):
Varies according to venue
What's On:

Over 700 arts events fill the concert halls, theatres, streets, and parks. Opens with a lavish children's parade along the seafront. Music on the streets at twilight and concert by the Detroit Symphony Orchestra (1998) in the evening. Plus street theatre etc
Historical Background:
1999 heralds the 33rd year promoting the very best cultural entertainment. Brighton Festival is Britain's largest celebration of the Arts
Media/Public Comments:
"A tantalising glimpse of the good life" The Independent
"A festival of contrasts - come and join us"
Brighton Festival Society Ltd
General Information:
Pick up a festival brochure in the town or call: 01273 292961.

visions98

The Festival of International Animated Theatre
Type of Festival:
Puppetry and Animated Theatre
Contact:
Lucia Reynolds - Administrator
Address:
University of Brighton Gallery
Grand Parade
Brighton
East Sussex
BN2 2JY
Tel. No: **01273 643012**
Fax No: **01273 643128**
E-mail: **clm1@brighton.ac.uk**
Date(s) of Festival:
5th - 31st October 1998
Times of Festival: **Various**
Cost for Adults: **Various**
Special discounts:

Discounts available for UB40s, OAPs, students and groups

Tickets available from:

Sallis Benney Theatre Box Office in University of Brighton

Routes by Car:

A23 from London to Brighton, A259 from East Coast and A27 from West Coast

Train/Other:

Direct trains from London Bridge, Victoria, Kings Cross, Bedford, Luton, Gatwick, Edinburgh, Bath

Venue: **Brighton University**

Facilities (Parking):

NCP car park, Church Street, Brighton

Facilities (Disabled):

Full disabled access to Sallis Benney Theatre

What's On:

Artists from around the world bring together a programme of lively shows, exhibitions, screenings, outreach projects. Highlights include: improvisation from Improbable Theatre, a racy version of Salome, animated fun from the world of Yello, and more

Historical Background:

visions98 is a biennial festival promoted by the University of Brighton. First launched in 1994 and it has a national and international profile. Reaching audiences across the country, visions "Satellite" festivals will take place in many UK venues

Media/Public Comments:

"Wonderful work that celebrates the possibilities of Theatre" The Guardian

General Information:

Also puppetry workshops for teachers and young people in schools, colleges and community groups and physical theatre workshops for practitioners

Charleston Festival

Type of Festival:

Arts and Literature

Contact: **Shaun Romain**

Address:

Charleston Farmhouse Charleston Trust Nr Firle Lewes East Sussex BN8 6LL

Tel. No: **01323 811626**

Date(s) of Festival:

27th - 31st May 1999

Times of Festival: **2pm - 5pm**

Cost for Adults: **£6 per event**

Tickets available from:

Shaun Romaine (see above)

Routes by Car:

Off A27 halfway between Brighton and Eastbourne

Train/Other:

London Victoria to Lewes

Venue: **Charleston Farmhouse**

Facilities (Parking):

Car park, tea room, toilets

Facilities (Disabled):

Disabled parking, disabled toilets, disabled access to events, limited disabled access to house

What's On:

Performances, talks relating to this years theme. Artists (TBC)

Charleston Manor Festival

Type of Festival: **Chamber Music**

Contact: **Sue Boxer**

Address:

12a Arlington Road

Eastbourne
East Sussex
BN21 1DJ
Tel. No: **01323 639548**
Fax No: **01323 416703**
Date(s) of Festival:
23rd - 28th June 1998
Times of Festival:
Masterclasses 23rd and 24th: 6pm. Concerts 26th: 8pm, Saturday 7.30pm, Sunday 5pm
Cost for Adults:
Concerts: £17.50, £12.50, £7.50
Masterclasses £3
Cost for Children: **Masterclasses £2**
Special discounts:**Students £5**
Tickets available from:
Box Office: Michelham Priory 01323 442121
Routes by Car:
Follow signs to Litlington off the A259 and A27
Train/Other:
Polegate Station is 4½ miles away; Seaford is 2½ miles
Venue: **Charleston Manor House**
Facilities (Parking):
Parking available. Refreshments available.
What's On:
Artistic director Robert Cohen (the cellist). Enjoy exquisite music, Italianate garden and grounds of the Manor House. Enjoy dinner in candlelit coach house, picnic in the garden, refreshments in marquee
Historical Background:
9th year under Robert Cohen's direction. However there have been other summer concerts since Lady Birley, a former owner, launched them in the mid-1930s
Media/Public Comments:
"Glorious music, atmosphere, like the Glyndebourne of Old"

Chiddingly Festival

Type of Festival:
Mixed Art, Craft and Folk
Contact: **Linda Bailey**
Address:
Old Stable Cottage
Tounsley
Blackboys
Uckfield
East Sussex
TN22 5HT
Tel. No: **01825 830747**
Date(s) of Festival:
24th September - 4th October 1998
Times of Festival: **Various**
Cost for Adults: **Various**
Routes by Car:
Located off A22 between Hailsham and Uckfield
Train/Other:
To Lewes Station or Tunbridge Wells.
Venue: **Chiddingly**
Facilities (Parking): **Parking**
Facilities (Disabled):
Access for disabled
What's On:
Music, theatre, craft events, workshops, concert, recitals, pub events.Watch, listen and participate in a range of events and workshop activities
Historical Background:
Set up to provide a platform for amateur and professional talents of all ages.
Media/Public Comments:
"The success of the small village of Chiddingly in acquiring such a splendid and well earned reputation for excellence for its annual Festival is quite remarkable" (Under Secretary of State for National Heritage)

Sherlock Holmes Festival

Type of Festival: **Literary**
Contact: **Mr Julian Roup**
Address:
Home Farm Cottage
Warren Road
Crowborough
East Sussex
Tel. No: **01892 663906**
Fax No: **01892 669200**
Date(s) of Festival:
1st weekend in July each year
Times of Festival: **All day**
Cost for Adults:
Various. Victorian Street market is free
Cost for Children: **Various**
Tickets available from:
Shops in Crowborough and at the Town Hall
Routes by Car:
A26 from Tunbridge Wells or Uckfield
Train/Other: **Crowborough Station**
Venue:
High Street, Crowborough
Facilities (Parking):
Town Centre parking
What's On:
Writers workshops, Victorian street market, music, mystery trails, walks, "Hound of the Baskervilles" dog show, short story competitions, cricket match, golf match. General celebration of the life and times of Sir Arthur Conan Doyle
Historical Background:
Crowborough was home to Sir Arthur Conan Doyle for the last 23 years of his life where he wrote a number of his Sherlock Holmes books
Media/PublicComments:
"Quintissentially English and eccentric" Der Spiegel
General Information:
Many people dress up in period costume. Visitors come from as far afield as Japan. There are 300 Sherlock Holmes societies around the world

Airborne '98

Type of Festival: **Air Festival**
Contact:
Marie Thompson,
Eastbourne Borough Council
Address:
Tourism and Community Services Dept
College Road
Eastbourne
East Sussex
BN21 4JJ
Tel. No: **01323 415442**
Fax No: **01323 638686**
Date(s) of Festival:
20th - 23rd August 1998
Times of Festival: **10am - 6pm daily**
Cost for Adults: **Free**
Cost for Children: **Free**
Tickets available from: **Not required**
Routes by Car:
A22 connects Eastbourne to London's M25
Train/Other:
80 mins from London Victoria; 45 mins from Gatwick Express coach from London Victoria
Venue: **Eastbourne**
Facilities (Disabled):
Good disabled access and disabled parking close by
What's On:
Red Arrows, aerobatic displays, parachute displays, helicopter rides, simulator rides, Birdman

Rally, RAF careers exhibition, arena events, trade stands, funfair, go-karting, firework display finale
Historical Background:
6th year of the event

Family Festival of Tennis

Type of Festival: **Sports**
Contact: **Marjorie Howie**
Address:
LTA
Queen's Club,
Barons Court
West Kensington
London W14 9EG
Tel. No: **0171 381 7000**
Fax No: **0171 381 5965**
Date(s) of Festival:
3rd - 8th August 1998
Times of Festival: **10am start**
Cost for Adults:
Free for spectators. Entry costs to be confirmed
Routes by Car:
A22 connects Eastbourne to London M25
Train/Other:
80 mins to London Victoria, 45 mins to Gatwick. Express Coach to London Victoria, Newhaven 20 mins, Dover 2 hrs away
Venue: **Devonshire Park.**
Facilities (Parking):
Parking at the Devonshire Park
Facilities (Disabled):
Disabled seating and parking
What's On:
Junior tennis and family events eg. father/son, mother/daughter and mixed doubles. Wimbledon's No 1 Court information and memorabilia. Refreshments
Historical Background:

Devonshire Park home of tennis for over 100 years. New £4.1 million Tennis Centre. Event has been running for 6 years

Hailsham Charter Market

Type of Festival:
Street Entertainment/Medieval Market
Contact: **Tim Dowsett**
Address:
Dowsett Associates
1st Floor Suite
11 High Street
Hailsham
East Sussex
BN27 1AL
Tel. No: **01323 442434**
Fax No: **01323 849922**
Date(s) of Festival:
12th September 1998
Times of Festival: **10am - 4pm**
Cost for Adults: **Free**
Cost for Children: **Free**
Tickets available from: **Not required**
Routes by Car:
A22 (8 miles north of Eastbourne)
Train/Other:
Polegate (Victoria/Eastbourne)
Venue: **High Street, Hailsham**
Facilities (Parking):
Excellent free local parking
What's On:
Street entertainment, Medieval market
Historical Background:
Over 10,000 people visited this event in 1997 and the festival is now in its second year

Hangleton and Knoll Community Festival

Type of Festival: **Traditional**
Contact: **Anna King**
Address:
Hangleton Community Centre
Harmsworth Crescent
Hove
East Sussex
Tel. No: **01273 410858**
Date(s) of Festival:
24th August - 4th September 1998
Times of Festival: **TBC**
Cost for Adults: **Free**
Cost for Children: **Free**
Tickets available from: **Not required**
Train/Other:
Hove Station or Brighton then catch Buses, 5, 5A or 5B
Venue:
Various indoor and outdoor venues within Hangleton
Facilities (Parking):
Parking in the area. Many events on recreational grounds, fields etc
What's On:
Sculpture trail, alien invasion weekend, Old Trades day, Memorabilia Day, live music, dancing, puppet theatre, funfair
Historical Background:
First started in 1979 by the residents within the community.
Media/Public Comments:
Praise from local newspapers and the general public

Hastings National Poetry Festival

Type of Festival: **Poetry**
Contact:
Josephine Austin
Editor of "First Time"
Address:

4 Burdett Place
George Street
Hastings
East Sussex
TN34 3ED
Tel. No: **01424 428855**
Fax No: **01424 428855**
Date(s) of Festival:
7th - 8th November 1998
Times of Festival: **2pm - 11pm**
Cost for Adults:
£5 for 2 days. £3 per day. Entry fee for each poem is £2. Entry form from J Austin (see above)
Cost for Children: **Half price**
Tickets available from:
Marina Pavilion, St Leonards on Sea
Routes by Car:
A21 from London, A27 from Brighton, A259 from Dover
Train/Other:
Charing Cross or London Victoria to Hastings
Venue: **Hastings**
Facilities (Parking): **Ample parking**
Facilities (Disabled):
Excellent facilities for disabled
What's On:
Listen to and perform own written work, meet and discuss poetry with small press editors. Meeting like minded people. Enjoy first class performances from established and non-established poets
Historical Background:
Began in 1968. 1998 is 30th anniversary to encourage original work and confidence to performers
Media/Public Comments:
"the most uncommercial, friendly, outgoing, encouraging, Poetry Festival still going and still non Arts supported"
"The Festival for the Poets by the Poets"

General Information:
Enjoy original exciting work from established Poets from all over Britain, Europe and the Commonwealth. If you want wall to wall poetry from Saturday afternoon to Sunday evening with only a short break to eat and sleep this Festival is a must

Hastings Young People's Festival

Type of Festival:
Arts, Film Animation
Contact: **Colin Booth**
Address:
Electro Studios
Seaside Road
St Leonards On Sea
East Sussex
TN38 0AL
Tel. No: **01424 718837**
Date(s) of Festival:
17th May - 30th May 1999
Routes by Car:
Hastings is on the A259 Coast Road from Worthing through to Dover and beyond
Train/Other:
London Charing Cross/Victoria
Venue:
Various venues within Hastings
Facilities (Parking):
Parking areas within the Town Centre
What's On:
Kite festival, film and animation festival, music events, beach sculpture, workshops, BMX jam and lots more
Historical Background:
Launched in 1993 as a children's Festival and has grown since.
Media/Public Comments:
"Best event in the Hastings calendar"

Herstmonceux Castle Medieval Festival

Type of Festival: **Medieval**
Contact: **Mr C Geisler**
Address:
The Malcolm Group Events Ltd
Ground Floor
3 Brunswick Place
Hove
East Sussex
BN3 1EA
Tel. No: **01273 723249**
Tel/fax:
24 hr info line: 0891 172902
E-mail: **malcolm@fastnet.co.uk**
Web site:
http: //stukenberg.com/malcolm/
Date(s) of Festival:
29th - 31st August 1998
Times of Festival: **10am - 6pm**
Cost for Adults: **£9**
Cost for Children: **£4 Ages 4-14**
Special discounts:
OAPs £8, group discounts
Tickets available from: **The castle**
Routes by Car:
A21 due south from Tunbridge Wells
Train/Other:
By rail to Polegate Station, shuttle bus stops every 30 mins at Polegate Station, North Street, Hailsham and Gardner Street, Hertsmonceux. Fare £1 return
Venue: **Herstmonceux Castle**
Facilities (Parking):
Free parking. Food and drink available
What's On:
Battle re-enactments, falconry, jousting, archery, longbow tournament, medieval crafts, fire eaters, Norse story teller, hand to hand combats, music, living history,

Medieval village, Medieval puppeteers, rousing music, sword play and theatre

Historical Background:
This festival was conceived in 1993 to mark the reopening of the 15th century moated castle. Following a 5 year growth plan the festival has become the largest annual event of its kind in England.

Media/Public Comments:
"The festival has proved to be a highly popular regional success and has reinforced its reputation as the largest medieval festival of its kind in the UK"

General Information:
The Malcolm Group is planning to make the event an even bigger attraction in 1998. 20,000 people passed through the gates over a 3 day period last year, even though the weather was wet on the Bank Holiday Monday

Southdown Real Ale and Cider Festival

Type of Festival: **Beer**
Contact: **Peter Mitchell**
Address:
26 The Drive
Shoreham by Sea
Lewes
East Sussex
Tel. No: **01273 462093**
Date(s) of Festival:
3rd - 4th July 1998
Times of Festival:
3rd: 11am-10.30pm. 4th: 11am - 3.30pm. 5th 5.30pm-10.30pm
Cost for Adults: **Various**
Special discounts:
Discount for CAMRA members
Tickets available from:
PO Box 2907, Brighton, BN1 3NT

Train/Other:
5 mins walk from Lewes Station
Venue: **Lewes Town Hall**
Facilities (Parking): **Town Parking**
Facilities (Disabled):
Disabled access and toilets
What's On:
Entertainment at each evening venue. Sample 50 real ales, traditional ciders and perries, country wines and bottled conditioned beers
Historical Background:
This Beer Festival is held in Lewes which has strong brewing traditions
Media/Public Comments:
All comments from visitors and media are very favourable

Festival at the Fort

Type of Festival:
Open Air Theatre and Jazz
Contact:
Ian Everest - Fort Manager
Address:
Newhaven Fort
Fort Road
Newhaven
East Sussex
Tel. No:
01273 517622 or Carole Buchain, Lewes District Council: 01273 484167
Fax No: **01273 512059**
Date(s) of Festival:
27th July - 24th August 1998
Times of Festival:
See below for programme details
Cost for Adults: **TBC**
Tickets available from:
Newhaven Fort
Routes by Car:
Off A259 from Brighton or Eastbourne
Train/Other:
Newhaven Station

Venue: **Newhaven Fort**
Facilities (Parking):
Ample parking and Refreshments
Facilities (Disabled):
Ample parking for the disabled
What's On:
ODDSOX in "Much Ado About Nothing" , 24th August at 7.30pm. Community Opera with Glyndebourne Education, 10th July at 7pm. "Jazz on a Summer's Night", 25th July at 7.30pm. OPHABDOM in "The Miller's Tale" 27th July at 7.30pm
Historical Background:
Napoleonic fort high on the cliffs above Newhaven harbour. Very colourful, unusual theatre
Media/Public Comments:
"Great family night out"
"Very popular. Early booking essential"
General Information:
Lots of music and audience participation

Rye Medieval Festival

Type of Festival: **Medieval**
Contact: **Norman Bennett**
Address:
Rye Medieval Society
Half House
Military Road
Rye
East Sussex
TN31 7NY
Tel. No: **01797 223404**
Date(s) of Festival:
1st - 2nd August 1998
Times of Festival: **9am - 5pm**
Cost for Adults: **Free**
Cost for Children: **Free**
Tickets available from:
Not required
Routes by Car:

Rye is on A259 from Folkstone to Brighton; 1¾ hours from London; 2 hrs from Chichester
Train/Other:
Main Stations Hastings to Ashford with local services to Rye
Venue:
Various venues within Rye Town Centre
Facilities (Parking):
Car parking nearby. Free camping if required
Facilities (Disabled):
Access for the disabled
What's On:
Medieval music, battle re-enactments, falconry, jousting, archery, longbow tournament, medieval crafts, medievel leech doctor, rune and tarot reader, jugglers, pole-lathe turner, music, living history, Viking village and storyteller, unicycling, stiltwalker
Historical Background:
The festival was started on Armada Day 1988. The festival celebrates the granting of Rye's Charter in 1289.
Media/Public Comments:
"Fabulous festival"
"One of the best shows in the South East"
"Festival is fun, free, friendly, and for the family"
General Information:
Grand procession through the town with bands playing and flags flying

Rye Festival

Type of Festival: **General Arts**
Contact:
Jenny Lee, Rye Festival Council
Address:
Eagle Cottages

Landgate
Rye
East Sussex
TN31 7LQ
Tel. No: **01797 222552**
Date(s) of Festival:
6th - 20th September 1998
Times of Festival: **Various**
Cost for Adults:
Varies from free to £12
Special discounts:
Concessions for students and (by arrangement) groups
Tickets available from:
For brochure write to Rye Festival, PO Box 33, Rye, TN31 7YB
Routes by Car:
A268 from London; A259 for East/West routes
Train/Other:
Rye is on the Marsh Link connecting with Eurostar and the London-Ashford line at Ashford and with the London-Hastings line at Hastings. Also a direct service from Eastbourne
Venue:
St Marys Church, The George Hotel, Rye Treasury, Methodist Church etc
Facilities (Parking):
Clearly marked car parks in Rye
Facilities (Disabled):
Some venues have disabled access
What's On:
Talks, concerts (all sorts of music from classical to jazz), drama, masterclasses, workshops, exhibitions, studio open days, walks, tours
Historical Background:
1998 sees the 27th Rye Festival. It was originally founded by popular demand for use to be made of the facilities of the beautiful St Marys Church which crowns Rye and can be seen for many miles on the approaches
Media/Public Comments:
"Rye Festival has established itself as one of the major arts events in the South East"
Observer Group
General Information:
Rye is well placed for touring East Sussex and South East Kent as well as being a tourist attraction in its own right

WEST SUSSEX

Arundel Festival

Type of Festival: **Mixed Arts**
Contact:
Julie Young
Festival Administrator
Address:
Arundel Festival Society
The Mary Gate
Arundel
West Sussex
BN18 9AT
Tel. No: **01903 883690**
Fax No: **01903 884243**
Date(s) of Festival:
21st - 31st August 1998

Various Cost for Adults:
Costs vary from event to event. Brochure published in June. Free copy from Festival Office
Tickets available from: **Festival Office**
Routes by Car:
Between Brighton and Chichester off the A27.
Train/Other:
Direct route from London Victoria and link to Chichester and Brighton
Venue: **Arundel**
Facilities (Parking):
Ample parking facilities in and around Town Centre
What's On:
Open air theatre, Arundel castle, concerts, events in historic venues, street theatre day, art galleries, river trips, antique shops, Wildfowl Trust, walks within the Castle Park. Visit The Black Rabbit Inn, situated by the River Arun
Historical Background:
1998 is the 21st festival. Started as a one off performance in Arundel Castle grounds to raise money for the Queens Silver Jubilee. A full mixed arts festival grew from this
Media/Public Comments:
"Festival at its best" The Times
General Information:
Arundel is a historic town dominated by the Castle and the river Arun. A beautiful setting for a festival only a few miles from the sea at Clymping, Bognor Regis, Littlehampton, Chichester and Worthing

Corpus Christi Carpet of Flowers and Floral Festival

Type of Festival:
Flower and Religious
Contact: **Rev Anthony Whale**
Address:
Arundel Cathedral
Cathedral House
Parsons Hill
Arundel
West Sussex
BN18 9AY
Tel. No: **01903 882297**
Fax No: 01903 885335
Date(s) of Festival:
10th - 11th June 1998
Times of Festival:
Wednesday: 9.30am - 9pm
Thursday: 10.30am - 5.30pm
Cost for Adults: **Free**
Cost for Children: **Free**
Routes by Car: **A27; A280**
Train/Other:
Arundel Station (London Victoria). Buses from Worthing, Littlehampton, Chichester, Barnham
Venue:
Arundel Cathedral, Arundel
Facilities (Parking):
Parking in the Town Centre
Facilities (Disabled):
Disabled access
What's On:
Carpet of flowers down length of Cathedral and other flower arrangements
Historical Background:
Continuous tradition since 1877. At 5.30pm on Thursday evening Bishop Cormac celebrates the Mass of Corpus Christi, which is followed by a procession of the Blessed Sacrament to the court-

yard of Arundel Castle for benediction, after which the procession returns

Media/Public Comments:
Widespread coverage from TV, radio and local press

General Information:
In the ancient worlds it was the custom to strew flowers in the path of important persons as a sign of respect and reverence. This custom was adopted by the Church to honour the Blessed Sacrament, carried in procession in the Festival of Corpus Christi

Chichester Festivities

Type of Festival: **Music and Arts**
Contact: **Amanda Sharp**
Address:
Chichester Festivities
Canon Gate House
South Street
Chichester
West Sussex
PO19 1PU
Tel. No: **01243 785718**
Fax No: **01243 527346**
Date(s) of Festival:
2nd - 14th July 1998
Times of Festival: **Various**
Cost for Adults: **Various**
Cost for Children: **Various**
Special discounts: **Various**
Tickets available from:
Box Office: 01243 780192
Routes by Car:
Chichester is situated on the South Coast off the A27. London 70 miles, Brighton 32 miles, A27. Southampton 37 miles M27/A27. Portsmouth 18 miles A27
Train/Other:
There is a rail service for festival goers. 22.40 hours service from Chichester to Three Bridges which connects with London, and a 22.52 hrs Monday-Saturday to Brighton. For details phone 0181 667 2780
Venue: **Chichester**
Facilities (Parking):
Chichester offers excellent parking facilities including the Avenue de Chartres triple deck car park and the Cattle Market accommodating a further 900 cars. Coach parking is situated in Cathedral way
What's On:
Concerts, theatre, Jazz and Real Ale Festivals, evensong, German Baroque, lunctime concerts, cathedral choir, opera, Humphrey Lyttelton and his band,cathedral concertos, an evening with David Puttnam, arts quiz hosted by Joan Bakewell, Nigel Kennedy and more
Historical Background:
Started in 1975 as a one-off to celebrate Cathedral's foundation. The events focused on the cathedral as well as venues across the City
Media/Public Comments:
"A sparkling Programme"
Daily Mail
"Everything seen and heard lingers in the mind"
The Sunday Times
General Information:
There are also art exhibitions, Sculpture in Paradise, lectures etc. Places to visit are Roman Palace at Fishbourne, Chichester Harbour, Goodwood House, Weald and Downland Open Air Museum, Uppark, Petworth, Chichester Cathedral, Pallant House

Festival of Flowers

Type of Festival: **Flower**
Contact: **Tim Bevan**
Address:
Chichester Cathedral Restoration Trust
The Royal Chantry
Cathedral Cloisters
Chichester
West Sussex
PO19 1PX
Tel. No: **01243 776922/782595**
Fax No: **01243 536190**
Date(s) of Festival:
28th - 30th May 1998
Cost for Adults: **Free**
Tickets available from:
Not required
Routes by Car:
A27 from Brighton and Worthing. A27, M27 from Bournemouth, Southampton. A29 from Crawley. A286, A3 from Guildford
Train/Other:
Chichester mainline Station from London Victoria
Venue: **Chichester Cathedral**
Facilities (Parking):
Chichester offers excellent parking facilities including the Avenue de Chartres triple deck car park and the Cattle Market accommodating a further 900 cars. Coach parking is situated in Cathedral Way
Facilities (Disabled):
Disabled parking and toilets available. Access for the disabled
What's On:
Spectacular display of flowers within Chichester Cathedral. Country fair, plant markets, lectures. All these events occur within the grounds of the cathedral
General Information:
Chichester is a historic Roman town housing the internationally known Festival Theatre. Nestled between the South Downs and the sea, the City and its surrounding areas are well worth a visit

Goodwood Motor Circuit Revival Meeting

Type of Festival:
Historic **Motor Sport**
Contact:
Rob Widdows
Goodwood Estate Co Ltd
Address:
Goodwood House
Goodwood Park
Chichester
West Sussex
Tel. No: **01243 755000**
Fax No: **01243 755005**
Date(s) of Festival:
18th - 20th September 1998
Times of Festival:
9am - 6pm (gates open at 6.30am)
Cost for Adults:
Friday: £10 in advance; £15 on the day. Saturday: £20 in advance; £25 on the day. Sunday: £30 in advance; £35 on the day. Weekend Ticket: £50 in advance
Cost for Children:
Under 12s free if accompanied by adult
Tickets available from:
Advance Ticket Hotline: 01243 787766 or Fax 01243 755005
Routes by Car:
Signposted from Chichester, Petworth, Midhurst and Portsmouth
Train/Other:
Nearest station Chichester. Taxi to Goodwood. Helicopter or light private plane at Goodwood Airfield by prior arrangement

Venue:
In the extensive grounds of Good-wood House, Goodwood Park
Facilities (Parking):
Plenty of free parking
Facilities (Disabled):
The area is flat and there is special access for disabled. Easily accessible by wheelchair
What's On:
Enjoy a full day of watching cars and the stars from the circuit's heyday. Goodwood Motor Circuit is nestled in the splendour of the rolling hills of the South Downs with Goodwood Race Course only a stones throw away
Historical Background:
50 years ago to the day (18 September 1948) the motor circuit was opened at Goodwood. It was here that Stirling Moss won his first ever major motor race. In a fitting tribute, Moss returns to Goodwood on the 50th anniversary.
Media/Public Comments:
This is the first time the circuit has been re-opened since 1966

Festival of Speed

Type of Festival: **Motor Sport**
Contact:
Rob Widdows
Goodwood Estate Co Ltd
Address:
Goodwood House
Goodwood Park.
Chichester
West Sussex
Tel. No: **01243 755000**
Fax No: **01243 755005**
Date(s) of Festival:
12th - 14th June 1998
Times of Festival:
9am - 6pm (gates open at 6.30am)

Cost for Adults:
Friday: £8 in advance; £10 on the day. Saturday: £15 in advance; £20 on the day. Sunday: £25 in advance only. Weekend ticket £40 in advance
Cost for Children:
Under 12s free if accompanied by adult
Tickets available from:
Advance Ticket Hotline:
01243 787766 or Fax: 01243 755005
Routes by Car:
Signposted from Chichester, Petworth, Midhurst, Portsmouth
Train/Other:
Nearest station, Chichester. Taxi to Goodwood. Helicopter or private planes can land by arrangement at the Goodwood Airfield
Venue:
In the extensive grounds of Good-wood House, Goodwood Park
Facilities (Parking):
Plenty of free parking
Facilities (Disabled):
The area is flat and there is special access for disabled. Easily accessible by wheelchair
What's On:
Mix with the cars and the stars. Watch the hill climb as cars race past the House and up the hill. Rally Sprint, Superbikes and Supercars. Full day of spectacular action on the track and in the air. Formula One and Indy blast their way through the Park.
Historical Background:
1998 is the 6th year of the Festival of Speed which has now established itself as being the foremost motor sport event of its kind in the world
Media/Public Comments:

Too many to mention, suffice to say, the event has world-wide coverage

General Information:
The ultimate garden party for motor racing enthusiasts. 1998's theme is "The Innovation Years" reflecting ground breaking technology from steam power to Space-Age Formula One. Also the Cartier "Style et Luxe" competition

Crawley Folk Festival

Type of Festival: **Folk Music**
Contact: **Mr D Whatmore**
Address:
c/o The Hawth
Hawth Avenue
Crawley
West Sussex
RH10 6YZ
Tel. No: **01293 552941 (admin)**
Fax No: **01293 533362**
E-mail: **hawth@enterprise.net**
Date(s) of Festival:
26th - 28th June 1998
Times of Festival:
Friday: 8.30am - 11.30pm;
Saturday: 12.30pm -11.30pm
Sunday: 12.30pm - 9pm
Cost for Adults:
Full weekend £25 or £5 per day
Cost for Children: **Full weekend £14**
Special discounts:
Daytime activities free under 12s
Tickets available from:
Hawth Box Office: 01293 553636
Routes by Car:
M23 Junction 10 follow Tourist Information signs to Hawth
Train/Other:
London Victoria (Brighton line)
Three Bridges
Venue:
The Hawth Avenue, Crawley
Facilities (Parking): **On site parking.**

Facilities (Disabled):
Facilities available for wheelchair users
What's On:
Friday night: Shane Macgowan and the Popes and support. Saturday daytime: Top British and Irish folk music and dance. Saturday night: Show of Hands and support. Sunday daytime: American folk music and dance
Historical Background:
Now in its 6th year supported by Crawley Borough Council
Media/Public Comments:
"Friendly family atmosphere with great music"

East Preston Festival Week

Type of Festival:
Traditional Village Festival
Contact: **Doug Medhurst**
Address:
East Preston Festival Committee
5 Chermont Close,
The Street
East Preston
West Sussex
Tel. No: **01903 771161**
Date(s) of Festival:
6th - 14th June 1998
Times of Festival: **Various**
Cost for Adults: **Most events free**
Cost for Children:
Special discounts: **None**
Routes by Car:
East Preston is off the A259
Train/Other:
London Victoria Line to Angmering Station.
Venue: **East Preston**
Facilities (Parking):
Parking facilities available

Facilities (Disabled):
Access for disabled at most venues
What's On:
Art with flowers exhibition, model railway display, fetes, carnival parade, celebrity cricket match, stoolball match with the BBC, tour of Infant School, open gardens, fashion show, dog show, antiques and craft fair, American line dancing and choral music
Historical Background:
1998 is the festival's 17th year. Started in 1981 to raise money for the Parish room for St Marys Church and completion of the Village Hall project. Started with a one day event and evolved into a 9 day event
Media/Public Comments:
General reaction was amazed that a small village manages over 60 events in the 9 days but still retains a village atmosphere for the festival
General Information:
The festival also offers coffee mornings, Sausage Sizzle with song, bingo, bridge, chess, bowls, whist drives, keep fit, tennis, tea dance and Songs of Praise

Gardens Festival

Type of Festival: **Garden**
Contact: **Ian Dean**
Address:
33 Chalk Lane
Sidlesham
Chichester
Tel. No: **01243 641284**
Date(s) of Festival:
17th - 18th April 1999
Times of Festival: **10am -5pm**
Cost for Adults: **£3**
Cost for Children: **£1.50**
Tickets available from:

At the gate
Routes by Car:
1½ miles north of Haywards Heath on Balcombe Road
Train/Other:
Haywards Heath mainline station (London Victoria) 1 mile away. Free bus service from station every 30 minutes
Venue:
Borde Hill Gardens, Haywards Heath
Facilities (Parking):
Free Car and coach parking
Facilities (Disabled):
Access for disabled
What's On:
Range of specialist nurseries, collectable plants, fine foods and wine. Gardeners Question Time with Roy Lancaster, floral displays, garden tours, brass band, garden tours,crafts etc
Historical Background:
1998 is the 8th year of the festival

Horsham Festival

Type of Festival: **Mixed**
Contact: **Terry Cullen**
Address:
Horsham Festival Committee
3 Beedingwood Drive
Colgate
Horsham
West Sussex
RH12 4TE
Tel. No: **01293 851760**
Date(s) of Festival:
11th - 12th July 1998
Times of Festival: **10am -10pm**
Cost for Adults: **Free**
Cost for Children: **Free**
Tickets available from:
Not required
Train/Other:

Horsham mainline Station (London Victoria)
Venue:
Horsham Town Centre
Facilities (Parking):
Car parks approximately 400 yds from park, toilets, refreshments
Facilities (Disabled):
Access for disabled
What's On:
Arena events, displays, exhibitions, side shows, charity stalls, funfair, bouncy castles . . .

Horsham Town Centre Festival

Type of Festival: **Music and Dance**
Contact:
Jeanne Coker - Leisure Services
Address:
Horsham District Council
Park House
North Street
Horsham
West Sussex
RH12 IRL
Tel. No: **01403 215265**
Fax No: **01403 215268**
Date(s) of Festival:
29th - 31st October 1998
Times of Festival: **10am - 10pm**
Cost for Adults: **Free**
Cost for Children: **Free**
Routes by Car:
Serviced by major routes from London, Brighton, Southampton
Train/Other:
Horsham mainline Station (London Victoria)
Venue: **Horsham Town Centre**
Facilities (Parking):
Parking, toilets, catering facilities, local restaurants
Facilities (Disabled):

Access for disabled
What's On:
Traditional street fairground including big wheel, dance, Battle of the Bands, music, street entertainment, sideshows
Historical Background:
Started in 1992 and due to its popularity has grown steadily over the years
Media/Public Comments:
"Brings life to Horsham at a quiet time of year"

Sussex Beer and Cider Festival

Type of Festival: **Beer**
Contact: **Stuart Elms**
Address:
Sussex Branch of CAMRA
15 Rackham Road,
Worthing
Hove
West Sussex
BN13 ILH
Tel. No: **01903 692370**
Fax No: **01903 692370**
Date(s) of Festival:
25th - 27th February 1999
Times of Festival:
25th: 6pm -10pm
26th: 11am - 3pm and 5pm -11pm
27th: 11am - 4pm and 6pm - 11pm
Cost for Adults: **Various**
Cost for Children: **N/A**
Special discounts:
Discounts for CAMRA members
Tickets available from:
Ticket Information Office:
46 Robson Road, Worthing
Train/Other:
Hove Station (easy walk). Venue on major bus routes
Venue:

Hove Town Hall, Norton Road
Facilities (Parking):
Town parking available
Facilities (Disabled): **Disabled access**
What's On:
Live entertainment, traditional pub games, CAMRA products stall

The Petworth Festival

Type of Festival:
Music, Art, Poetry, Jazz
Contact: **Mrs Jean Hugget**
Address:
**The Petworth Festival
40 Orchard Close
Petworth
West Sussex
GU28 0SA**
Tel. No: **01798 343906**
Fax No: **01798 342232**
Date(s) of Festival:
6th - 29th July 1998
Times of Festival: **Various**
Cost for Adults: from **£5 - £12**
Cost for Children: **Under 14s free**
Special discounts: **None**
Tickets available from:
Tourist Information, Market Square, Petworth
Routes by Car:
Petworth is on the intersection of A272, A283, A285
Train/Other:
Pulborough (London, Victoria) Haslemere (London, Waterloo) Portsmouth (Connex South East)
Venue:
Leconfield Hall, Petworth House (Marble Hall), Petworth Park, Duncton Roman catholic Church, St Marys Church
Facilities (Parking):
Parking in Town Centre, toilets, restaurants and tea shops
Facilities (Disabled):

Disabled access except to Leconfield Hall
What's On:
Jazz, organ recitals, opera, classical concerts, string quartets, poetry, square dance, kites in Petworth Park, lecture on the history of photography, Oriental decorative arts, choral and instrumental concert, secret gardens of Petworth, Tibetan dances
Historical Background:
Festival has run for 20 years, originally music, now broader based and much larger
Media/Public Comments:
Excellent reviews of the 1997 festival by the local Midhurst and Petworth Observer

South East Festival of Craftmanship

Type of Festival: **Crafts**
Contact: **Dr Diana Owen**
Address:
**Property Manager
Petworth House
Petworth
West Sussex**
Tel. No: **01798 342207
(Info Line: 01798 343929)**
Fax No: **01798 343929**
Date(s) of Festival:
**19th - 27th September 1998
(Note: exceptions 24th and 25th schools and colleges only)**
Times of Festival: **1pm - 5.30pm**
Cost for Adults: **£5 (admission to Petworth House; festival free)**
Special discounts:
10% reduction for groups of 15+; free entry to National Trust members
Tickets available from:

On the door Petworth House
Routes by Car:
A272/A283 to centre of Petworth
Train/Other:
Pulborough Station then taxi
Venue:
Petworth House, Petworth
Facilities (Parking): **Free Parking**
Facilities (Disabled): **Wheelchairs
provided. Access for disabled**
What's On:
**Exhibitions, demonstrations, talks,
craft shop, workshops and
masterclasses**
Historical Background:
1998 is the festival's first year
General Information:
**A celebration of craftsmanship in
the South East in co-operation
with the National Trust backed by
the Lottery. An unique opportunity
to see contemporary crafts displayed alongside the superb
historical collection of Petworth
House**

Victorian Seaside Festival

Type of Festival:
Music and Entertainment
Contact:
**Kim Long
Community Services Dept**
Address:
**Worthing Borough Council
Portland House,
Richmond Road
Worthing
West Sussex
BN11 1HP**
Tel. No: **01903 239999 Ext. 2507**
Fax No: **01903 207035**
Date(s) of Festival:
8th - 9th August 1998

Times of Festival:
**Saturday: 10am -10pm
Sunday: 10am - 5pm (may finish
at 10pm Sunday if there is a fire-
work display)**
Cost for Adults: **Free**
Cost for Children: **Free**
Tickets available from: **Not required**
Routes by Car:
A 27 and A279, M23 and M25
Train/Other:
Worthing Central Station
Facilities (Parking):
**Ample parking within the town cen-
tre. Victorian bar at Rutherfords,
food stalls, ice cream stalls, ginger-
bread stalls etc**
What's On:
**Models exhibition in the marquee,
military gun display, open air art
exhibition,   Pierot Clown, Punch
and Judy, funfair, Jelly Rollers,
Wurlitzer organ concert, photo ex-
hibition, children's entertainment,
giant chess and draughts and
much more**
Historical Background:
**Started as "Wilde" weekend to
celebrate 100 years since Oscar
Wilde wrote "The Importance of
Being Earnest" in Worthing, re-
named to encompass more scope**
Media/Public Comments:
**"Just one big and happy family"
Evening Argus
"Happy faces all round"
Herald Newspaper**

Tyne and Wear

Houghton Feast

Type of Festival: **Traditional**
Contact: **Mr John Murphy**
Address:
14 Pleasure Beach
South Shields
Tyne & Wear
NE33 2JZ
Tel. No: **0191 4546239 and**
0831 458774
Date(s) of Festival:
2nd - 10th October 1998
Times of Festival:
6pm -10pm daily
Saturday 2pm - 10pm for funfair
Cost for Adults: **Free to funfair**
Tickets available from: **Not required**
Routes by Car:
Close to A19 and A1M, Sunderland
4 miles
Venue: **Houghton-Le-Spring**
What's On:
Various activities during the week:
music, art exhibitions, pipe bands,
firework display and funfair
Historical Background:
The festival is approximately 95
years old
Media/Public Comments:
"Highlight of the year for
Houghton-Le-Spring"
General Information:
Fairground is opened by the Mayor
of Sunderland at 6pm on the first
day of the fair. This fair caters for
all age groups from children's rides,
traditional to "white knuckle" rides

Newcastle Comedy Festival

Type of Festival: **Comedy**
Contact: **Gillian Wilson**
Address:
Newcastle Comedy Festival
1 Pink Lane
Newcastle upon Tyne
Tyne & Wear
NE1 5DW
Tel. No: **0191 230 4406**
Fax No: **0191 230 4484**
Date(s) of Festival:
5th - 21st November 1998
Times of Festival: **Various**
Cost for Adults: **Various**
Cost for Children:
Concessions for children
Special discounts:
Concessions available for UB40s,
OAPs and students
Tickets available from:
Tyne Theatre: 0191 232 0899
LiveTheatre: 0191 232 1232
Playhouse and Gulbenkian:
0191 232 5151
City Hall: 0191 261 2606
Tyneside Cinema: 0191 232 8289
Hyena Café: 0191 232 6030
Venue:
Various venues within Newcastle
City Centre
Facilities (Parking):
Parking facilities close to most ven-
ues

Facilities (Disabled):
Wheelchair access to auditoria, toilet and refreshment areas. Contact Box Office to make arrangements
What's On:
Top national and international comedians at a variety of venues 300 comedians and 200 shows. Something to suit everyone

North Shields International Fish Quay Festival

Type of Festival: **Music**
Contact: **Carol Alevroyianni**
Address:
North Tyneside Council
7 Northumberland Square
North Shields
Tyne & Wear
NE30 IQQ
Tel. No: **0191 2005415**
Fax No: **0191 2005798**
Date(s) of Festival:
23rd - 24th May 1999
Times of Festival: **Various**
Cost for Adults: **Free**
Cost for Children: **Free**
Routes by Car:
A19 via Tyne Tunnel from the South. Park at Metro Stations and Metro into North Shields
Train/Other:
Newcastle Central Station - Metro link to North Shields. Ferry from South Shields to North Shields
Facilities (Parking):
Accessible Park and Ride Scheme call: 0191 200 7896 for details. Accessible buses call Nexus for details
Facilities (Disabled):
Access for disabled
What's On:

Featuring Bookman Eksperyans, Jools Holland, Dr DidJ,Celtarabia, Sine, Peatbog Fairies, pop bands, firework display, Blessing of the fleet, blues night, disability arts cabaret, boat trips, street theatre,pageant display, exhibitions, craft markets etc
Historical Background:
Originally the Fisherman's Regatta, then became Fishquay Festival in 1987. Emphasis on music developed over the years and now a major music event
Media/Public Comments:
"Europe's biggest free music festival". "Britain's most popular street party". "The music and the atmosphere are second to none"
General Information:
There is a children's arena: games, bouncy castles, soft play, funfair etc

Cookson Country Festival

Type of Festival:
Music, Theatre, Arts
Contact:
Michele Maving - Leisure Services
Address:
Central Library
Prince George Square
South Shields
Tyne & Wear
NE33 2PE
Tel. No: **0191 4271717 Ext: 2056**
Fax No: **0191 4270469**
Date(s) of Festival:
4th July - 9th August 1998
Times of Festival: **Various**
Cost for Adults: **Free**
Cost for Children: **Free**
Tickets available from:
Not required

Routes by Car: **A1(M) to A194**
Train/Other:
Newcastle upon Tyne, Metro to Sheffield
Venue:
Bents Park, Town Hall, Customs House, Pirate Day at Sandhaven, Amphitheatre
Facilities (Parking):
Lots of parking. Pay and display along seafront
Facilities (Disabled):
Limited disabled access
What's On:
4th July opening parade, Leo Sayer, Music and Dance Day, Memphis Belle Swing Orchestra, Mill Dam Festival, tribute to the stars, Pirate Day, The Billy Lewis Drifters, Family Fun Day, Paul Daniels, Roy Walker . . .
Historical Background:
The festival started over 10 years ago to enhance and prolong the holiday season in South Tyneside for both the residents and the visitors
Media/Public Comments:
"The Cookson Country Festival is all about free family fun. Average Sunday attendance 6000 people"
General Information:
South Tyneside Council present this annual free festival which includes open air concerts, brass band season, children's parties every Tuesday and Thursday during the school holidays, live music, Saturday Specials, street theatre, Sunday spectaculars . . .

Whitley Bay International Jazz Festival

Type of Festival: **Traditional Jazz**
Contact: **Mike Durham**
Address:
60 Highbury
Newcastle upon Tyne
Tyne & Wear
NE2 3LN
Tel. No: **0191 281 2935**
Fax No: **0191 281 5121**
Date(s) of Festival:
10th - 12th July 1998
Times of Festival:
Friday 8pm to midnight
Saturday noon - 1am
Sunday noon - 11.30pm
Cost for Adults:
Full weekend £25, Friday night £5, Saturday or Sunday all day £12
Cost for Children: **Half price**
Special discounts:
Students 25% discount
Tickets available from:
Park Hotel, Tynemouth
Routes by Car:
From Newcastle A1058 coast Road all the way to the seafront. Hotel is on the left
Train/Other:
Newcastle upon Tyne Central then metro train to Cullercoats. Newcastle airport is 20 miles away, taxi or Metro Train link
Venue: **Park Hotel, Tynemouth**
Facilities (Parking): **Free Parking**
Facilities (Disabled): **Ramp Access**
What's On:
21 bands representing the finest in traditional jazz from ragtime to swing. Also street parade, jazz church service, jam sessions
Historical Background:

Festival now in its eighth year
Media/Public Comments:
**"Attendances have been up every
year for the past five years"**
General Information:
**All under one roof - three rooms
with music at all times**

WARWICKSHIRE

Town and Country Festival

Type of Festival: **Family**
Contact: **Sarah Knott - Manager**
Address:
**Town and Country Festival
Stoneleigh Park
Stoneleigh
Warwickshire
CV8 2GA**
Tel. No: **01203 696969**
Fax No: **01203 696900**
Date(s) of Festival:
29th - 31st August 1998
Times of Festival:
**Saturday/Sunday: 9.30am - 7pm
Monday: 9.30am - 6.30pm**
Cost for Adults: **£6.50 on the day**
Cost for Children:
£3.50. Under 5s free
Special discounts:

£6 in advance. Over 5s £3 in advance
Tickets available from:
**Credit Card Hotline:
01203 693000
Advanced tickets by post:
01203 696969 for leaflet**
Routes by Car:
5 mins off A46, Stoneleigh Junction.
Train/Other: **Coventry Station**
Venue:
Stoneleigh showground, Stoneleigh
Facilities (Parking): **Free parking**
Facilities (Disabled):
Disabled priority parking, wheelchair access (free rides for disabled children on Saturday morning)
What's On:
650 exhibitors, crafts, clothing, antiques, motoring manufacturers, live music, children's circus, mounted pony games, monster action truck and stunt display, funfair, off road vehicles, new cars, etc
Historical Background:
Festival is 27years old and is regarded as the biggest family fun day out in the Midlands
Media/Public Comments:
"Crowds poured in to soak up the festival atmosphere . . . " Evening Telegraph

Phoenix 1998

Type of Festival: **Music**
Contact: **Dora Masullo**
Address:
**Mean Fiddler
Information Line
Stratford upon Avon
Warwickshire**
Tel. No:
Info Line: 0181 963 0940
Fax No:

Dora Masullo: 0181 961 5743
Date(s) of Festival:
16th - 19th July 1998
Times of Festival: **Various**
Cost for Adults:
**Weekend £75 includes camping,
Single £27.50 (in advance)**
Tickets available from:
**TicketMaster: 0541 500044
Also available from: 0171 344 0044**
Routes by Car:
**Junction 15 M40, Junction 11, M40
at Banbury**
Train/Other: **Stratford upon Avon**
Venue:
**Longmaston Airfield, Stratford
upon Avon**
What's On:
**300 acts on 6 stages, music, dance,
circus and comedy. Ocean Colour
Scene headlining on 17th, New Or-
der on 18th, Prodigy on 19th**

Stratford upon Avon Poetry Festival

Type of Festival: **Poetry readings**
Contact:
Roger Pringlen - Director
Address:
**The Shakespeare Birthplace Trust
The Shakespeare Centre
Henley Street
Stratford upon Avon
Warwickshire
CV37 6QW**
Tel. No: **01789 204 016**
Fax No: **01789 296 083**
Date(s) of Festival:
**Sunday evenings 28th June - 23rd
August 1998**
Times of Festival:
7.30pm and 8pm
Cost for Adults: **Various**
Tickets available from:

**The Shakespeare Bookshop,
Henley Street**
Routes by Car:
**Junction 15 off M40, A46 to Strat-
ford then A439**
Train/Other: **Stratford upon Avon**
Venue: **Shakespeare Centre**
Facilities (Parking):
**Nearest public car park, Windsor
Street**
Historical Background:
**Now in its 45th session the aim of
the poetry festival is to present po-
etry from as many different
periods as possible and to provide
opportunities for contemporary
poets to be heard**

Warwick and Leamington Festival

Type of Festival: **Music**
Contact:
**Mr Richard Phillips
Festival Director**
Address:
**Northgate
Warwick
Warwickshire
CV34 4JL**
Tel. No: **01926 407606**
Date(s) of Festival:
1st - 11th July 1998
Times of Festival:
**Throughout the day and evening
concerts.**
Cost for Adults: **£2.50-£20**
Special discounts:
**Student standbys £1 (½ hour be-
fore performance)**
Tickets available from:
**Warwick and Leamington Festival
Box Office: 01926 496277**
Routes by Car:
Junction 15 M40, A46 to Warwick

and Royal Leamington Spa
Train/Other:
Marylebone station, London and Birmingham, Snow Hill. 45 minutes from Birmingham International Airport
Venue:
Various venues within Warwick and Leamington
Facilities (Parking): **Town parking**
Media/Public Comments:
A fun, varied festival. Something for all the family

WEST MIDLANDS

Birmingham International Jazz Festival

Type of Festival: **Music**
Contact: **Clare Jepson-Homek**
Address:
P O Box 944
Edgbaston
Birmingham
West Midlands
B16 8UT
Tel. No: **0121 454 7020**
Fax No: **0121 454 9996**
Date(s) of Festival:
29th June - 12th July 1998

Times of Festival: **11am - 11pm**
Cost for Adults:
90% events free. Others from £3-£15 (includes concession rate)
Tickets available from:
C Jepson-Homek (see above)
Routes by Car:
M40/M42/M5/M6 all routes to City Centre
Train/Other:
Birmingham, Snow Hill or Birmingham, New Street
Venue:
Approximately 70 venues within the City including Ronnie Scotts, Adrian Boult Hall, MAC, plus pubs, restaurants, streets, shops, churches etc
Facilities (Parking): **City parking**
What's On:
UK's biggest jazz event hosting over 280 performances. Mardi Gras New Orleans Parade, King Pleasure and the Biscuit Boys, The Notting Hillbillies, Bob Kerr and His Whoopee Band, Digby Fairweather and the First Class Sounds, Beiderbecke and all that jazz
Historical Background:
1998 heralds the 14th festival. Previous headliners have included some of the great names in jazz including Dizzy Gillespie, Cab Colloway, Miles Davis, Clark Terry, BB King, John McLaughlin. 250,000 people attended the 1997 festival

New Solihull

Type of Festival: **Music**
Contact: **Geoffrey Gibbons**
Address:
The Elms
Balsall Street

Balsall Common
West Midlands
CV7 7AR
Tel. No: **01676 535818**
Date(s) of Festival:
8th - 15th May 1999
Times of Festival:
Afternoons and evening programme of events
Cost for Adults: **Various**
Cost for Children:
Concessions available
Special discounts:
Concessions available
Tickets available from:
Box Office:
0121 7046962 Library Theatre, Solihull Arts Complex, Homer Road
Routes by Car:
M42 Solihull Junction
Train/Other: **Solihull Station**
Venue:
At Alphege Church, St James Church, Solihull Library Theatre
Facilities (Parking): **Town parking**
Facilities (Disabled):
Access for disabled
What's On:
Concerts, choir concert (Nocturne), organ recital, song recital, jazz evening, piano trio playing Beethoven, Ravel and Mendelssohn, orchestral concert, classical and contemporary music for guitar, violin and piano recital and more..
Historical Background:
The festival was founded in 1988 by the present promoter. Originally supported by Solihull City Council now privately run by the Friends of Solihull Festival
Media/Public Comments:
"Highly recommended"

Walsall Leather Festival

Type of Festival:
Craft/Industrial Heritage
Contact: **Francesca Wagstaff**
Address:
Walsall Leather Museum
Littleton Street West
Walsall
West Midlands
Tel. No: **01922 721153**
Fax No: **01922 725827**
Date(s) of Festival:
31st July - 2nd August 1998
Times of Festival: **10am - 5pm**
Cost for Adults: **Free**
Cost for Children: **Free**
Tickets available from:
Not required
Routes by Car:
The Museum is situated on A4148 Littleton Street, West Ring Road. From M6 Junctions 7,9, or 10 head for Town Centre
Train/Other:
Walsall Station is a 5 minute walk from the Museum
Venue:
Walsall Leather Museum
Facilities (Parking):
Parking in Day Street car park. Museum has shop and toilet
Facilities (Disabled):
Full disabled access with lift and toilet
What's On:
Leather work demonstrations including saddler, leather carving, plaiting etc. Horse parade, horse and carriage rises, exhibitions, children's activities. Live entertainment
Historical Background:
Walsall is the capital of the British leather goods industry and this three day carnival celebrates the town's traditional trade

Walsall Celebrates

Type of Festival: **Street Theatre**
Contact: **Antonia Compa**
Address:
Leisure and Community Services
Civic Centre
Walsall
West Midlands
Tel. No: **01922 653170**
Fax No: **01922 721682**
Date(s) of Festival:
8th - 16th August 1998
Times of Festival: **Various**
Cost for Adults: **Free**
Cost for Children: **Free**
Tickets available from:
Not required
Routes by Car:
From M6 Exits 7,9, or 10 head for
Town Centre
Train/Other:
Walsall Station
Venue:
Various venues including Walsall
Town Centre and Walsall Arbore-
tum
Facilities (Parking): **Town parking**
What's On:
Outdoor festival of street theatre
General Information:
Leisure and Community Services,
Civic Centre: 01922 653183

WILTSHIRE

Amesbury Carnival

Type of Festival: **Carnival**
Contact:
Linda Robson/Jackie Walker
Address:
Amesbury Visitor Information
Centre
Redworth House,
Flower Lane
Amesbury
Wiltshire
SP4 7HG
Tel. No: **01980 622833**
Fax No: **01980 625541**
Date(s) of Festival:
11th July 1998
Times of Festival:
Procession at 12 noon. 1pm arena
displays
Cost for Adults: **Free**
Cost for Children: **Free**
Tickets available from:
Not required
Routes by Car:
A303 Amesbury. Signposted from
there
Train/Other:
Salisbury Station. Bus to Amesbury
Venue: **Amesbury Town Centre**

Facilities (Parking): **Parking available**
What's On:
Carnival procession, arena displays, motorbike display teams, marching bands, jugglers, fairground rides and attractions etc

Bradford upon Avon Town Festival

Type of Festival:
Music, Drama, Arts
Contact:
Roger Andrews - Chairman
Address:
**Bradford upon Avon Town Festival Committee
11 Churches
Bradford upon Avon
Wiltshire**
Tel. No: **01225 867853**
Date(s) of Festival:
27th June - 5th July 1998
Times of Festival: **Various**
Cost for Adults: **Various**
Routes by Car:
M4 to Junction 18 South on A36 and then A363 to Bradford on Avon
Train/Other:
Bradford upon Avon
Venue:
Various venues within Bradford upon Avon
Facilities (Parking):
Adequate car parking in the centre of the town

Devizes Festival

Type of Festival: **Arts**
Contact: **Stephen Brazier**
Address:
**Devizes Festival Committee
34 Long Street
Devizes
Wiltshire**

SN10 1NT
Tel. No: **01380 728151**
Date(s) of Festival:
10th - 27th June 1998
Cost for Adults: **£3 - £8**
Cost for Children: **Varies**
Special discounts:
UB40s, OAPs, students: half price at the door
Tickets available from:
Devizes Books, Sidmouth Street, Devizes
Routes by Car:
A342 from Chippenham, A361 from Marlborough, A36 from Salisbury
Train/Other:
Chippenham or Pewsey By narrow boat on Kennet and Avon Canal
Venue: **Devizes**
Facilities (Parking):
Easy parking in market place
Facilities (Disabled):
Disabled access
What's On:
The festival covers a wide range of interests: classical, folk, jazz, world, rock music, contemporary dance, poetry readings, comedy, local history and environmental issues, brewery tours
Historical Background:
The Festival has been running for 18 years. The aim is to provide high quality professional performances
General Information:
Annual Show at Handel House Contemporary Gallery, Sidmouth Street, Devizes (£1000 prize). Cycle rides and walks in the surrounding countryside

Larmer Tree Music Festival

Type of Festival:
Folk Roots and World Music
Contact:
Julia Safe and James Shepard
Address:
13 St Marks Road
Tollard Royal
Salisbury
Wiltshire
SP1 3AY
Tel. No: **01722 415223**
Fax No: **01722 415223**
E-mail:
info@larmertree.demon.co.uk
Web site: **www.lamertree.demon.co.uk**
Date(s) of Festival:
10th - 12th June 1998
Times of Festival:
Friday: 6pm - 1pm;
Saturday/Sunday: 9am - midnight
Cost for Adults:
Weekend: £45. Friday £10. Saturday £25. Sunday £25
Cost for Children: **Under 5's free**
Discounts for under 17s
Tickets available from:
Booking form from: 01722 415223. Credit card bookings
Routes by Car:
Just off A354 Salisbury - Blandford road then follow special signs. Do not follow signs to Tollard Royal
Train/Other:
Nearest station Salisbury then catch bus or taxi.
Venue:
Larmer Tree Grounds, Tollard Royal, nr Salisbury
Facilities (Parking):
Free parking. Camping facilities, tents, caravans, campervans, toilets and showers

Facilities (Disabled):
Disabled access and facilities. An easy access camping area will be provided with specially adapted toilets
What's On:
Over 30 bands on 4 stages including a marquee and main garden stage. Acts include Edward II, The Flatville Aces, The Well-Oiled Sisters, Carmina and lots more. Huge free workshop programme, children's venue "The Larmer Parler", funk rock, hillbilly, jazz, blues etc
Historical Background:
James Shepard discovered the Larmer Tree in 1989 whilst out jogging on the Cranborne Chase. He immediately decided it would be a perfect venue for a music festival. Initially it was a festival of jazz and blues music attended by approximately 200 people
Media/Public Comments:
"The surprise of the Larmer Tree is its unique setting, its diverse programming and compact site"
"Brilliant weekend - see you next year for sure - thanks a lot"
"My favourite festival on the circuit"
General Information:
The Larmer Tree Festival is hidden in the wilds of Cranborne Chase on the Wilts/Dorset Border. The grounds were laid out in 1889 by archaeologist General, Pitt-Rivers (though the Larmer Tree itself blew down in 1894)

WORCESTERSHIRE

British VW Festival

Type of Festival: **VW**
Contact: **Mac Howarth**
Address:
45 Dowlers Hill Crescent
Greenlands,
Redditch
Worcestershire
B98 7QZ
Tel. No: **01527 457890.**
E -mail: **mac.howarth@virgin.net**
Date(s) of Festival: **4th - 5th July 1998**
Times of Festival:
8pm - 6pm day visitors. Gates open
24 hrs for camping
Cost for Adults:
£6. £6.50 per unit (caravan or tent)
Cost for Children: **Under 14s free**
Tickets available from:
Details of advanced booking: Mac
Howarth (see above)
Routes by Car:
Venue is just outside Malvern. En-
trance on the B4208 just after the
crossroads with the B4209. Well
signposted
Venue:
Three Counties Showground
Facilities (Parking):
Ample parking, campsite good

range of caterers and licensed
bars, shop, first aid etc
Facilities (Disabled):
Disabled parking areas
What's On:
Trade stands, autojumble, club dis-
plays, exhibitions, concours
competitions, "Berk Bros" theatre
Co, workshops, juggling, driving
competitions, special themed dis-
play, family and children's
entertainment, "It's a Knockout"
type competitions, convoys etc
Historical Background:
Festival founded many years ago
as Bug-In but renamed British VW
Festival. The event is run by dedi-
cated team of enthusiasts from
some of the major VW Clubs in
Britain. It has grown to be one of
the main VW events
Media/Public Comments:
"The British VW Festival is now
one of the focal points of the tra-
ditional VW scene in the UK and
justifiably so - it's a true celebra-
tion of everything that is special
about the VW"

Vanfest '98

Type of Festival:
VW Transporter Festival
Contact: **Simon Holloway**
Address:
Wessington House
2 Milton Lane
Steventon
Great Malvern
Worcestershire
Tel. No: **01235 831520**
Fax No: **01235 831 520**
Date(s) of Festival:
19th - 20th September 1998
Times of Festival:
Gate open at midday Friday of the

show weekend
Cost for Adults:
£6. £6.50 per camping unit per night
Cost for Children: **Under 15s free**
Tickets available from:
Vanfest '98, 48 Denleigh Road, Kingswinford, DY6 8PS
Routes by Car:
8 miles off the M5 or M50 (Junctions 7 or 8) and then follow signs
Venue:
Three Counties Showground, Malvern
Facilities (Parking):
On site parking, camping, (pets permitted), catering and bar
Facilities (Disabled):
On site disabled parking,
What's On:
Trade stands, autojumble, craft fair, vehicle sales, special vehicle displays, full evening entertainment (Friday and Saturday nights), live bands and discos, Cooking in a Camper display, children's entertainment and creche, Vantech stand
Historical Background:
Organised by the Type 2 Owners Club. Vanfest is now enjoying its 5th year and has become a growth industry as an ever increasing number of VW fans discover the attractions of the venerable VW van
Media/Public Comments:
"The show organised by van fans for fans with vans and vans with fans"
The show has been well covered in the VW Press. Also on Channel 4 "Ride On" and BBC Top Gear "Cars the Star"
General Information:
Main display theme will be based around "Devon and Danbury" conversions. Also a good selection of DIY conversions

Oliver Cromwell Jazz Festival
Type of Festival: **Jazz**
Contact:
Dierdre Thompson - Secretary
Address:
Jazz Festival Office
18 Riverside Close
Upton-upon-Severn
Worcestershire
WR8 0JN
Tel. No: **01684 593254**
Fax No: **01684 593254**
Date(s) of Festival:
26th - 28th June 1998
Times of Festival:
Midday Friday - 11pm Sunday
Cost for Adults:
Weekend £33 (in advance, £40 on the day. Friday £9. Saturday £18. Sunday £14
Cost for Children: **Under 14s free**
Special discounts: **None**
Tickets available from:
Jazz Festival Office (see above)
Routes by Car:
M5 (north) Junction 7, A44 Worcester. M5 (south) Junction 8, M50 to Junction 1 A38 Malvern
Train/Other:
6 miles from Great Malvern Station, Worcester 11 miles
Venue:
12 venues which include 4 large marquees, Fish Meadow, Upton-upon-Severn Town Centre. All venues are within easy walking distance
Facilities (Parking):
Free parking for ticket holders at Fish Meadow (follow signs). Camping and caravan site which include hot showers, water, toilets and refuse points
Facilities (Disabled):
Disabled access to most venues. All

venues are within easy distance from one another

What's On:

75+ bands in 12 venues featuring various styles of jazz, New Orleans, big bands, Dixieland, "Hot Club" Comedy, traditional. etc. Large jazz parade, jazz and blues bands, male voice choirs, jazz church service, riverboat trips etc

Historical Background:

Festival was founded in 1986. Upton has historical connections with the Civil War, hence the name "Oliver Cromwell". There are plaques marking some of the historic events, such as the spot where Cromwell addressed his troops prior to the Battle of Worcester

Media/Public Comments:

"Here we go again for our annual jazz jamboree on the banks of the Severn ... highlights of the festival include the Saturday morning "Mardi-Gras" Parade through Upton, the Sunday morning service at the Parish Church and the riverboat trips to Conway Castle"

YORKSHIRE

Beverley and East Riding Early Music Festival

Type of Festival: **Music**

Contact: **Gill Baldwin**

Address:

P O Box 226

York

Yorkshire

YO30 5ZU

Tel. No: **01904 658338**

Fax No: **01904 612631**

Date(s) of Festival:

Last weekend in May 1999 (TBC)

Times of Festival: **Various**

Cost for Adults: **Various**

Special discounts:

Concessions available

Tickets available from:

Beverley Tourist Information Centre, Guildhall, Register Square, Beverley: 01482 884354

Routes by Car: **Public car parks**

Train/Other:

Disabled access to all areas

Venue:

Various venues within Beverley

Facilities (Parking):

Public car parks

Facilities (Disabled):

Disabled access to all venues

What's On:

Highlights include: The Tallies Scholars in Beverley Minster on Friday 22nd May, New London Concert on Saturday 23rd May in Beverley Minster and the King's Consort in St Marries Church on 24th May

Historical Background:

Started in 1988 and now acknowledged as the cultural festival of the region

Beverley and East Riding Folk Festival

Type of Festival: **Music**
Contact: **Chris Wade**
Address:
Beverley and East Riding Folk Festival
2 Star Road, North Dalton
Driffield
Yorkshire
YO25 9UR
Tel. No: **01377 217662**
Fax No: **01377 217754**
Date(s) of Festival:
19th - 21st June 1998
Times of Festival:
Friday evening 8pm - midnight Sunday
Cost for Adults:
£33 for the weekend
Cost for Children:
Half price (Under 6s free)
Special discounts:
£30 if booked in advance
Tickets available from:
Festival Office or 01482 867430
Routes by Car:
A1079 from York. A15 to Humber bridge. M62 from the west and south
Train/Other:
To Beverley Station via Hull. Bus via Beverley from York or Bridlington
Venue: **Various venues in Beverley**
Facilities (Parking):
Park available at main Leisure Centre venue
Facilities (Disabled):
Disabled access possible with assistance from attendants
What's On:
Concerts, dances, workshops, informal sessions, street shows, children's events, special gospel concert in Beverley Minster with London Community Gospel Choir
Historical Background:
Dates back to 1983 when it was originated as the Beverley Folk Festival
Media/Public Comments:
"The major cultural event in Beverley: a festival for all tastes and all ages"

Bradford Festival

Type of Festival: **Community Arts**
Contact:
Rob Welsh - Bradford Festival
Address:
Provincial House
Centenary Square
Bradford
Yorkshire
BD1 1NH
Tel. No: **01274 309199**
Fax No: **01274 724213**
Date(s) of Festival:
26th June - 11th July
Times of Festival: **Various times**
Cost for Adults: **Free**
Cost for Children: **Free**
Tickets available from: **Not required**
Routes by Car:
M1 to M62 to M606
Train/Other:
Via Leeds - Bradford
Venue:
Café Bradford in Centenary Square in the Centre of Bradford and Peel Park, Bradford
Facilities (Parking): **Town parking**
Facilities (Disabled):
Good disabled access and toilets
What's On:
The whole of Centenary Square is taken over as Café Bradford where visitors can enjoy music, food and drink, street entertainment, street

theatre, carnival sculpture, dance. Also meal (170,000 visitors in 1997) in Peel Park followed by a Firework Finale

Historical Background:
1998 is the 12th festival celebrating Bradford as a multicultural city enjoying the cultures from people from all around the world. It is a coming together of cultural harmony

Media/Public Comments:
"The meal is the best family free day out in the country"
"The festival is the largest community arts festival in the country" Rob Walsh - Publicity Officer

General Information:
The Bradford festival is a summer highlight, filling the city with music, colour and laughter. Exciting events, international performers and a host of musical style around the city, making it the largest community arts festival in Britain

Bridlington Arts Festival

Type of Festival: **Art**
Contact: **Mel Jones**
Address:
Bridlington Arts Festival Limited
64 Quay Road
Bridlington
Yorkshire
YO16 4HX
Tel. No: **01262 604826**
Date(s) of Festival:
30th April - 9th May 1999
Cost for Adults:
Various. Most local events approximately £3 - £4.
Tickets available from:
Spa Theatre, Bridlington:

01262 678258
Routes by Car:
Main roads from Hull, York and Scarborough
Train/Other:
From Hull or Scarborough
Venue:
Bridlington and Spa Theatre, Bridlington
Facilities (Parking):
No specific parking
Facilities (Disabled):
Wheelchair access at main venue
What's On:
Theatre, travelling storytellers, drama, dance companies, land art, beach sculpting, drama workshops, photographic workshops, postcard competitions
Historical Background:
13th year of festival, growing and improving with every year

Calderdale Walking Festival

Type of Festival: **Walking**
Contact: **Ed Westbrook**
Address:
Calderdale Tourism
1 Bridgegate
Hebden Bridge
Yorkshire
HX7 8EX
Tel. No: **01422 842830**
Fax No: **01422 845266**
Date(s) of Festival:
26th September - 11th October 1998
Times of Festival: **Various**
Cost for Adults: **Most events free**
Tickets available from: **Not required**
Routes by Car:
From M62 (between Junctions 21 and 26) from east, west and south.

A646 and A629 from north
Train/Other:
Access by Pennine Leisure Link from Manchester, Blackpool, Preston, Leeds and York
Venue:
Various venues in Calderdale
What's On:
50 guided walks for all abilities, orienteering events, talks on walking themes, walking exhibitions and photographic competition, countryside advice and courses
Historical Background:
2nd year of local authority run event with help from walking clubs etc
Media/Public Comments:
"The biggest concentration of walks and walking events ever held in a single district" Rambling Today
General Information:
Supported by The Great Outdoors magazine; its editor, Cameron MacNeish will launch the festival and give an illustrated talk. Cameron will also present "Wilderness Walks" on BBC2

Cleckheaton Folk Festival

Type of Festival: **Music and Dance**
Contact: **Geoffrey Pickles**
Address:
7 Listerdale
Littletown
Liversedge
Cleckheaton
Yorkshire
WF15 6EN
Tel. No: **01924 404346**
Fax No: **01924 404346**
Date(s) of Festival:
3rd - 5th July 1998
Times of Festival: **All weekend**

Cost for Adults:
£17 in advance. £22 on the weekend
Cost for Children: **Half price**
Special discounts:
OAPs, UB40s, students £1 off
Tickets available from:
G Pickles (see above)
Routes by Car:
M62 Junction 26 then follow signs for Cleckheaton
Train/Other:
To Dewsbury then bus to Cleckheaton
Venue:
Cleckheaton Town Hall and various other venues in town
Facilities (Parking):
Central parking. Camping and caravan site available £1.50 person/night
Facilities (Disabled):
Access for disabled in most of the venues. Please telephone for details
What's On:
Concerts, ceilidhs, children's creche, street entertainment, craft fair, workshops and meets. Artists include: Harvey Andrews, Noel Murphy, Dig Disley, Dave Webber, Annie Feniman, Robb Johnson, Vikki Clayton, Les Barker and many more
Historical Background:
Small town festival which has run for 11 years on the first weekend in July
Media/Public Comments:
"The best value for money festival in the country"

Harrogate International Youth Music Festival

Type of Festival: **Music, Dance, Arts**
Contact:
Sharon Brewster, Festival Manager
Address:
Perform Europe
Deepdene Lodge
Deepdene Avenue
Dorking
Surrey
Tel. No: **01306 744360**
Fax No: **01306 744361**
Date(s) of Festival:
2nd - 9th April 1999
Times of Festival:
Performances in the Harrogate area throughout the week
Cost for Adults:
All major concerts £4, other community performances free
Cost for Children:
All major concerts £2.50
Tickets available from:
Festival Booking Office:
01306 744360
Train/Other:
Major lines from Leeds and York
Venue:
Harrogate and surrounding areas
What's On:
Festival Parade through Centre of Harrogate. The festival has been bringing together over 1,000 instrumentalists, singers and dancers from all over the world. In 1998 there are groups from Russia, Sweden, Australia, Spain, Canada and USA
Historical Background:
In 1999 the festival celebrates its 27th year

Harrogate International Festival

Type of Festival: **Multi-Arts**
Contact:
William Culver Dodds
Festival Director
Address:
Harrogate International Festival Ltd
1 Victoria Avenue
Harrogate
Yorkshire
HG1 1EQ
Tel. No: **01423 562303**
Fax No: **01423 521264**
Date(s) of Festival:
24th July - 8th August 1998
Times of Festival:
Cost for Adults: **Varies**
Tickets available from:
Harrogate International Festival Ltd
Routes by Car:
A61 connects to all major routes (M1 via Leeds direct from A1)
Train/Other: **Harrogate Station**
Venue: **Harrogate**
Facilities (Parking):
Varies from venue to venue. Please call for details
What's On:
Jazz festival, stand up comedy "Laffs at the Baths", cream of classical performances. Harrogate Fiesta, open air events featuring world music, street theatre, children's entertainment and more
Historical Background:
The festival was founded in 1966 and has expanded to include the jazz, street theatre, and "Laff at the Baths" comedy festivals
Media/Public Comments:
"The North of England's leading Arts Festival" The Times

Hebden Bridge Arts Festival

Type of Festival: **Arts**
Contact:
Hebden Bridge Arts Festival Ltd
Address:
Tourist Information Centre
West End
Hebden Bridge
Yorkshire
HX7 9EX
Tel. No: **01422 842864**
Fax No: **01422 846837**
E-mail: **101371.443@compuserve.com**
Website:
www.hebdenbridge.co.uk/Festival
Date(s) of Festival:
13th June - 12th July 1998
Times of Festival: **Various**
Cost for Adults:
Various. Many events are free
Special discounts:
Concessions available
Tickets available from:
Tourist Information Centre (see above)
Routes by Car:
A646 from Halifax. Junction 26 off M62 from Manchester to Leeds
Train/Other: **Hebden Bridge Station**
Venue:
Various venues within Hebden Bridge
Facilities (Parking):
Parking within the Town Centre
What's On:
Classical music, photography exhibitions, theatre, film, art exhibitions, sculpture, textile exhibitions, open air music, dance, cabaret, poetry, street acts, children's workshops, jazz bands, rock bands, choirs, street entertainment . . .
Historical Background:
Started in 1993 by local artists to promote arts in Hebden Bridge
Media/Public Comments:
"The streets become a gallery, the town becomes a stage"

Pennine Spring Music

Type of Festival: **Classical Music**
Contact: **Penelope Anne Fletcher**
Address:
New Inn House
10 Brookhampton Street
Ickleton
Saffron Walden
Essex
CB10 1SP
Tel. No: **01799 530463**
Fax No: **01799 531499**
Date(s) of Festival:
27th - 30th May 1998
Times of Festival: **8pm start**
Cost for Adults: **£5**
Cost for Children: **£3**
Special discounts: **No concessions**
Tickets available from:
Tourist Office, Hebden Bridge: 01422 842532
Train/Other:
Hebden Bridge Station
Venue:
Parish Church, Heptonstall, Hebden Bridge
Facilities (Parking):
Parking available
What's On:
This year's music: Bach, Beethoven, Barber, Gershwin, Copeland, Haydn, Parry, Ives, Mozart, Puccini, Rossini, Sibelius, Delibes, Schubert, Verdi etc
Historical Background:
The festival is now into its 12th year

Huddersfield Contemporary Arts Festival

Type of Festival:
Music and Contemporary Arts
Contact:
Maria Bot - General Manager
Address:
Huddersfield Festival
Music Dept
University of Huddersfield
Huddersfield
Yorkshire
HD1 3DH
Tel. No: **01484 425082**
Fax No: **01484 425082**
Date(s) of Festival:
18th - 29th November 1998
Times of Festival: **10am - 11pm**
Cost for Children:
Concessions available
Special discounts:
Concessions available for OAPs, UB40s, students, Registered Disabled, Stage Pass and Kirklees Passport holders
Tickets available from:
01484 430528 or Festival Box Office, Lawrence Batley Theatre, Queens Square, Huddersfield
Routes by Car: **Off the M62**
Venue:
Various venues within Huddersfield
Facilities (Disabled):
Good access for disabled
What's On:
Orchestral, concerts (computer generated tape compositions), theatre, Paul Ruders in conversation, Young Composers Award, opera, film, musical performances, dance, cellos of the BBC Philharmonic, electric guitar and lots more
Historical Background:

Founded in 1978. In 1983 the arrival of Xenakis in Huddersfield and the extraordinary impact and daring of his music marked this festival's coming of age. Visitors descended from all over Britain to absorb this musical experience
Media/PublicComments:
"Huddersfield...byword for the best in contemporary music" Daily Telegraph
"Thoroughly welcoming. It is easy for anyone to come here and listen to rare music, talk to renowned composers in the bar, attend all manner of workshops, forums and films..." Sunday Times
General Information:
Discussions, lectures, talks, workshops, films - many of these can be found for free throughout the festival's 12 days. Opportunities to meet and talk with composers at the regular rendezvous sessions at the Festival Café

Ilkley Literature Festival

Type of Festival: **Literature**
Contact: **David Porter**
Address:
Ilkley Literature Festival
The Manor House
Ilkley
Yorkshire
LS29 9DT
Tel. No: **01943 601210**
Fax No: **01943 817079**
Date(s) of Festival:
29th March 1998 - 12th December 1998
Times of Festival: **Various**
Cost for Adults: **Various**
Cost for Children: **Various**
Tickets available from:

The Manor House (see above)
Routes by Car:
Ilkley is on the A65, 15 miles west of Leeds
Train/Other:
Ilkley Station. Regular services from Leeds and Bradford. Buses from Leeds, Bradford, Keighley and Skipton
Venue: **Ilkley**
Facilities (Parking): **Good parking**
Facilities (Disabled):
All venues are accessible to disabled
What's On:
Events, exhibitions, readings, discussions, theatrical one-man shows etc
Historical Background:
Founded in 1973, Ilkley Literature Festival celebrates its 25th anniversary in 1998 with a full calendar of events from Easter to Christmas

V98

Type of Festival: **Music**
Contact: **Bob Angus**
Address:
Maztec Ltd
491a Holloway Road
London
N19 4DD
Tel. No: **0171 272 2442**
Fax No: **0171 263 2434**
Date(s) of Festival:
22nd - 23rd August 1998
Times of Festival: 12 noon - 11pm
Cost for Adults:
£62 weekend with camping. £55 without camping. £30 day ticket
Special discounts:
Please make cheques payable to SG Box Office. Send to V98, P O Box 2052, London W1A 1HH. Add £2 booking fee for day tickets; £3 for weekend. Can be purchased

from Virgin Megastores (no booking fee)
Hotline: **0870 165 5555**
Tickets available from:
Credit Card Hotlines: 0113 244 4600; 0115 912 9198; 0161 832 1111
Train/Other:
Details of trains on 0345 48 49 50. Nearest stations are Leeds and Garforth. Local buses running to and from the site and the main train stations
Venue:
Temple Newsam, Leeds
Facilities (Parking): **On site parking**
Facilities (Disabled):
Car park for disabled, a special viewing platform on both outdoor stages and toilets for the disabled. No separate tickets are required. Stewards on site briefed on care and facilities for the disabled
What's On:
Please refer to the Chelmsford, Essex venue
Historical Background:
As with previous "V" Festivals the full line up will swap venues overnight for the second day ensuring that all 110,000 Festival goers will join the V98 experience
General Information:
Please refer to the Chelmsford V98 (Essex)

City Voice '98

Type of Festival: **Literature**
Contact:
Jane Stubbs/Michelle Whitehead
Address:
Library HQ
32 York Road
Leeds
Yorkshire
LS9 8TD

Tel. No: **0113 2143337**
Fax No: **0113 2143339**
Date(s) of Festival:
30th May - 13th June 1998
Times of Festival: **Various**
Cost for Adults:
Most events free, some charges for workshops
Tickets available from:
Library HQ (see above)
Venue:
Leeds City Centre: libraries, cafes and theatres
Facilities (Parking):
Limited parking for city centre venues
Facilities (Disabled):
Most venues have level access
What's On:
Celebrates writers and readers. Highlights include: 5 performances of new writing created specifically for City Voice, reading promotion, author visits, storytelling and a Bengali celebration. Other highlights include Soap on the Internet, writing workshops etc
Historical Background:
After the first ever City Voice '97, the innovative "Festival of Words" returns. A unique celebration of literature in Leeds, City Voice brings the world of reader and writer together. This years celebration will be packed with dynamic new writing
Media/Public Comments:
"It is essential to platform the City's talent"(reader from last year)
General Information:
To join the mailing list phone 0113 214 3337. City Voice is a collaboration between the Leeds Word Arena and Leeds Library and Information Service

Middleham Festival

Type of Festival:
Music, Arts, Historic, Racing. Crafts
Contact: **The Rev David Eyles**
Address:
The Rectory
Middleham
Yorkshire
DL8 4RB
Tel. No: **01969 622276**
Date(s) of Festival:
3rd - 12th July 1998
Times of Festival: **Various**
Cost for Adults: **Various**
Cost for Children:
Some reductions
Tickets available from:
Domus,   Market   Square, Middleham: 01969 623497
Routes by Car: **A6108 From Leyburn**
Train/Other:
Thirsk or Northallerton
Venue:
In and around the Royal, loyal and ancient township of Middleham
Facilities (Parking):
Good Town parking
What's On:
Flower festival, living history, music, New Orleans jazz, exhibitions, tea dances, drama, pub uuizzes, concerts, heritage events, comedy, live music, line dancing, stable visits, festival service, guided walks, medieval market, tours, BBQ etc
Historical Background:
Richard III lived in Middleham Castle for 10 years before he became King, then Middleham was known as "the Windsor of the North". The festival is a celebration of Richard's Coronation, Britain's Racing Industry and the town's beauty

General Information:
More recently Middleham has been known as "the Newmarket of the North" where the gallops once used by Richard III have seen many famous winning race horses trained

Middlesborough Mela

Type of Festival: **Music**
Contact: **Judith Croft**
Address:
Community Development, Leisure and Libraries
P O Box 69
Vancouver House
Middlesborough
Yorkshire
TS1 1EL
Tel. No: **01642 263839**
Fax No: **01642 221866**
Date(s) of Festival:
19th July 1998
Times of Festival: **Free**
Cost for Adults: **Free**
Tickets available from: **Not required**
Routes by Car:
A66 or A19 into Middlesborough
Train/Other:
Middlesborough Station
Venue:
Albert Park, Linthorpe Road, Middlesborough
Facilities (Parking):
Parking available on Clairville Common
What's On:
Popular Asian art forms including folk performances, popular music and dance. Children's entertainment, fashion stalls, craft stalls, food stalls
Historical Background:
8th year of Mela with a blend of popular performance and family entertainment to suit everyone.
Media/Public Comments:
"A feast of Bhangra Music"
"Thoroughly enjoyable day"
"The sizzling smell of Masala and thumping beats of the dohl filled the sweltering air at the North East's biggest Asian festival in Teeside"

Writearound

Type of Festival: **Writing**
Contact: **Andy Croft**
Address:
Buzzwords/Cleveland Arts
Gurney House
Middlesborough
Yorkshire
TS5 6RP
Tel. No: **01642 262424**
Fax No: **01642 262429**
Date(s) of Festival:
16th - 23rd October 1998
Cost for Adults: **TBC**
Cost for Children: **TBC**
Venue:
Various venues in Middlesborough
What's On: **TBC**
Historical Background:
Emerged out of community writing, education and amateur writing group in the late 80s. Now in its 9th year
Media/Public Comments:
"Writearound 1997 brought a number of extremely distinguished writers to Teeside notably Simon Aromatise, Kate Chantey, Matthew Sweeney, Matt Simpson and Linda France at the same time as making room for local writers to showcase their work"
General Information:
Writearound is an independent organisation which promotes,

develops and supports literary activity on Teeside aiming to bring the best of national writing to Teeside and to encourage local writers

Ryedale Festival

Type of Festival:
Classical Music and Theatre
Contact: **Helen Heron**
Address:
Festival Office
The Old Meeting House
Helmsley
Yorkshire
YO6 5DW
Tel. No: **01439 771518**
Fax No: **01439 771518**
Date(s) of Festival:
17th July - 1st August 1998
Times of Festival:
Events staged all day and evening
Cost for Adults: **Various**
Special discounts:
Discounts for Friends of Ryedale Festival
Tickets available from:
Festival Office: 01439 771518
Venue:
Various venues in the Ryedale area including Duncombe Park, St Marys Priory, Old Malton, Ampleforth Abbey Church, Helmsley etc
Facilities (Parking):
Parking available at all venues
Facilities (Disabled):
Access for disabled people at 90% of venues
What's On:
The events are staged in a variety of venues including some of the finest houses and churches in the countryside of North Yorkshire. Attending events can be combined
with walking on the moors, architectural interests, visiting local pubs and restaurants
Historical Background:
Ryedale Festival has been running for 14 years. 1998 is the third year it has been directed by Malcolm Layfield
General Information:
1998 is the year the festival is moving into an exciting new area with a spectacular fireworks concert in the grounds of Duncombe Park in August

Saltburn International Folk Festival

Type of Festival:
Folk Music, Dance and Song
Contact: **John Taylor**
Address:
Fern Cottage
Dalehouse
Straithes
Saltburn
Yorkshire
TS13 5DT
Tel. No: **01947 840928**
Date(s) of Festival:
31st July - 2nd August 1998
Times of Festival:
Friday noon - midnight. Saturday 9am-midnight. Sunday 9am - midnight
Cost for Adults: **£22**
Cost for Children:
10-16 years half price. Under 10s free
Tickets available from:
Tourist Information Office: 01287 622422
Train/Other:
Main line to Darlington, train to Saltburn
Venue:

Various venues within Saltburn

Facilities (Parking):
Ample parking. Campsite, £6 for weekend providing season ticket holders

Facilities (Disabled):
Disabled parking available. Access to all venues for disabled

What's On:
Concerts, ceilidh, singaround, craft stalls, Punch and Judy, dance displays and street entertainment

Scarborough Angling Festival

Type of Festival: **Angling**

Contact: **Avril Gillies**

Address:
23 Pollard Gardens
Scarborough
Yorkshire

Tel. No: **01723 859480**

Date(s) of Festival:
19th - 27th September 1998

Times of Festival: **Various**

Cost for Adults: **Various**

Tickets available from:
Avril Gillies (see above) and tackle shops in Scarborough

Routes by Car:
A165 from Bridlington. A171 from Whitby. A170 from Pickering

Train/Other: **Scarborough Station**

Venue:
Coastal areas of Scarborough, Whitby, Flamborough

Facilities (Parking):
Vast Area. The festival does not have any special parking arrangements.

What's On:
Junior and senior boat fishing, junior and senior shore fishing, junior parr competitions (6-11yrs), junior march (6-17 yrs), junior and senior

freshwater fishing , roving competitions, boating competitions. Plus All England Open Codling Championship

Historical Background:
Started by Scarborough's townsmen around 1910 and has steadily increased in size over the years

General Information:
The festival is trying to increase the number of junior, disabled and ladies participation and hopefully over the years there will be a good increase in their numbers

Scarborough Fayre Traditional English Dance and Music Festival

Type of Festival:
Traditional English Dance and Music

Contact: **Jim Clarke**

Address:
"Red Worms"
Helperthorpe
Malton
Scarborough
Yorkshire

Tel. No: **01944 738422**

E-mail:**Jim.McCaffery@ dial.pipe.co**

Date(s) of Festival:
28th May - 6th June 1999

Times of Festival: **10am - 11.30pm**

Cost for Adults:
£108 season ticket. £2-£5 per event

Cost for Children: **Half price**

Tickets available from:
On the door or Jim Clarke (see above)

Venue:
Scarborough Spa Conference Centre

Facilities (Parking): **Easy parking**

Facilities (Disabled):
Full access for disabled
What's On:
Dance demonstrations, street theatre, craft demonstrations, historical re-enactments, dance and music workshops, pub sessions, beach parties, ceilidhs, children's activities. Join the dancers, musicians, Vikings, Saxons, and English Civil War Soldiers
Historical Background:
Celebrates England's oldest festival at the end of the Millennium.
Media/Public Comments:
"Not to be missed" Open Morris Newsletter

Sowerby Bridge Rushbearing Festival

Type of Festival: **Traditional**
Contact: **Mrs R Knights**
Address:
9 Bright Street
Sowerby Bridge
Yorkshire
HX6 2ES
Tel. No: **01422 831896**
Date(s) of Festival:
5th - 6th September 1998
Times of Festival: **10.30am - 5pm**
Cost for Adults: **Free**
Cost for Children: **Free**
Tickets available from:
Not required
Routes by Car:
2½ miles from Halifax. Near M62 exits 22 or 24
Train/Other:
Sowerby Bridge Station is on the Manchester/Leeds and York Line
Venue:
Along streets of Sowerby Bridge, Sowerby, Ripponden, calling at churches and pubs

Facilities (Parking):
Free car parking in Sowerby Bridge
What's On:
Follow the colourful Rushcart as it is pulled along its 10 mile route through hilltop villages and valley bottom towns by 60 men accompanied by morris dancers. Visit events along the route i.e. street entertainment, fun fairs, canal events, bands, markets . . .
Historical Background:
Rushbearing originally served the purpose of transporting rushes to church for use as floor covering in the winter. Each year the old rushes were cleared out and new rushes were taken by cart. The tradition was revived in Sowerby for the Queens Jubilee 1977
Media/Public Comments:
"A very attractive and colourful event. Lots of music and Morris dancing" Publicity Officer
General Information:
Sowerby Bridge is in the heart of the splendid Calderdale area - rich in countryside, heritage and traditions. Visit the historic Piece Hall, Shibden Hall, Hebden Bridge, clogs being made at Mytholmroyd, Austin and Morris cars at Automobolia and much more

Moor and Coast Festival

Type of Festival:
Traditional Music, Dance, Arts
Contact: **Glen Rogers**
Address:
Moor and Coast
9 Windsor Terrace
Whitby
Yorkshire

YO21 1ET
Tel. No: **01947 820408**
Fax No: **01947 820408**
Date(s) of Festival:
14th - 16th May 1999
Cost for Adults: **£29 weekend ticket**
Cost for Children:
£14.50 weekend ticket
Special discounts: **None**
Tickets available from:
Moor and Coast (see above)
Venue:
Various venues within Whitby
Facilities (Parking):
Town centre parking
What's On:
Bands, dances, street entertainment, singers, workshops, singarounds, musicians sessions, etc. Artists including Vin Garbutt, Roy Bailey, Jez Lowe, Keith Donnelly, Enda Kenny, Chris Parkinson, Roger Wilson, Gaelforce, The Wilsons, John Wright Band and Lucky Bags

Sword Spectacular Festival

Type of Festival:
Traditional Music and Dance
Contact:
Vince Rutland - Festival Secretary
Address:
37 Church View
Brompton
Northallerton
Yorkshire
DL6 2QX
Tel. No: **01609 780536 (home)**
E-mail: **Rutland@onyxnet.co.uk**
Date(s) of Festival:
21st -25th May 1998
Times of Festival:
All day and evening
Cost for Adults:

£25 weekend include camping.
£13.50 camping. Individual event tickets also available
Cost for Children:
Over 10s half price. Under 10s free
Tickets available from:
Festival Secretary (see above)
Routes by Car:
From A1 and York - A64/A169.
From Teeside and north - A171.
From Scarborough - A171
Train/Other:
Service from Middlesborough to Whitby
Venue:
Various venues in and around Whitby, Redcar, Goathland, York
Facilities (Parking):
Parking available. Campsite (flat) at Whitby Community College with catering on site
What's On:
Dancing, street performances, ceilidhs, workshops, parades, gala concerts, international sword dance groups from Belgium (4), Italy and France, plus almost 30 from UK. Displays of traditional sword dancing from Northumbria and Yorkshire
Historical Background:
Follows successful first festival in Scarborough in 1996

York Early Music Festival

Type of Festival: **Music**
Contact: **Gill Baldwin**
Address:
P O Box 226
York
Yorkshire
YO30 5ZU
Tel. No: **01904 658338**
Fax No: **01904 612631**

Date(s) of Festival:
3rd - 12th July 1998
Times of Festival: **Various**
Cost for Adults: **Various**
Tickets available from:
Festival Box Office:
01937 584123
Train/Other: **York Station**
Facilities (Parking): **Public car parks**
Facilities (Disabled):
Disabled access to most venues
What's On:
Highlights include: The Gabriele Consort and Players, Academy of Ancient Music, Ton Koopman, Nigel North, Emma Kirkby and the medieval York mystery plays on wagons
Historical Background:
Started in 1977 Britain's premium festival of early music attracting artists and visitors from all over the world

Jorvik Viking Festival - Jolablot

Type of Festival: **Historic Pageant**
Contact:
Jorvik Viking Centre
Address:
Coppergate
York
Yorkshire
YO1 9WT
Tel. No: **01904 643211**
Fax No: **01904 627097**
Date(s) of Festival:
19th December - 21st February 1999
Times of Festival: **Various**
Cost for Adults:
Many events are free. Prices for feasts, ceilidhs, combat arena will be confirmed in January 1999
Tickets available from:

Jorvik Viking Centre
Routes by Car:
York is reached from A59, A19, A1079 and A1 (via A64)
Train/Other:
York Station
Venue:
Various venues within the centre of York
Facilities (Parking):
Town Centre parking
What's On:
Viking combat (battle re-enactment), Viking procession, boat burning ceremony, Viking feasts, festival ceilidhs. Visit Jorvic Viking Centre
Historical Background:
Inspired by "Jolablot", a celebration held by the Vikings to mark the end of the winter
Media/Public Comments:
"It brightens up the winter in York and is just as much fun for local residents as for tourists"
A York Resident

York Festival of Food and Drink

Type of Festival: **Food and Drink**
Contact: **Patrick Loy/Jane Sowden**
Address:
City of York Council
20 George Hudson Street
York
Yorkshire
YO1 6WR
Tel. No: **01904 554433**
Fax No: **01904 554429**
Date(s) of Festival:
19th - 27th September 1998
Times of Festival: **Various**
Cost for Adults:
Various. Many events free

Special discounts:
Family tickets available
Tickets available from:
York Tourist Information Centres in Exhibition Square and George Hudson Street: 01904 621756
Routes by Car:
A64 from south and west, A1079 from east; A19 from north. Use Park and Ride (signposted from major routes)
Train/Other:
Direct rail services from London, Edinburgh, Manchester and Birmingham
Venue:
Various venues within York City Centre
Facilities (Parking):
Park and Ride. City Centre parking
Facilities (Disabled):
Disabled parking available in City Centre and majority of venues have good disabled access
What's On:
Nescafe World Street café, Festival Food Theatre, free live cookery shows from local and celebrity chefs i.e. Ready Steady Cook's Patrick Anthony and James Martin, themed food markets, festival feasts, wine and beer tasting, "Masterchef" type competitions
Historical Background:
First held in 1997 and now the largest "City Wide" food festival in the UK with over 75 events
Media/Public Comments:
**BBC Radio York, Minster FM extensive coverage, including 3 live broadcast shows, numerous interviews, on-air promotions.
BBC Radio 4 - Woman's Hour**
General Information:

Discover York's traditional pubs, diverse restaurants, café society, and great nights out in First Stop, York's "Days and Nights"Guide, available from the Tourist Information Centre, York Central Library, and Minster FM reception

SCOTLAND

Aberdeen International Youth Festival

Type of Festival: **Performing Arts**
Contact: **Nicola Wallis**
Address:
**3 Nutborn House
Clifton Road
London
SW19 4QT**
Tel. No: **0181 946 2995**
Fax No: **0181 944 6507**
Date(s) of Festival:
5th - 15th August 1998
Times of Festival:
Throughout the day and each evening at 7.30pm
Cost for Adults: **£5 - £25**
Cost for Children: **About £2.50**

Special discounts:
25% discount for students, OAPs and UB40s
Routes by Car:
A92 from south and A96 from the north
Train/Other: **Aberdeen Station**
Venue:
Various venues within Aberdeen city centre including Aberdeen Art Gallery
Facilities (Parking):
Plenty of parking in city centre
Facilities (Disabled):
Disabled access to most venues
What's On:
Major exhibition of work created by young artists. Concerts, dance and drama performances presented by some of the world's top quality youth arts groups
Historical Background:
Started in 1973 mainly as an International Youth Orchestra Festival. Over the years has expanded into a major multi-arts festival incorporating education, visual arts and a touring programme throughout NE Scotland

Braemar Gathering

Type of Festival:
Traditional Scottish Sports
Contact: **William Meston**
Address:
Coilacriech Ballater
Braemar
Scotland
AN35 5UH
Tel. No: **01339 755377**
Fax No: **01339 755377**
Date(s) of Festival:
5th September 1998
Times of Festival: **9.30am - 5pm**
Cost for Adults:

Standing areas £5, Ringside seats £8 , Seats in uncovered stand £10
Cost for Children: **£1**
Tickets available from: **On the gate**
Routes by Car:
A93 (60 miles west of Aberdeen, 50 miles north of Perth)
Train/Other:
Nearest station is Perth
Venue:
Princess Royal and Duke of Fife Memorial Park, Braemar
Facilities (Parking): **Free parking**
Facilities (Disabled):
Parking and access for disabled
What's On:
Highland dancing, tug of war, solo piping, running events. Heavy events such as tossing the caber, pipe bands etc
Historical Background:
Association formed in 1817 although events were held in Braemar previous to this
General Information:
The Gathering is the most famous in Scotland. It regularly attracts crowds of around 20,000. Members of the Royal Family usually attend

Burning of the Clavie

Type of Festival: **Fire**
Contact: **Dan Ralph (Clavie King)**
Address:
"Cladach"
Brander Street
Burghead Moray
Scotland
IU30 2UD
Tel. No: **01343 835773**
Fax No: **01343 830739**
Date(s) of Festival: **11th January 1999**
Times of Festival:
Lit at 6pm. Finished at 7.30 am approximately

Cost for Adults: **Free**
Cost for Children: **Free**
Tickets available from: **Not required**
Routes by Car:
North on A9, head for Elgin, 9 miles towards the coast
Train/Other:
To Elgin by train. To Inverness by plane
Venue: **Burghead town streets**
Facilities (Parking):
Unlimited parking (arrive in good time)
What's On:
Join in with the crowds following the burning tar barrel around the streets of Burghead finishing up on Doorie Hill. People scramble to obtain a piece of burning barrel for good luck. This is a celebration of Burghead's New Year which carries on until daylight.
Historical Background:
Probably originates from the Pict and Viking periods. It is peculiar to Burghead
Media/Public Comments:
"Unique ceremony, very atmospheric and primitive"

Dufftown Highland Games

Type of Festival:
Scottish Culture and Traditional Sport
Contact:
Mr Arthur Brown - Secretary
Address:
Dufftown District Games Ltd
Ashville
Church Street
Dufftown Moray
Scotland
Tel. No:

01340 820265 (day)
01340 820342 (evening)
Fax No: **01340 820265**
Date(s) of Festival:
25th - 31st July 1998
Times of Festival: **11am - 5pm**
Cost for Adults: **TBC**
Cost for Children: **TBC**
Special discounts:
Concessions available for bus parties. Please telephone: Dufftown District Games Ltd (see above)
Tickets available from:
Dufftown District Games Ltd
Routes by Car:
Dufftown is half way between Aberdeen and Inverness. 45mins from Aviemore
Train/Other: **Keith (10 miles)**
Venue:
Mortlach Primary School sports field, Hill Street
Facilities (Parking):
Ample parking, toilets, tea tent
Facilities (Disabled):
Disabled access and toilets for disabled on site
What's On:
A traditional Scottish Highland Games: Highland dancing, athletics, hill racing, heavy athletics caber, hammer and weights. Also massed pipe bands, children's events, overseas visitors race, stalls, food stalls
Historical Background:
Dufftown Highland Games is over 105 years old
Media/Public Comments:
"A wonderful day for all"
General Information:
See all the colour, culture and majesty of Scotland at Dufftown Highland Games. Also many historic buildings in the area

Dumfries and Galloway Arts Festival

Type of Festival: **Arts**
Contact:
Mrs Sheena Widdall
Administrative Assistant
Address:
Festival Office
Gracefield Arts Centre
28 Edinburgh Road
Dumfries
Scotland
DGI INW
Tel. No: **01387 260447**
Fax No: **01387 260447**
Date(s) of Festival:
22nd - 31st May 1998
Times of Festival: **Various**
Cost for Adults: **£4.50 - £12.50**
Cost for Children: **£3**
Special discounts:
Concessions for UB40s and students only
Tickets available from:
Festival Office: 01387 260447
Routes by Car: **M6, A74, A75**
Train/Other: **Carlisle to Dumfries**
Venue:
Dumfries and surrounding areas
Facilities (Parking): **Town parking**
Facilities (Disabled):
Disabled access to most venues
What's On:
Art and craft exhibitions, orchestral concerts, literary events, folk and jazz sessions, children's events, intimate classical recitals
Historical Background:
The festival, now in its 19th year, is run by an enthusiastic group of volunteers and aims to bring the highest quality in music, art, poetry, jazz, folk and children's events
Media/Public Comments:
"Sell out success"
"Top class entertainment"
Comments made by visitors
General Information:
Enjoy the surrounding countryside by walking, cycling, pony trekking, visiting numerous castles and beauty spots

Dundee Jazz Festival

Type of Festival: **Jazz Festival**
Contact: **Dundee Rep**
Address:
I Tay Square
Dundee
Scotland
DDI IPB
Tel. No: **01382 223530**
Date(s) of Festival:
9th - 13th June 1998
Times of Festival: **Various**
Cost for Adults: **Various**
Special discounts:
Concessions available
Tickets available from:
Rep Box Office (see above)
Venue:
Various venues within Dundee
What's On:
Humphrey Lyttelton and his band, Salsa Celtica, Bill Bruford's Earthworks, Kevin Murray's Jazz in a Cold Climate, Roots Salutes the Sax, Alison Burns, Violet Leighton, The Penny Dainties etc
General Information:
The Jazz Club featuring Nimmo Bros, Gerry Culley's piano trio, Little Wolves, Dundee University Big Band, Comme Prima Feat Colin Steele

Dunkeld and Birnam Arts Festival

Type of Festival: **Music, Art**
Contact:
Dunkeld Tourist Information Centre
Address:
The Cross
Dunkeld
Scotland
Tel. No: **01350 727688**
Fax No: **01350 727688**
Date(s) of Festival:
25th - 28th June 1998
Times of Festival: **Various**
Cost for Adults: **Various**
Cost for Children:
Concessions for under 15s
Special discounts:
Concessions for OAPs
Tickets available from:
Tourist Information: 01350 727688
Routes by Car:
A9 North from Perth for 12 miles
Train/Other:
From Edinburgh, Glasgow and Inverness to Dunkeld and Birnam Station
Venue:
Various venues within Dunkeld and Birnam
Facilities (Parking):
Parking in Town Centre
Facilities (Disabled):
Disabled access to most venues
What's On:
Exhibitions, craft fairs, promenade organ recital, gala opening concert, concerts, forest expeditions, workshops, festival talk, poetry readings, country market, music, festival pageant, family fun, picnic in the park, festival supper and cabaret

Edinburgh Fringe Festival

Type of Festival: **Performing Arts**
Contact:
Hilary Strong - Director
Address:
The Fringe Society
180 High Street
Edinburgh
Scotland
EH1 1QS
Tel. No: **0131 226 5257**
Fax No: **0131 220 4205**
E-mail: **admin@edfringe.com** Web site: **http://www.edfringe.com**
Date(s) of Festival:
9th - 31st August 1998
Times of Festival: **All day**
Cost for Adults:
Various. Average price is £6
Cost for Children:
Half price (some events)
Special discounts:
A few events offer discounts
Tickets available from:
The Fringe Society (see above)
 Train/Other:
Edinburgh Waverely or Haymarket train stations. St Andrews bus station
Venue:
200 venues across Edinburgh
Facilities (Parking): **City parking**
What's On:
Expected to host over 1000 performing companies along with an estimated 500,000 visitors
Historical Background:
The Festival was created in 1947 and was seen as a post war initiative to re-unite Europe through culture. However six Scottish companies and two English gate-crashed the festival and were referred to as "Festival

Adjuncts" this was replaced by "Fringe"

Media/Public Comments:

"the scene of the biggest arts party in the western world" The Herald
"an event of global importance" The Scotsman
"the fringe is quite simply the biggest side-show in the world" Mail on Sunday

General Information:

From its modest beginnings 50 years ago some of the best dramatists, comedians, actors, poets have emerged - Dudley Moore, John Cleese, Michael Palin, Victoria Wood, Harry Enfield, Jack Dee, Paul Merton, Emma Thompson, Tom Stoppard and Rowan Atkinson to name but a few

Edinburgh Book Festival

Type of Festival: **Literature**
Contact: **Faith Liddell**
Address:
Scottish Book Centre
137 Dundee Street
Edinburgh
Scotland
EH11 1BG
Tel. No: **0131 228 5444**
Fax No: **0131 228 4333**
E-mail **edadmin@edbookfest.co.uk**
Date(s) of Festival:
15th - 31st August 1998
Times of Festival: **10am - 11pm**
Cost for Adults: **Up to £7.50**
Special discounts:
Concessions available
Tickets available from:
Hotline: 0897 500 010
Venue:
Various venues within Edinburgh

Facilities (Parking):
City Centre parking
Facilities (Disabled):
Disabled parking and access
What's On:
300+ events featuring nationally and internationally renowned authors plus the hottest new writing talents. Discussions, lectures, readings, demonstrations, workshops, musical events, theatre, book tents, 1930s Belgian Mirror tent, and more
Historical Background:
The festival began in 1983 to celebrate the written word. It normally attracts over 70,000 visitors
Media/Public Comments:
"Juxtaposes the established with the sub culture and is blithely balanced between happy entertainment and higher illumination"

Edinburgh International Festival

Type of Festival:
Theatre, Dance, Music, Opera
Contact:
Penny Mills
Press and Marketing Officer
Address:
21 Market Street
Edinburgh
Scotland
EH1 1BW
Tel. No: **0131 473 2001**
Fax No: **0131 473 2002**
Web site: **www.go.edinburgh.co.uk**
Date(s) of Festival:
16th August - 5th September 1998
Times of Festival: **Various**
Cost for Adults: **£5 - £50**
Cost for Children:
Under 18s (matinees only) half price

Special discounts:
Groups of 10+10% discount. Half price tickets on the day. Half price OAPs, UB40s, students for selected events. Half price for Stagepass, Equity, MU cardholders
Tickets available from:
Festival Office (see above) or tel: 0131 473 2000/fax: 0131 473 2003. Ticket sales at venues
Routes by Car:
Not advisable to bring cars into the City Centre as very congested at this time. Many taxis and bus services serving the festival venues. LRT Festival Bus passes available
Train/Other:
Central Edinburgh. Edinburgh airport has easy access to the city
Venue:
Various theatres, concert halls etc in Edinburgh
Facilities (Parking):
Parking within the festival area is difficult. Suggest parking away from area and taking taxi/bus to festival venues
Facilities (Disabled):
All venues accessible to disabled
What's On:
Over 170 performances of opera, dance, theatre, music, insight, talks and study days, Usher Hall concerts, Bank of Scotland concert series, ballet, fireworks concert, University festival lecture and lots more
Historical Background:
The festival was founded in 1947
Media/Public Comments:
"Nothing less than a sensation" The Scotsman
General Information:
Welcome to the thrilling atmosphere of one of the world's great celebrations of the arts. Also during this time Edinburgh hosts the Book Festival, International Jazz and Blues Festival, Military Tattoo Festival and International Film Festival

Edinburgh International Science Festival

Type of Festival:
Science and Technology
Contact: **Pauline Mullin**
Address:
149 Rose Street
Edinburgh
Scotland
EH2 4LS
Tel. No: **0131 220 3977**
Fax No: **0131 220 3987**
Web Site: **www.go.edinburgh.co.uk**
Date(s) of Festival:
3rd - 18th April 1999
Times of Festival: **Various**
Cost for Adults:
Various, many events free
Cost for Children:
Various, many events free
Special discounts:
Concessions available
Tickets available from:
Pauline Mullin (see above)
Venue: **Edinburgh**
What's On:
250 events over 16 days - science shows, exhibitions, workshops, debates and lectures, walks and tours
Historical Background:
Started in 1989 and has grown from an event attracting 58,000 people to one which attracts over 175,000
General Information:
The world's largest festival devoted to the celebration of Science

and Technology. Now copied throughout the world

Glenmoray Elgin Highland Games

Type of Festival: **Sports**
Contact: **Mrs Marion Allen**
Address:
13 Alba Place
Elgin
Moray
Scotland
Tel. No: **01343 541856**
Date(s) of Festival: 18th July 1998
Cost for Adults: **£3**
Cost for Children: **Half price**
Special discounts: **OAPs Half price**
Tickets available from: **At the event**
Venue: **Morriston Park, Elgin**
Facilities (Parking):
Car parking available
Facilities (Disabled):
Parking for disabled but limited access to toilets
What's On:
Traditional Highland heavy events. Tossing the caber, hammer throwing etc. Highland dancing, pipe bands, track events, side stalls, bouncy castles etc
Historical Background:
The first games were held in 1970 and has gone from strength to strength ever since
Media/Public Comments:
"Good day out"

Eyemouth Seafood Festival

Type of Festival:
Music, Seafood, Crafts
Contact:
Mrs F Waddell - Secretary
Address:
2 Barefoots Road
Eyemouth
Berwickshire
Tel. No:
01890 750618 (evenings)
Date(s) of Festival:
13th - 14th June 1998
Cost for Adults: **£2**
Cost for Children: **Free**
Special discounts: **OAPs £1**
Tickets available from: **At the gate**
Routes by Car:
Only 1½ miles off A1, 50 miles from Edinburgh, 65 miles from Newcastle
Train/Other:
To Berwick upon Tweed. By sea from Forth and Tyne
Venue: **Harbour Road, Eyemouth**
Facilities (Parking):
Overflow car parks and shuttle service to festival
Facilities (Disabled):
Parking for disabled
What's On:
Fresh iced seafood displays. Traditional boats and yachts, seafood cookery demonstrations, celebrity Ready Steady Cook, crafts, photographic exhibition, model boats, water sports, children's workshop, touch tank with local fish, musicians and entertainers, ceilidhs and more
Historical Background:
Fifth year of the festival. Celebration of wonderful seafood caught off the coast of Berwickshire. Eat spit roasted shark and a huge range of seafood
Media/Public Comments:
"Good value for money"
"Excellent atmosphere"
"Something for everyone"
General Information:

Most of the venues are in marquees in case of inclement weather. In June 2000 the festival will be staging an International Seafood Festival

Eyemouth Herring Queen Festival

Type of Festival: **Traditional**
Contact: **Mr J Barrie**
Address:
21 Gumsgreem Crescent
Eyemouth
Scotland
Tel. No: **018907 50232**
Date(s) of Festival:
25th - 27th July 1998
Times of Festival:
25th: 10am - 8pm, 26th: 12noon - 6.30pm, 27th: 10am - 11pm
Cost for Adults: **£1**
Cost for Children: **Under 12s free**
Special discounts: **None**
Tickets available from: **At the gate**
Routes by Car:
9 miles north of Berwick upon Tweed, 2 miles off A1
Train/Other: **Berwick upon Tweed**
Venue:
Harbour Road, Eyemouth
Facilities (Parking): **Parking available**
Facilities (Disabled):
Disabled parking within yards of the festival site
What's On:
Fishing fleet (30 boats) escorting the Queen into harbour, Crowning Ceremony, parades, firework display. Also enjoy music and children's activities
Historical Background:
54th crowning. Established in 1939. Stopped during Second World War
General Information:

Attendance in 1997 was 11,200 generating £123,000 for the area

Gatehouse of Fleet Festival of Music, Art and Crafts

Type of Festival:
Traditional Music, Arts and Crafts
Contact: **George McCulloch**
Address:
4 Carneys Corner
Gatehouse of Fleet
Kirkcudbrightshire
Scotland
DG7 2HW
Tel. No: **01557 814030**
Fax No: **01557 814030**
Date(s) of Festival:
26th - 28th March 1999
Times of Festival: **10am - 1am daily**
Cost for Adults:
Weekend ticket £10. Varying prices for each event
Cost for Children: **Half price**
Special discounts:
25% discount for OAPs, students and UB40s
Tickets available from:
G McCulloch (see above)
Routes by Car:
On A75 midway between Dumfries and Stranraer
Train/Other:
Dumfries Station. Buses from Dumfries to Stranraer
Venue:
Various venues within Gatehouse of Fleet
Facilities (Parking):
Good car parking near venues
Facilities (Disabled):
Disabled access to most venues
What's On:

Craft fair, art exhibitions, poetry readings, singing and original tune competitions, singarounds, festival party with real ales, concerts, pub shows, adult and children's fun musical workshops etc

Historical Background:
Springtime festival in this historic Old Galloway town (population 1,000)

Media/Public Comments:
"A truly family event suitable for all ages"

Midsummer Night's Dram

Type of Festival:
Music and Real Ale
Contact: **George McCulloch**
Address:
4 Carneys Corner
Gatehouse of Fleet
Kirkcudbrightshire
DG7 2HW
Tel. No: **01557 814030**
Fax No: **01557 814030**
Date(s) of Festival: **20th June 1998**
Times of Festival: **7pm - 11pm**
Cost for Adults: **£2.50**
Cost for Children: **£1**
Special discounts: **None**
Tickets available from:
G McCulloch (see above)
Routes by Car:
On the A75 midway between Dumfries and Stranraer
Train/Other:
Dumfries Station. Buses from Dumfries and Stranraer
Venue:
Ruined Castle, outside Gatehouse of Fleet between Dumfries and Stranraer
Facilities (Parking):

Good car parking near venue
Facilities (Disabled): **Not suitable**
What's On:
Many musicians performing in the majestic surroundings of ancient castle ruins with panoramic views over the Irish Sea. Enjoy a free dram of whisky on arrival, real ales in cellar bar and sizzling barbecue
Historical Background:
15th century ruined castle maintained by Historic Scotland
Media/Public Comments:
"A great event for all the family"

Gatehouse of Fleet Gala

Type of Festival: **Village Gala**
Contact: **John W Davidson**
Address:
Harpers Wood
Memory Lane
Gatehouse of Fleet
Kirkcudbrightshire
DG7 2BB
Tel. No: **01557 814765**
Date(s) of Festival:
26th July - 2nd August 1998
Cost for Adults: **Free**
Cost for Children: **Free**
Tickets available from:
Not required
Routes by Car:
On A75 midway between Dumfries and Stranraer
Venue: **Gatehouse of Fleet**
Facilities (Parking): **Good parking**
What's On:
Pipe bands and dancing, torchlit procession and fireworks, model aircraft, field day, sports, competitions, pet show, concerts, forest walks
Historical Background:
40 years of Gala Activities

Oktober Beerfest

Type of Festival: **Music and Real Ale**
Contact: **George McCulloch**
Address:
4 Carneys Corner
Gatehouse of Fleet
Kirkcudbrightshire
DG7 2HW
Tel. No: **01557 814030**
Fax No: **01557 814030**
Date(s) of Festival:
3rd October 1998
Times of Festival: **1pm - 6pm**
Cost for Adults: **£2**
Cost for Children: **£1**
Special discounts:
OAPs, UB40s and students £1.50
Tickets available from:
G McCulloch (see above)
Routes by Car:
On A75 midway between Dumfries and Stranraer
Train/Other:
Dumfries Station
Venue:
Ruined Castle, outside Gatehouse of Fleet between Dumfries and Stranraer
Facilities (Parking):
Good car parking
Facilities (Disabled):
Not suitable for disabled
What's On:
Many musicians performing in the majestic surroundings of ancient castle ruins with panoramic views over the Irish Sea. Enjoy a free dram of whisky on arrival, real ales in cellar bar and sizzling barbecue
Historical Background:
15th century ruined castle maintained by historic Scotland
Media/Public Comments:
"A great event for all the family"

Glasgow International Jazz Festival

Type of Festival: **Music**
Contact:
Gillian Garrity - Administrator
Address:
Glasgow International Festival
18 Albion Street
Glasgow
Scotland
G1 1LH
Tel. No: **0141 552 3552**
Fax No: **0141 552 3592**
E-mail **glasgow@jazzfest.co.uk**
Web site: **www.jazzfest.co.uk**
Date(s) of Festival:
26th June - 5th July 1998
Times of Festival: **Various**
Cost for Adults: **£8 - £15**
Special discounts:
Concessions available for students, OAPs, disabled, and UB40s
Tickets available from:
Ticket Centre: 0141 287 5511 or Glasgow Tourist Information: 0141 204 4480
Venue:
The historic Merchant city area in Glasgow city centre
Facilities (Parking):
Street parking, City car parks
Facilities (Disabled):
All venues are accessible to the disabled
What's On:
Highlights include: Michael Brecker Quintet, Jimmy Smith, Buddy Guy, Ladysmith, Black Mambazo
Historical Background:
The festival was founded in 1987 and 1998 will be its 12th year. Previous years it has featured the world's greatest jazz and blues artists such

as **BB King, Tony Bennett, Miles Davies, George Benson, Stephane Grappelli, Herby Handcock, Betty Carter and many more**

Media/Public Comments:
"The most dramatic and imaginative of any UK Jazz Festival"
The Guardian
"This is perhaps Britain's most prestigious event"
The Daily Telegraph
"The largest most diverse Festival of its kind in the UK" The Independent

Celtic Connections

Type of Festival: **Music**
Contact: **Colin Hynd**
Address:
The Glasgow Royal Concert Hall
2 Sauchiehall Street
Glasgow
Scotland
G2 2NY
Tel. No: **0141 332 6633**
Fax No: **0141 333 9123**
Date(s) of Festival:
14th - 31st January 1999
Times of Festival: **Various**
Cost for Adults: **Various**
Cost for Children: **Various**
Special discounts:
Concessions available
Tickets available from:
Ticket Centre: 0141 287 5511
Routes by Car:
M8 from Edinburgh (East) turn off Junction 16 and follow signs
Train/Other:
Queen Street Station (2 mins)
Central Station (10 mins)
Venue: **Glasgow Royal Concert Hall**
Facilities (Parking): **City parking**
Facilities (Disabled):
A special access information bro-

chure and programme of events on tape or in braille format are available on the Accessibility Hotline: **0141 353 4137**
What's On:
Concerts, art exhibitions, workshops, come and trys, live broadcasts, debates, talks and film screenings
Historical Background:
The festival started in 1994 to present traditional and Celtic concerts in Glasgow's major venue throughout the low season
Media/Public Comments:
". . . Celtic connections, from the most modest beginnings, has become a runaway success. . . A festival which combines international artists with the profoundly local variety"

Hawick Summer Festival

Type of Festival:
Family Entertainment
Contact: **Mrs Evelyn Sangster**
Address:
3 Dovecote Mews
Hawick
Scotland
TD9 9QL
Tel. No: **01450 375263**
Date(s) of Festival:
8th - 23rd August 1998
Times of Festival: **Various**
Cost for Adults:
Various, many events are free
Cost for Children:
Discounts available
Special discounts:
Concessions available for OAPs
Tickets available from: **At the venue**
Routes by Car:

From the south M6 and then A7 northwards

Venue:
Various venues within Hawick Town Centre. The craft fayre takes place within Hawick Town Hall

Facilities (Parking):
Town Centre parking

Facilities (Disabled):
Access for disabled

What's On:
3 day craft and antiques fayre, Scots nights, open air entertainment, walks, music, dance, workshops for children, road race, model rail exhibition

Historical Background:
1998 heralds the 15th festival

Media/Public Comments:
"Well worth a visit"

General Information:
An action packed two weeks of high quality family entertainment

Borders Festival of Jazz and Blues

Type of Festival:
Jazz and Blues Music

Contact: James Dunlop

Address:
4 Fairneylaw Place
Hawick
Roxburghshire
TD9 7QG

Tel. No: 01450 377278

Date(s) of Festival:
11th -13th September 1998

Times of Festival: All day

Cost for Adults:
3 day ticket £24; 1 day ticket £10 (after 31st July 1998)

Special discounts:
Discounted 3 day ticket £20; 1 day ticket £8 (before 31st July 1998)

Routes by Car:
A7 Carlisle - Birmingham

Train/Other:
Carlisle, Berwick, Edinburgh

Venue: Hawick Town

Facilities (Parking):
Free parking in town centre. Camping and caravaning site

What's On:
A three day event of jazz and blues played by a wide variety of talented musicians. Soak in the atmosphere of this popular festival set in an area of magnificent scenery. Take time out to visit historical sites, fishing, golf and great walks

Historical Background:
Festival is in its 3rd year

Media/Public Comments:
The bands, locals, radio, press, visitors all say "Excellent"

General Information:
Supported by Scottish Borders Enterprise and Local Committees and councillors who are all pleased to continue their support

Highland Festival

Type of Festival: Arts

Contact: Alison Logsdail

Address:
40 Huntley Street
Inverness
IV3 5HR

Tel. No: 01463 719000

Fax No: 01463 716777

Date(s) of Festival:
22nd May - 6th June 1998

Times of Festival: All day

Cost for Adults:
Various. Some events free

Cost for Children:
Concessions for children

Special discounts:
Concessions available

Tickets available from:
Festival Information Line:
01463 711112
Routes by Car:
A9 is the main route to Highlands from the South
Train/Other:
Daily from Edinburgh, Glasgow, Aberdeen and London including sleeper service. Easy Jet, BA fly from London to Inverness daily
Venue:
Throughout the Highlands and the Islands
Facilities (Parking): **Varied**
What's On:
A celebration of arts and culture throughout the Highlands and Islands of Scotland. Highlights of the programme include new productions by some of Scotland's leading talent, tours by UK and International artists. Street entertainment, masterclasses etc
Historical Background:
1998 is the 3rd annual Highland Festival

Kelburn Festival of Flight

Type of Festival: **Flight**
Contact:
David Shields
Development Manager
Address:
Kelburn Country Centre
South Offices
Fairlie
Nr Largs
Tel. No: **01475 568685**
Fax No: **01475 568121**
Date(s) of Festival:
23rd - 25th May 1998
Times of Festival: **10am - 5pm**

Cost for Adults:
£4.50 (includes entrance to the Kelburn Country Centre)
Cost for Children: **£3**
Special discounts:
OAPs, UB40s and students £3. Family tickets (2 adults, up to 3 children) £13
Tickets available from: **On the door**
Routes by Car:
1 mile south of Largs on the A78
Train/Other:
Nearest station is Largs. Free mini bus service 11.45am and 1.45pm to Kelburn
Venue: **Kelburn Country Centre**
Facilities (Parking):
Free parking, designated coach parking
What's On:
Aerobatic displays, flypasts, hot air balloons, parakarting, kite flying, radio controlled airship, birds of prey displays, model aircraft flying displays, model rocket workshops, teddy bear parachuting, kite making workshops, children's competitions, etc
Historical Background:
The first festival was in 1996. Kelburn's link with flight is the present Earl of Glasgow's great uncle the Hon Alan Boyle who was one of the first Magnificent Men in their Flying Machines
General Information:
As well as entrance to the festival the cost also gives the visitor entrance to Kelburn's Country Centre and its many attractions including "The Secret Forest", Scotland's most unusual visitor attraction

The Killin Traditional Music and Dance Festival

Type of Festival:
Traditional Music and Dance
Contact:
Mr Alex Stewart
Festival Secretary
Address:
2 Dochart Road
Killin
Perthshire
FK21 8SN
Tel. No: **01567 820224**
E-mail
10675 1.2564@compuserve.com
Date(s) of Festival:
19th - 21st June 1998
Times of Festival: **Various**
Cost for Adults:
£30. Family £90. OAPs £25
Camping: tent/caravanette £7;
caravan: £14
Cost for Children: **Under 16s £25**
Special discounts:
Adult £27.50, family £85, under 16s
£22.50, OAPs £22.50
(booked before 1st June 1998)
Tickets available from:
Mr Alex Stewart (see above) make
cheques payable to: The Killin Initiative
Routes by Car:
Killin is midway between Oban
and Aberdeen. Maps can be obtained from the local Tourist Office:
01567 820254
Train/Other:
There will be a festival bus available,
by prior booking, to meet any of the
trains at Crianlarich Station, or any
of the buses which may terminate
at Callander. The bus is also available to visitors arriving from the
ferry. The bus also runs between the
various venues.
Venue:
Main concerts and ceilidhs take
place at McLaren Hall, Killin, other
venues staged throughout the village
Facilities (Parking):
Ample parking in the village. Festival camp, Breadalbane Park is in
the centre of the village. There is
a dedicated family area within the
campsite
What's On:
Concerts, workshops, storytelling,
competitions, ceilidhs, open stage,
drama, traditional music and song.
Also artists including Old Blind
Dogs, Tomas Lynch, Beware of the
Dog alias Ron Cavana, Gino Lupari,
Brian McNeil and Ian Bruce
Historical Background:
The festival began in 1995. In 1996
the Killin Initiative won national
recognition when the Scottish
Tourist Board Thistle Award for
the best Area Tourist Initiative
was presented to the village
General Information:
Killin is situated amid the hills and
glens of Highland Perthshire, at the
head of Loch Tay, close to the geographic centre of Scotland

T in the Park

Type of Festival: **Music**
Contact: **Big Day Out**
Address:
North Lodge Stables
Auchineden, By Blanefield
Glasgow
G63 9AX
Tel. No:
Tourist InformationOffice:
01990 992244

Date(s) of Festival:
11th – 12th July 1998
Cost for Adults:
£54 weekend ticket; £29 day ticket. £7.50 camping ticket
Tickets available from:
Hotlines: 0141 3398383 and 01698 265081
Train/Other:
Shuttle bus services run from main towns
Venue: **Kintross in Fyfe**
What's On:
Main Stage: Prodigy, Corner Shop, Pulp, Robbie Williams, Space and the Seahorses
Langholm Common Riding
Type of Festival: **Traditional**
Contact: **R J Hill**
Address:
Bank of Scotland Buildings
Langholm
Scotland
DG13 0AD
Tel. No: **013873 80428**
Fax No: **013873 81144**
Date(s) of Festival: **31st July 1998**
Cost for Adults:
Free public events: £3 admission for afternoon
Cost for Children: **£1**
Special discounts: **£1 for OAPs**
Tickets available from:
Box Office: 013873 80428
Routes by Car:
M6 to Carlisle, then A7 to Langholm
Train/Other:
From Carlisle or Lockerbie
Venue:
Main Streets of Langholm and the Castleholm
Facilities (Parking):
2 good sized car parks and street parking

What's On:
Ceremonial processions led by the Cornet and his mounted supporters and accompanied by the Brass, Pipe and Flute Bands and later by Emblem Bearers including a Rider's chase and the crying of the fair. In the afternoon there is horse racing, Cumberland wrestling and Highland dancing
Historical Background:
In 1759 a Court decided that certain lands and certain rights and privileges in other lands belonged to the community. The boundaries of the communal land had to be defined. Each year a single horseman checked the boundary marks and reported any encroachment
General Information:
Series of Ride outs and dances are held during the fortnight beforehand and also a Common Riding concert

The Highlands and Islands Festival

Type of Festival: **Music and Dance**
Contact: **Neil Sinclair - Chairman**
Address:
Gleanndaloch
Connel
Oban
PA37 1PA
Tel. No: **01631 710201**
Date(s) of Festival: **1st - 2nd May 1999**
Times of Festival: **Various**
Cost for Adults:
Single events 50p. All day events: £1.50. Concerts various
Tickets available from:
Oban Music and Book Shop, Main Street, Oban
Routes by Car: **On the A816**

Venue:
Various venues within Oban town
Facilities (Parking): **Ample parking**
What's On:
Competitions: Highland dancing, piping, accordion, piano, fiddle, clarsach, singing, Scottish instrumental groups and woodwind and brass. Cups and medals are awarded in competitive classes and in open sections. Fringe events, grand concert and dance
Historical Background:
The objectives of the festival are to promote and develop the traditional and historical arts of Highlands and Islands music and dance. In 1997, 1,500 adults and children throughout the mainland and islands took part
Media/Public Comments:
"Meal-an-Naidheachd air Luchd-buannachd na Feis air fad"
Translated means "Congratulations to the Festival Champions"

Orkney Science Festival

Type of Festival:
Educational/Entertainment
Contact: **Howie Firth**
Address:
8 Broad Street
Kirkwall
Orkney
Scotland
Tel. No: **01 85687 6214**
Fax No: **01 85687 6284**
Date(s) of Festival:
4th - 11th September 1998
Times of Festival: **Various**
Cost for Adults: **Various**
Tickets available from:
Howie Firth (see above)

Routes by Car:
Drive to Scrabster, Caithness, take car across to Stromness
Train/Other:
From Edinburgh/Glasgow to Thurso then onto ferry. Or plane to Kirkwall Airport
Venue:
Various venues within Kirkwall and Stromness
Facilities (Parking): **Available**
Facilities (Disabled):
Access for disabled people
What's On:
Talks, lectures, activities, ceilidhs St Magnus Festival
Type of Festival: **Music**
Contact: **Dorothy Rushbrook**
Address:
Strandal Nicolson Street
Kirkwall
Orkney
Scotland
Tel. No: **01 85687 2669**
Fax No: **01 85687 2204**
Date(s) of Festival:
19th - 24th June 1998
Times of Festival: **Various**
Cost for Adults: **Various**
Tickets available from:
D Rushbrook (see above)
Routes by Car:
Drive to Scrabster, Cathness, take car ferry across to Stromness (15 miles from Kirkwall)
Train/Other:
From Edinburgh/Glasgow to Thurso then onto ferry or by plane to Kirkwall Airport
Venue:
Kirkwall and surrounding area
Facilities (Parking): **Available**
Facilities (Disabled):
Good access for disabled
What's On:

Concerts, recitals, drama, dance, pottery, visual Arts
Historical Background:
Founded in 1977 by Sir Peter Maxwell Davies to promote music, drama and the arts in the area
Media/Public Comments:
"... A continuing miracle" The Herald

Scottish International Festival

Type of Festival:
Traditional Scottish Games
Contact: **George McCulloch**
Address:
4 Carneys Corner
Gatehouse of Fleet
Scotland
DG7 2HW
Tel. No: **01557 814030**
Fax No: **01557 814030**
Date(s) of Festival:
3rd August 1998
Times of Festival: 1pm - 6pm
Cost for Adults:
£3 includes free admission to all games
Cost for Children: **£1.50**
UB40s, OAPs, students £2
Tickets available from:
G McCulloch (see above) or pay on entry
Routes by Car:
Dumfries and Castle Douglas on A75 then A713 to Parton, Castle Douglas
Train/Other:
Dumfries Station. Bus from Dumfries or Ayr
Venue:
Mango Byron, Loch Ken Holiday Park, Parton, Castle Douglas
Facilities (Parking):

Car parking next to venue
Facilities (Disabled):
Excellent for disabled
What's On:
World Gird 'N' Clique Championships, tossing the sheaf, hurling the curling stave, snail racing, spinning the peer, Balmaclellan skittles, flingin' the herd's bonnet etc. Participate in all the games. Also there are a number of side shows
Historical Background:
1998 heralds the 16th festival
Media/Public Comments:
"A great event for all the family"

Peebles Jazz Festival

Type of Festival: **Jazz Festival**
Contact: **Daniel T Ward**
Address:
23 Connor Ridge
Peebles
Scotland
EH45 8HN
Tel. No: **01721 721207**
Date(s) of Festival:
7th May - 9th May 1999
Times of Festival: **Various**
Cost for Adults:
Single session ticket £4. Rover ticket £15
Tickets available from:
Booking Office: Green Tree Hotel, Peebles or above address
Routes by Car:
From Edinburgh (1 hr), Newcastle (2 hrs), Carlisle (2 hrs), Glasgow (2 hrs)
Venue:
Various hotels and clubs in Peebles
Facilities (Parking):
Ample parking. 2 large caravan sites. Swimming pool in Leisure Centre
Facilities (Disabled):
Limited access for disabled

What's On:
**Traditional/Dixieland jazz.
Honestas Marching Band, festival
band, other artists to be confirmed**
Historical Background:
**1999 is the 5th year of the festival.
Initially started with only three
bands and now has seven. Plans to
increase in the future**
Media/Public Comments:
**"As numbers attending have gradu-
ally increased - it would seem our
reputation is spreading"**
General Information:
**Peebles is a small, friendly market
town set in beautiful Borders countryside. Only 20 miles from
Edinburgh, the attractions of the
big city are readily available**

Potfest Scotland

Type of Festival: **Ceramics Market**
Contact: **Geoff Cox**
Address:
**Stoddahgate Barn
Penruddock,
Penruddockrith
Cumbria
CA11 0RY**
Tel. No: **017684 83820**
Date(s) of Festival:
13th - 14th June 1998
Times of Festival:
10am to 5pm each day
Cost for Adults: **£1.50**
Cost for Children: **Free**
Special discounts: **OAPs £1**
Tickets available from: **At the gate**
Routes by Car: **Off the A9**
Train/Other:
**On the Perth-Crieff Road (2 miles
from the town centre)**
Venue:
The Agriculture Centre - Perth
Facilities (Parking):

**Free parking. Restaurant and bar
on site**
Facilities (Disabled): **Disabled access**
What's On:
**150 ceramic artists from all over
the UK with guests from Holland
and Belgium selling their work**
Historical Background:
**First in a three year build up to a
major International festival by 2000**

Perth Festival of the Arts

Type of Festival: **Arts**
Contact:
Sandra Ralston - Administrator
Address:
**Perth Festival of the Arts
3-5 High Street
Perth
Scotland
PH1 5JS**
Tel. No: **01738 475295**
Fax No: **01738 475295**
Date(s) of Festival:
21st - 31st May 1998
Times of Festival: **Various**
Cost for Adults: **Various**
Tickets available from:
**Box Office at Perth Theatre:
01738 472706**
Routes by Car:
**M90 from Edinburgh, A80 from
Glasgow, A9 from Inverness.**
Train/Other: **Perth Station**
Venue:
**Various venues within Perth City
Centre**
Facilities (Parking):
City Centre parking
Access for disabled
What's On:
**Orchestral (The Berlin Symphony,
Royal Scottish National Orches-**

tra), opera, festival chorus, **Cleo Laine, John Dankworth, Ned Sherrin, Wendy Craig and Francis Matthew in "Matters Matrimonial", Jools Holland, Riverside Art Mart, Scottish artists, and many more**
Historical Background:
Festival is now in its 27th year and includes a rich mix of arts

River Tweed Festival

Type of Festival: **Canoeing**
Contact: **W Bruce**
Address:
2 Hutlerburn Cottages
Ettrick
Selkirk
Scotland
TD7 5HL
Tel. No: **01750 52238**
Fax No: **01750 52238**
Date(s) of Festival: **7th June 1998**
Times of Festival: **10.30am - 3pm**
Cost for Adults:
Entries £4.50. Spectators Free
Cost for Children:
Entries £3 for juniors
Tickets available from:
Above address or on the day
Routes by Car:
From any direction join the A7 to Selkirk, then onto the B707 towards Clovenfords, Innerleithen and Peebles
Venues:
Fairnlee, Yair Bridge, Selkirk, Scottish Borders
Facilities (Parking):
Free Parking and toilets. Non alcoholic drinks will be available
Facilities (Disabled):
Access to many areas by disabled
What's On:
The day will start off with a Slalom,

then the river race will begin farther upstream to finish at Fairnlee followed by the Rapid Race. At the end of the day there will be a Duck Race and finally prize giving
Historical Background:
This event was first organised by request of the Scottish Borders Enterprise, it is run by a local club, Selkirk Canoe Club. Primarily a fun event with an aim to encourage new participants to the sport
General Information:
All proceeds to the event go to the Selkirk Canoe Club which is a non-profit making organisation

Skye and Lochalsh Festival (Feis an Eilein)

Type of Festival:
Traditional Music and Dance
Contact: **Duncan MacInnes**
Address:
S.E.A.L.L. Community Arts
Opstaig House
Teangue
Isle of Skye
Scotland
Tel. No: **01471 844207**
Fax No: **01471 844411**
Date(s) of Festival:
17th - 24th July 1998
Times of Festival:
Some daytime events and most evenings
Costs for Adults:
Approximately £3. Concerts/ceilidhs approximately £5
Special discounts:
£1 off OAPS, students, UB40s
Tickets available from:
Box Office (see above)
Routes by Car:
To Kyle of Lochalsh/Mallaig then

Ferry/Bridge. It would be best to take a car as public transport is minimal
Train/Other:
To Kyle of Lochalsh or Mallaig then bus
Venue:
Throughout the Island
Facilities (Parking): **Available**
Facilities (Disabled):
Please give prior notice
What's On:
Excellent Celtic/traditional bands, dancing, world music, Celtic electric, ceilidhs, workshops, concerts, dances, theatre
Historical Background:
1998 is the 7th Feis
Media/Public Comments:
"This festival has a real buzz about it"
General Information:
Enjoy the stunning scenery of Skye

St Andrews Highland Games

Type of Festival: **Highland Games**
Contact: **Mr Ian Grieve**
Address:
54 Crawford Gardens
St Andrews
Fife
Scotland
KY16 8XQ
Tel. No: **01334 476305**
Fax No: **01334 463537**
Date(s) of Festival: **26th July 1998**
Times of Festival: **1pm - 5pm**
Cost for Adults: **£3**
Cost for Children: **£1**
Tickets available from: **At the gate**
Routes by Car:
50 miles from Edinburgh (1hour)
Venue:
North Haugh, St Andrews

Facilities (Parking):
Ample parking. Beer tent and refreshments
Facilities (Disabled): **Disabled access**
What's On:
Traditional Highland Games, running and cycling, pipe band, piping, Highland dancing, heavyweights. Also funfair and stalls

Stonehaven Folk Festival

Type of Festival:
Traditional and Contemporary Folk
Contact: **Meg Findlay**
Address:
7 Rodney Street
Stonehaven
Scotland
Tel. No: **01569 765 733**
Date(s) of Festival:
10th - 12th July 1998
Times of Festival: **Various**
Cost for Adults:
Most individual events are £10. Weekend ticket £30
Tickets available from:
Pat Cruse: 01569 763519
Routes by Car:
A90 north towards Aberdeen
Train/Other:
Main East Coast route
Venue:
Various venues within Stonehaven
Facilities (Parking): **Town parking**
Facilities (Disabled):
Access to all events for disabled. Help given if required
What's On:
Concerts, ceilidhs, workshops, pub sessions, Aqua Ceilidh, Arthur Argo Memorial Concert, World Championship Paper and Comb

competition, children's concert

Historical Background:

The festival is now 10 years old and has gained much respect as a friendly well organised event.

Media/Public Comments:

Paper and Comb Competition in 1997 made National Press, TV and Radio

Strathearn Music Festival

Type of Festival: **Music**

Contact:

Crieff Tourist Information Centre

Address:

Town Hall
High Street
Crieff
Scotland

Tel. No: **01764 652578**

Fax No: **01764 655422**

Date(s) of Festival:

29th July - 2nd August 1998

Cost for Adults:

Between £3 and £6. Some events are free.

Special discounts:

Concessions available

Tickets available from:

Tourist Information Office (see above)

Train/Other:

Closest stations are Gleneagles, Dunblane or Perth or bus from Perth or Stirling to some venues

Venue:

Various venues throughout Strathearn, i.e. Crieff, Cumrie, St Fillans, Lochearnhead, Auchterarder

Facilities (Parking): **Available**

What's On:

Diverse music festival encompassing brass, jazz, folk, blues, opera, Cajun, traditional groups

Media/Public Comments:

"A music festival which caters for all musical tastes"

"Hunter" British and Scottish Gold Panning Championships

Type of Festival: **Mining**

Contact: **Carole Davies**

Address:

Museum of Lead Mining
Wanlockhead
Scotland
ML12 6UT

Tel. No: **01659 74387**

Fax No: **01659 74481**

Date(s) of Festival:

23rd - 24th May 1998 (and Sunday 13th September 1998)

Times of Festival:

10am - 5pm
(Sunday 13th 12.30pm - 4.30pm)

Cost for Adults: **£3.50**

Cost for Children: **Half price**

Special discounts: **Family ticket: £10**

Tickets available from: **The gate**

Routes by Car:

M74 to Abington or A76 to Sanquhar

Train/Other:

To Sanquhar then 8 miles to venue

Venue:

Lead Mining Museum, Wanlockhead

Facilities (Parking):

Parking available. Visitor shop, tea room.

Facilities (Disabled):

Disabled access to all venues

What's On:

Gold panning, gold panning demonstrations, guided mine tours, miner's cottages, miner's library, Visitor Centre

WALES

Musicfest Aberystwyth

Type of Festival: **Music**
Contact: **Louise Amery**
Address:
Aberystwyth Arts Centre
Penglais
Aberystwyth
Wales
SY23 3DE
Tel. No: **01970 622889**
Fax No: **01970 622883**
Date(s) of Festival:
18th - 31st July 1998
Times of Festival:
Daily evening concerts.
Summer School concerts each
lasting a week
Cost for Adults: **Varies by event**
Tickets available from:
Arts Centre Ticket Office:
01970 623232
Routes by Car:
The Arts Centre is on University
Campus in Aberystwyth on A487
Train/Other: **Aberystwyth Station**
Venue:
Aberystwyth   Arts   Centre,
Penglais, Aberystwyth

Facilities (Parking):
Plenty of parking, café, etc
Facilities (Disabled):
Disabled access
What's On:
Daily concerts featuring music com-
posed since 1900, plus world music,
jazz. Summer school courses for
strings, wind, piano, percussion, com-
posers, jazz, trombone, saxophone,
singers and improvisation. Also ex-
hibitions, craftshop, bookshop etc
Historical Background:
Now in its 12th year the festival is
an established event on the classi-
cal music calendar

Welsh International Film Festival

Type of Festival: **Film making**
Contact: **Grant Vidgen**
Address:
Premiere Cymru Wales
CYF
6G Parc Gwyddoniaeth
Cefn Llan,
Aberystwyth
Wales
SY23 3AH
Tel. No: **01970 617995**
Fax No: **01970 617942**
Date(s) of Festival:
13th - 22nd November 1998
Times of Festival: **Various**
Cost for Adults:
£4 for opening and closing galas,
£3 for all other screenings. Talks
free
Special discounts:
Buy tickets for 5 different films and
get one free. Purchase Dragon
Pass. Ticket for all the Celluloid
Wales Strand £25
Tickets available from:

Arts Centre: 01970 623232
Train/Other:
Aberystwyth Station
Venue:
4 main venues around Aberystwyth including the Commodore Theatre, Arad Gochm Ceredigion Museum and Aberystwyth Arts Centre
Facilities (Parking):
Town Centre parking. For brochure ring Tourist Information Office: 01803 852861
Facilities (Disabled):
Facilities for disabled are limited
What's On:
The festival is the premier film event for Wales celebrating Welsh film making in an international context. Rare chances to see work not normally available in Welsh or even British cinemas.
Historical Background:
Established in 1989, the festival has become one of the fastest growing film events in Europe with a reputation of being, friendly and relaxed with an accessible programme encompassing art-house and mainstream cinemas
Media/Public Comments:
**"The 10 day festival injects some £250,000 into the local economy" "Our commitment to new and young Welsh film makers is highlighted by the prestigious DM Davies Award (£25,000+)"
WIFF Publicity Office**
General Information:
Interest in Welsh film increased substantially following the first Oscar nomination in 1994 for the Welsh language Epic "Hedd Wyn". Welsh films in Welsh and English have always been offered a platform in Aberysywyth

Poetryfest

Type of Festival: **Poetry**
Contact: **Louise Amery**
Address:
Aberystwyth Arts Centre
Penglaais
Aberystwyth
Wales
Tel. No: **01970 622889**
Fax No: **01970 622883**
Date(s) of Festival:
3rd - 11th July 1998
Times of Festival:
Varies by event - daily
Cost for Adults: **Various**
Tickets available from:
Arts Centre: 01970 623232
Routes by Car:
Arts Centre is on the University Campus on A487
Train/Other: **Aberystwyth Station**
Venue:
Aberystwyth Arts Centre, Aberystwyth University Campus
Facilities (Parking):
Plenty of parking, café, etc
Facilities (Disabled):
Disabled access available
What's On:
A special festival placing Welsh poetry of both languages in an international context. Short residential courses also available. Plus craftshop, bookshop, exhibitions etc
Historical Background:
Now in its 3rd year, Poetryfest is growing in renown and attracts leading international poets

North Wales International Music Festival

Type of Festival: **Classical Music**
Contact:
Mrs Jill Mort - Administrator
Address:
Festival Office
High Street
Asaph
Denbighshire
LL17 0RD
Tel. No: **01745 584508**
Fax No: **01745 584508**
Date(s) of Festival:
19th - 26th September 1998
Times of Festival:
11am - 7.30pm
Cost for Adults: **£2.50 - £15**
Cost for Children:
Discounts available
Special discounts:
Available upon request, plus party discounts
Tickets available from:
Festival Office (see above)
Routes by Car:
A55 from Chester (east), Llandudno (west), A525 from Denbigh (south)
Train/Other:
To Rhyl from Crewe (London 3 hrs), Manchester and North; Bus from Rhyl and Denbigh
Venue: **St Asaph Cathedral**
Facilities (Parking):
Ample parking, refreshments, toilets close by. Local accommodation
Facilities (Disabled):
Access for disabled
What's On:
Concerts in the cathedral every morning and evening plus children's events, some late night events. The final concert will be given by the BBC national orchestra of Wales conducted by Mark Wigglesworth
Historical Background:
Began in 1972 by Artistic Director, the late William Mathias. Now one of the leading festivals in Wales
General Information:
St Asaph is set in the beautiful Denbighshire countryside. Enjoy the coastline of North Wales and its surrounding areas, including Snowdonia National Park and the Island of Anglesey

Barmouth Arts Festival

Type of Festival: **Arts**
Contact: **Mrs M Jones - Secretary**
Address:
1 Epworth Terrace
Barmouth
Wales
LL42 1PN
Tel. No: **01341 280392**
Date(s) of Festival:
6th - 12th September 1998
Times of Festival: **Mostly 8pm**
Cost for Adults: **£2 - £6**
Cost for Children: **£1**
Special discounts: **Parties**
Tickets available from:
Mrs M Jones (see above) or at the door
Train/Other:
Via Shrewsbury. Barmouth Station
Venue: **Dragon Theatre, Barmouth**
Facilities (Parking):
Parking available
Facilities (Disabled):
Access for disabled
What's On:
Bass trio, variety show, Richard Digance, lunch with speaker, crafts display, Spanish Flamenco, organ

and tenor, pianist, Welsh Choir, art exhibition . . .

Historical Background:
Festival is in its 24th year. Barmouth is the first area of land given to the National Trust

Media/Public Comments:
Local press very supportive and are members of "Festivals of Wales"

General Information:
Barmouth is a small seaside town on the edge of Snowdonia National Park, wonderful scenery and a noted walking area

Brecon Jazz Festival

Type of Festival: **Music**

Contact:
Deborah Anthony/Mandy Wix

Address:
Brecon Jazz Festival and Gallery
Watton Chambers
Brecon
Wales
LO3 7EF

Tel. No: **01874 625557**
Fax No: **01874 622387**

Date(s) of Festival:
7th - 9th August 1998

Times of Festival: **6pm - 11pm**

Routes by Car: **A470 from Cardiff (1½ hours from Bristol)**

Train/Other:
Abergavenny Station

Venue: **Brecon Town Centre**

Facilities (Parking):
Park and Ride. Town café, bars and restaurants

Facilities (Disabled):
Disabled reserved parking in Town Centre

What's On:
100 concerts, street bands, open air bandstands, indoor concerts. Street stalls and street entertainment

Historical Background:
Now in its 15th year, Brecon Jazz is one of the most popular festivals of its kind in Europe

Media/Public Comments:
"The most enjoyable of all Britain's festivals" The Times
"Brecon Jazz is an astonishing success story" Daily Telegraph

National Eisteddfod of Wales

Type of Festival:
Music, Dance, Art and Crafts

Contact: **Elevi Twynog Davies**

Address:
Eisteddfod Office,
40 Parc Ty Glas
Llanishen
Cardiff
CF4 5WU

Tel. No: **01222 763 777**
Fax No: **01222 763 737**

Date(s) of Festival:
1st - 8th August 1998

Times of Festival:
10am - 10pm every day except Sunday 2nd August

Cost for Adults: **£6.50 - £9.50**

Cost for Children:
Under 12s free when accompanied by adult

Special discounts:
Students £3, OAPs £4

Routes by Car: **M4**

Train/Other: **Bridgend Station**

Venue:
Bridgend Town. Eisteddfod in English means "Sitting together"

Facilities (Parking):
Free parking close to venue

What's On:
Over 300 stalls, colourful bardic ceremonies, choirs - over 6000 competitors, Wales' largest contem-

porary art and crafts exhibition, children's activities
Historical Background:
Dates back to mid-19th century, although the first Eisteddfod was held in 1176

Gwyl Ifan

Type of Festival: **Folk Dance**
Contact: **Dai James**
Address:
**Cumni Dawns Caerdydd
50 Prospect Drive
Llandaf
Cardiff
CF5 2HN**
Tel. No: **01222 563989**
Date(s) of Festival:
20th - 21st June 1998
Times of Festival:
Friday evening - Sunday lunchtime
Cost for Adults:
Weekend package: £65.70 including B&B in 5 star Park Hotel, lunch Saturday, festival feast Saturday evening and all events and transport included
Tickets available from:
01222 563989/or Park Hotel
Routes by Car:
A48(M), M4 or A470 to City Centre
Train/Other:
Cardiff Central, local train to Cardiff Queen Street (or short taxi ride)
Venue:
Various venues within Cardiff City
Facilities (Parking):
Parking available within the City Centre. Some parking within the grounds of the hotel
Facilities (Disabled):
No special facilities for the disabled. However hotel is 5 star standard, so assistance is always on hand

What's On:
Welsh barn dance, dancing, dance tours, grand procession through City Centre, Taplas (feast and dance), workshops, traditional Welsh folk music, dance teams in their spectacular costumes, guest teams from the Czech Republic, Scotland, Cornwall and England
Historical Background:
Began in 1977 by Cumni Dawns Werin Cherdydd (the official folk dance team of the City of Cardiff) as one-day adult dance festival and soon expanded into the largest festival of its type and a full weekend

The North Wales Bluegrass Music Festival

Type of Festival: **Music and Dance**
Contact: **Gill Williams/John Les**
Address:
**"Woodstock"
Llanrwst Road
Glan Conwy
Wales
LL28 5SR**
Tel. No:
01492 580454 of 01492 515921
Fax No: **01492 580454**
Date(s) of Festival:
3rd - 5th July 1998
Times of Festival:
7pm Friday evening through until 6pm Sunday evening
Cost for Adults: **TBC**
Cost for Children:
13yrs+ half price. Under 13s free
Routes by Car:
A55 Expressway. Turn off to Conwy
Train/Other:
Railway station is right in the middle of Conwy, 5 mins walk from the festival site

Venue:
Bodlonders Park, Civic Hall Audi-torium, Castle Street, Conwy
Facilities (Parking):
Large level car park
Facilities (Disabled):
Access for disabled, toilet facilities on festival site and main audito-rium, wheelchair access to all venues including marquee
What's On:
8 bluegrass concerts. 24 hour pickin' sessions. 30 bluegrass bands and Old Time music bands, 3 dance groups. Instrument workshops, 3 dance workshops etc
Historical Background:
The festival is 10 years old this year. It began in a field in Abergele, moved to Trefin in the Conwy Val-ley. The festival outgrew the area and 4 years ago moved to its present site (7 acres)
Media/Public Comments:
Everyone says, "it's brilliant"
General Information:
Continuous pickin' round the clock on the 7 acre level festival camp-site. A family event in the beautiful medieval town of Conwy

Gwyl Criccieth Festival

Type of Festival: **Music**
Contact:
Pam McLaughlin - Criccieth Arts Association
Address:
52 High Street
Criccieth
Gwynedd
Wales
LL52 0EY
Tel. No: **01766 522778**
Fax No: **01766 522778**
Date(s) of Festival:

16th - 21st June 1998
Times of Festival: **Various**
Cost for Adults: **From £3 to £12**
Cost for Children:
Under 16s half price
Tickets available from:
Criccieth Arts Festival Office (see above)
Routes by Car:
A55 Coast road to Bangor then south to Criccieth
Train/Other:
London to Criccieth or London to Bangor and bus to Criccieth. Na-tional Express bus to Criccieth
Venue:
Various venues in Criccieth and surrounding areas
Facilities (Parking):
Ample parking, camping, good B&B, hotels etc
What's On:
Opera, National Youth Jazz Or-chestra, variety show, young artists on piano, cello, oboe, violin, New Cambrian Ministreets playing early Welsh instruments plus children's events - circus skills, pottery mak-ing, face painting, bouncy castles, fireworks etc
Historical Background:
11th annual festival. One of this year's highlights is the acclaimed production of Offenbach's "Tales of Hoffman" - New Cambrian Min-strels and Opera Box

Fishguard Music Festival

Type of Festival: **Classical Music**
Contact: **Mrs Marion Butler**
Address:
Festival Office
Fishguard
Wales

SA65 9BJ
Tel. No: **01348 873 612**
Fax No: **01348 873 612**
Date(s) of Festival:
25th July to 1st August 1998
Times of Festival: **Various**
Cost for Adults: **Various**
Tickets available from:
Festival Office: 01348 873612
Routes by Car: **M4**
Venue:
Various venues within Fishguard and surrounding areas
Facilities (Parking): **Ample parking**
Facilities (Disabled):
Access for disabled
What's On:
Concerts, featuring the BBC National Orchestra of Wales, masterclasses, workshops, children's programme etc
Historical Background:
The festival was founded in 1970 and is a major event in Wales
Media/Public Comments:
"An international music event with famous musicians"
"Music making of the highest order. Famous for it"

Gower Festival

Type of Festival: **Classical Music**
Contact: **Maurice Broady**
Address:
Gower Festival Society
59 Hendrefoilan Road
Swansea
Wales
Tel. No:
01792 207924 or 01792 419449
Date(s) of Festival:
18th - 31st July 1998
Times of Festival: **Various**
Cost for Adults: **Mostly £10**
Cost for Children: **Under 15s half**

price if accompanied by adult
Special discounts:
Discounts for block bookings. 15-25 yr olds 25% off, disabled 25% off
Tickets available from:
Booking Office: Grand Theatre, Singleton Street, Swansea: 01792 475715 (from 23rd June)
Venue:
Gower Churches: Oystermouth, Cheriton, Reynoldston, Oxwich, Newton, Penrice, Llandewi, Bishopston, Pennard Churches
Facilities (Parking):
Parking available
Facilities (Disabled):
Access may be difficult for the disabled
What's On:
Swansea Bach Choir, Halle Brass, classical accordion, piano, violin, National Youth Choir, Gammbyssa Choir (Sweden), Katona Guitar Duo, Delme Quartet, Tudor songs, folk songs, National Youth Brass Band of Wales, lectures, festival ramble
Historical Background:
The festival began in 1976 and is growing each year
Media/Public Comments:
"The Gower festival aims to bring good music to every part of Gower, taking advantage of the excellent acoustics of the many beautiful parish churches, which have accommodated the festival since its birth"

Llandrindod Wells Drama Festival

Type of Festival: **Theatre**
Contact: **Roger King**
Address:
Foxwood
8 Crabtree Green
Llandrindod Wells

Wales
LD1 6EP
Tel. No: **01597 822480**
Date(s) of Festival:
4th - 9th May 1998
Times of Festival:
7.45pm each evening
Cost for Adults: **£4**
Cost for Children: **£2**
Special discounts:
Patron Voucher scheme. Discounts for groups of 10+
Tickets available from:
Roger King (see above)
Routes by Car: **A470**
Train/Other:
Direct from Swansea or Shrewsbury
Venue:
Albert Hall, Ithon Road, Llandrindod Wells
Facilities (Parking):
Car parks close to all venues
Facilities (Disabled):
Access for disabled
What's On:
Amadeus, Entertaining Mr Sloane, Second From Last in the Sack Race, One Flew Over The Cuckoo's Nest, The Cavalcaders
Historical Background:
Longest running drama festival in the UK (65 years)
Media/Public Comments:
"Prestigious and of a very high standard"
General Information:
Good local amenities eg. hotels, guest houses and unrivalled countryside

Llandrindod Wells Victorian Festival

Type of Festival: **Victorian**
Contact: **Victorian Festival Office**
Address:
Town Hall
Memorial Gardens
Llandrindod Wells
LD1 4DL
Tel. No: **01597 823441**
Fax No: **01597 835905**
Date(s) of Festival:
22nd - 30th August 1998
Times of Festival:
Most events free
Tickets available from:
Victorian Festival Office (see above)
Venue: **Llandrindod Wells**
What's On:
Male voice choir, music hall melodramas, Victorian Ball, jazz, Welsh night, Murder Mystery Banquet, Magic Night, torchlight procession, children's workshops, bandstand concerts, costume parades, exhibitions, talks, Victorian fairground, costume hire etc
Historical Background:
This Victorian Festival celebrates its 17th year. Attracting some 35,000 visitors, largely to the dramatic change achieved in the reversion to the Victorian era, the effect of horses and carriages, Victorian window displays and costumes etc
Media/Public Comments:
"The town's unspoilt architecture provides a perfect backdrop to the celebrations"
General Information:
Llandrindod Wells Victorian Festival is a 1985 Daily Crest Heritage Award winner, a 1986 Wales Tourist Board winner

The Llandudno Victorian Extravaganza

Type of Festival:
Traditional Victorian Steam Fair
Contact: **Mr W T Deacon**
Address:
13 Deganley Avenue
Llandudno
Wales
LL30 2YB
Tel. No: **01492 875152**
Date(s) of Festival:
1st - 3rd May 1999
Times of Festival: **9am - 9.30pm**
Cost for Adults: **Free**
Cost for Children: **Free**
Tickets available from:
Not required
Routes by Car:
From Chester: A55, A470. From South Wales: A470 from Cardiff. From Mid Wales A5 and A470
Train/Other:
London-Crewe/Llandudno
Holyhead - Llandudno
Venue: **Llandudno Town**
Facilities (Parking):
Town parking available
What's On:
Daily parades, street entertainment, displays of steam engines, competitions, tram rides.
Historical Background:
Started in 1986 and designed to bring the Victorian atmosphere back to the town
Media/Public Comments:
"Starts the holiday season off with a bang"
General Information:
Explore the Victorian town of Llandudno and Great Rome Country Park, as well as using the town as a base to explore the Snowdonia National Park

Llangollen International Jazz Festival

Type of Festival: **Jazz**
Contact: **Mr R Potts**
Address:
Farthings
Riveacre Road
Hooton Park
South Wirral
Tel. No: **0151 339 3367**
Fax No: **0151 339 3367**
Date(s) of Festival:
8th -11th May 1999
Times of Festival: **3 days continuous**
Cost for Adults:
£25 for whole weekend
Tickets available from:
Mr Potts (see above)
Venue:
7 venues within Llangollen
Facilities (Parking):
Town parking. All venues easy walk from one another
What's On:
Continuous music. Many styles of jazz.
Historical Background:
1999 heralds the festival's 14th year
Media/Public Comments:
"Probably the friendliest festival in Europe"
General Information:
Visit Telford's aqueduct, the famous narrow gauge railway, ancient abbey and enjoy the surrounding countryside of Llangollen

Llangollen International Musical Eisteddfod

Type of Festival:
Music, Song and Dance
Contact: **Maureen A Jones**
Address:
Eisteddfod Office
Llangollen
Wales
LL20 8NG
Tel. No: **01978 860236**
Fax No: **01978 861300**
Date(s) of Festival:
7th - 12 July 1998
Times of Festival:
Tuesday-Saturday: 9am -10.30pm
Sunday: 5pm - 10pm
Cost for Adults: **From £4**
Cost for Children: **From £2**
Special discounts:
10% off for groups of 10+
Tickets available from:
Eisteddfod Office (see above)
Routes by Car:
From Shrewsbury A5, from Chester A483 onto A5391
Train/Other:
London Euston to Ruabon (5 miles from Llangollen) then by bus or taxi
Venue: **Llangollen**.
Facilities (Parking):
2,500 car parking spaces, 70 coach parking spaces. Fast food outlets, restaurant facilities etc
Facilities (Disabled):
Access for disabled i.e. ramps, toilets
What's On:
Competitors rehearsing in colourful national costumes, 25 Welsh craft shops, exhibitions, overseas competitors national crafts, South American crafts, souvenirs, com- petitors parade, also concerts, workshops, competitions etc
Historical Background:
In 1947 Llangollen launched its first Musical Eisteddfod. 1953 saw the visit of the Oberkirchen Children's Choir who brought their song "The Happy Wanderer". In 1968 a young tenor, Placido Domingo made his first UK appearance
Media/Public Comments:
"It has to be experienced to be believed" The Independent
"Six days of magic" Daily Post
"The only surprising things about miracles, however small, is that they sometimes happen" Dylan Thomas
General Information:
The festival attracts over 6500 people representing some 47 countries and an audience of nearly 100,000. Thousands also enjoy the many glimpses of the festival via the TV coverage in particular the "Choir of the World Competition" which is transmitted live

Llantilio Crossenny

Type of Festival: **Music**
Contact: **D S Milner**
Address:
Llanddewi House
Llanddewi Skirrid
Abergavenny
Llantilio Crossenny
Wales
Tel. No: **01873 856928**
Date(s) of Festival:
14th - 17th May 1998
Times of Festival:
Day and evening concerts
Cost for Adults: **£3 - £12**

Tickets available from:
D.S. Milner (see above)
Routes by Car:
Llantilio Crossenny is halfway between Monmouth and Abergavenny on the B4233
Venue:
St Teilos 12th century Church
Facilities (Parking):
Ample parking and toilet facilities
What's On:
Llantilio Festival Opera presents: "Orpheus and Eurydice", orchestral concert with Llantilio Festival Orchestra, festival evensong and The Carnival Band, who are classically trained graduates playing strictly for fun!
General Information:
To inaugurate the festival the Carnival Band concert on Thursday 14th May will be followed by a buffet reception. The price is £3 (including wine). Make an early reservation

Tydfil Festival

Type of Festival: **Arts**
Contact: **Mr G James/Mrs D Rees**
Address:
Merthyr Tydfil Borough Council Central Library High Street Merthyr Tydfil Wales CF47 5AF
Tel. No: **01685 723057**
Fax No: **01685 370690**
Date(s) of Festival:
Whole of October 1998
Times of Festival: **Various**
Cost for Adults: **Many events free**
Cost for Children: **Free**
Venue:
Held throughout the County

What's On:
Community concerts, workshops/seminars, lectures, performances, author visits, competitions, workshops
Historical Background:
Started in 1995 as a week long literary festival. Celebrates new unitary authority
Media/Public Comments:
"We all appreciated this event enormously. It really was superb"
"We were thoroughly absorbed made publishing look so easy. Valuable advice"
"Cleverly constructed . . . there was seriousness and spontaneous laughter"

Gwyl Gregynog Festival

Type of Festival: **Music**
Contact: **Nia Price**
Address:
Gwyl Gregynog Festival Gregynog Newtown Wales SY16 3PW
Tel. No: **01686 650224**
Fax No: **01686 650656**
Date(s) of Festival:
23 - 28th June 1998
Times of Festival:
Afternoon and evenings
Cost for Adults: **£3 - £12.50**
Tickets available from:
Festival Office: 01686 650101
Routes by Car:
Gregynog is situated 5 miles north of Newtown, Powys
Train/Other:
Direct rail links to Birmingham and from there to London (Euston) and Manchester
Venue:

Gregynog, University of Wales, Newtown

Facilities (Parking):
Ample free parking in the grounds

Facilities (Disabled):
Access for disabled. Ramps to selected entrances and large toilets in main building

What's On:
Recitals, choral, orchestral, outdoor spectacular   jazz   night. Masterclasses, annual awards etc. Concert goers are welcome to enjoy the grounds for picnics and walks

Historical Background:
Between 1924 and 1964 Gregynog was the home of the Davies Sisters who founded the Gregynog Music Festival attracting Vaughan Williams, Edward Elgar, Sir Adrian Boult, Gustav Holst etc. In 1988 the festival was revived.

Media/Public Comments:
"The Gregynog Festival was one of the most enjoyable experiences of last summer"
Daily Telegraph
"If there is a more perfect setting for a music festival…then someone please direct me to it" Daily Post

General Information:
The Festival is one of Britain's finest music Festivals. Under the artistic direction of Anthony Rolfe Johnson, one of Britain's finest operatic tenors, the festival has attracted musicians from all over the world

Mid Wales Festival of Transport

Type of Festival:
Transport from turn of century

Contact:
Mr Mike Exton - Festival Chairman

Address:
Stanley Street
Seven Stars Road
Welshpool
Wales
SY21 7JH

Tel. No:
01938 553680
01938 553947(evenings)

Fax No: **01938 553680**

Date(s) of Festival:
11th - 12th July 1998

Times of Festival: **10am - 5pm**

Cost for Adults: **£3.50**

Cost for Children: **Under 16s free**

Tickets available from: **The gate**

Routes by Car:
Via A458 from Shrewsbury. A483 from north and south

Train/Other:
Shrewsbury - Aberystwyth Line. Welshpool airport

Venue: **Powys Castle**

Facilities (Parking): **Free parking**

Facilities (Disabled):
Disabled parking

What's On:
Classic collectors vehicles of all types. Motorcycles, cars, light and heavy commercials, fire engines, military vehicles, agricultural vehicles etc. Collectables, steam vehicles, trade stands, autojumble, continuous arena activity, Olde Tyme Fairground

General Information:
Now the largest motoring event in Wales. A superb family weekend

St Davids Cathedral Festival

Type of Festival: **Classical Music**
Contact:
Llywela V Harris - Administrator
Address:
65 Goat Street
St Davids
Pembrokeshire
SA62 6RQ
Tel. No: **01437 720271**
Fax No: **01437 721885**
Date(s) of Festival:
23rd - 31st May 1998
Times of Festival:
Evening concerts each day and 2 5pm recitals by young musicians
Cost for Adults: **From £3 - £16**
Cost for Children: **Half price**
Special discounts:
UB40s, students, disabled: half price
Tickets available from:
Festival Office (see above)
Routes by Car:
London M4; A40, Haverford West then onward to St Davids
Train/Other:
Paddington - Haverford West and St Davids. Fishguard ferry from Ireland
Venue: **St Davids Cathedral**
Facilities (Parking):
Ample parking, camping for caravans, tents etc. Good local accommodation
Facilities (Disabled):
Wheelchair access, hearing loop, disabled toilets etc
What's On:
Evening concerts featuring professional performers (soloists, ensembles and orchestras), late afternoon recitals in which younger musicians are invited to take part

Historical Background:
Founded in 1979 and entitled the St Davids Bach Festival the present pattern of music making was established. In 1991 the title was changed to reflect a wider repertoire and the larger involvement of the cathedral choirs. Royal Patron: Her Majesty the Queen
Media/Public Comments:
"A feast of classical music during the last week of May in the superb ambience and acoustics of St Davids Cathedral, the National Shrine of Wales. An ideal opportunity to enjoy the pleasures by day of the Pembrokeshire coast with music in the evening"
General Information:
St Davids is set in the beautiful Pembrokeshire Coast National Park. People still flock to St Davids in their thousands as they did throughout the Middle Ages when the shrine of St David was a significant place of pilgrimage

Saundersfoot in Bloom Flower Festival

Type of Festival: **Flower**
Contact:
Mrs R Hayes - Hon Secretary
Address:
1 Belle Vue
Ridgeway
Saundersfoot
Pembrokeshire
SA69 9JZ
Tel. No: **01834 812880**
Date(s) of Festival:
14th - 18th July 1998
Times of Festival: **10am - 8pm**
Cost for Adults:
Free but donations appreciated

Cost for Children: **Free**
Tickets available from: **Not required**
Routes by Car: **A477/B4316**
Train/Other: **Saundersfoot Station**
Venue:
St Issels Church, Saundersfoot
Facilities (Parking):
Parking available. Refreshments
Facilities (Disabled):
Access for wheelchairs on request
What's On:
Floral displays. Community effort with 34 organisations taking part
Historical Background:
First held in St Issells Church in 1984
General Information:
Half of the proceeds of the event are used to buy flowers, plants etc for the troughs and tubs placed around Saundersfoot and the other half is donated to The Children's Society

Swansea Festival of Music and the Arts

Type of Festival:
Classical Music, Drama, Dance, Art
Contact:
Susan Croall - Administrator
Address:
9 Gabalfa Road
Swansea
Wales
SN2 8NF
Tel. No: **01792 205318**
Fax No: **01792 205318**
Date(s) of Festival:
3rd - 24th October 1998
Times of Festival: **Various**
Cost for Adults: **From £5 - £19**
Cost for Children: **25% discount**
Special discounts:
Concessions available for students,

UB40s
Tickets available from:
Grand Theatre Box Office:
01792 475715
Routes by Car:
M4 exit Junction 42
Train/Other: **Swansea Station**
Venue:
Bran Gwyn Hall and Grand Theatre
Facilities (Parking): **CCTV parking**
Facilities (Disabled):
Disabled facilities available
What's On:
London Philharmonic Orchestra, BBC National Orchestra for Wales, London Chamber Orchestra, Dance String Quartet, Ballet Rambert, Italian Films, Teatoo De Dragon Puppets, Art Exhibition, Welsh National Opera etc
Historical Background:
Founded in 1948 as a week of orchestral concerts to bring high quality classical music to the area. Celebrating 50th anniversary in 1998
General Information:
1998 brings an Italian theme to the festival

Tenby Arts Festival

Type of Festival:
Classical Folk Dance and Theatre
Contact: **Mrs Julie Watts**
Address:
Crossing Cottage
Penally
Tenby
Wales
Tel. No: **01834 842291**
Fax No: **01834 845898**
Date(s) of Festival:
18th - 26th September 1998
Times of Festival:
Lunchtimes, afternoons and eve-

nings
Cost for Adults: **Up to £9**
Cost for Children:
Concessions available
Special discounts:
Student concessions
Tickets available from:
**Devalence Pavilion, Upper Frog
Street, Tenby: 01834 842974
(after 9th September)**
Routes by Car:
**M4 from London. Coach services
are also available**
Train/Other:
**Rail links from London and all ma-
jor towns to Swansea then link rail
to Tenby station 5 mins from Town
Centre**
Venue:
**The Devalence and St Marys
Church**
Facilities (Parking):
Multi storey car park in town centre
Facilities (Disabled):
Access for disabled at all venues
What's On:
**Classical concerts, lectures, folk
music, Celtic music and talks, art
exhibitions, drama by the Tenby
Players**
Historical Background:
**Festival is now in its 7th year with
a growing reputation in Wales and
England**
General Information:
**The festival is held in the walled
town of Tenby which is part of the
Pembrokeshire National Park**